MJC

PRENTICE HALL
BIOLOGY
The Living Science
The Human Body

Kenneth R. Miller, Ph.D.
Professor of Biology
Brown University
Providence, Rhode Island

Joseph Levine, Ph.D.
Science Writer and Producer
Adjunct Assistant Professor of Biology
Boston College
Boston, Massachusetts

PRENTICE HALL
Upper Saddle River, New Jersey
Needham, Massachusetts

PRENTICE HALL
BIOLOGY
The Living Science

The Human Body

Components

   Student Edition
   Teacher's Edition
   Laboratory Manual and Annotated Teacher's Edition
   Teaching Resources
   BioLog and Annotated Teacher's Edition
   Transparency Box with Teacher's Guide
   Computer Test Bank
   BioVue

> *The photograph on the cover shows two modern dancers using their athletic abilities to perform amazing movements.*

Credits begin on page 200.

ISBN 0-13-434276-3

1 2 3 4 5 6 7 8 9 10   01 00 99 98 97

PRENTICE HALL
Simon & Schuster Education Group
A VIACOM COMPANY

Staff Credits for Prentice Hall *Biology: The Living Science*

Advertising and Promotion: Judy Goldstein, Carol Leslie, Rip Odell
Business Office: Emily Heins
Design: Laura Jane Bird, Kerri Folb, Kathryn Foot, AnnMarie Roselli, Gerry Schrenk
Manufacturing and Inventory Planning: Katherine Clarke, Rhett Conklin
Market Research: Eileen Friend, Gail Stark
Media Resources: Martha Conway, Libby Forsyth, Vickie Menanteaux, Maureen Raymond, Emily Rose, Melissa Shustyk
National Science Consultants: Charles Balko, Patricia Cominsky, Jeannie Dennard, Kathleen French, Brenda Underwood
Pre-Press Production: Carol Barbara, Kathryn Dix, Paula Massenaro
Production: Christina Burghard, Elizabeth O'Brien, Marilyn Stearns, Elizabeth Torjussen
Science Department
   Director: Julie Levin Alexander
   Editorial: Laura Baselice, Joseph Berman, Christine Caputo, Maureen Grassi, Rekha Sheorey, Lorraine Smith-Phelan
   Marketing: Arthur Germano, Andrew Socha, Kathleen Ventura, Jane Walker Neff, Victoria Willows
   Technology Development: Matthew Hart
Electronic Services: Greg Myers, Cleasta Wilburn

Acknowledgments

Many people contributed their ideas and expertise in the preparation of *Biology: The Living Science*. Among them are the biology teachers, writers, and consultants whose names are listed here. Their contributions are gratefully acknowledged.

Teacher Advisory Panel

Leslie Ferry Bettencourt
Lincoln High School
Lincoln, Rhode Island

Jean T. (Caye) Boone
Hume-Fogg Academic High School
Nashville, Tennessee

David A. Dowell
Carmel High School
Carmel, Indiana

Deborah H. Fabrizio
Seminole High School
Seminole, Florida

Yvonne Favaro
Fort Lee High School
Fort Lee, New Jersey

Steve Ferguson
Lee's Summit High School
Lee's Summit, Missouri

Patricia Anne Johnson
Ridgewood High School
Ridgewood, New Jersey

Mamie Lew
George W. Brackenridge High School
San Antonio, Texas

Ned C. Owings
Florence School District One
Florence, South Carolina

Kathey A. Roberts
Lakeside High School
Hot Springs, Arkansas

College Reviewers

Brian Alters, Ph.D.
Harvard University
Cambridge, Massachusetts

Lauren Brown, Ph.D.
Illinois State University
Normal, Illinois

Maura Flannery, Ph.D.
St. John's University
Jamaica, New York

Ann Lumsden, Ph.D.
Florida State University
Tallahassee, Florida

Gerry Madrazo, Ph.D.
University of North Carolina
Chapel Hill, North Carolina

Cynthia Moore, Ph.D.
Washington University
St. Louis, Missouri

Laurence D. Mueller, Ph.D.
University of California
Irvine, California

Carl Thurman, Ph.D.
University of Northern Iowa
Cedar Falls, Iowa

High School Reviewers

Louise Ables
A & M Consolidated High School
College Station, Texas

Bernard Adkins
Wayne High School
Wayne, West Virginia

Tony Beasley
Science Consultant
Nashville, Tennessee

Victor Choy
John Oliver Secondary School
Vancouver, British Columbia, Canada

Gary Davis
Albuquerque Academy
Albuquerque, New Mexico

Barbara Foots
Houston Independent School District
Houston, Texas

Elaine Frank
Durant High School
Plant City, Florida

Truman Holtzclaw
Sacramento High School
Sacramento, California

Michael Horn
Centennial High School
Boise, Idaho

Jerry Lasnik
Agoura High School
Agoura, California

Marva Moore
Hamilton Southeast High School
Fishers, Indiana

Michael O'Hare
New Trier High School
Winnetka, Illinois

Susan Plati
Brookline High School
Brookline, Massachusetts

James Pulley
Science Consultant
Independence, Missouri

Eddie Rodriguez
Math Science Academy
San Antonio, Texas

Beverly St. John
Milton High School
Milton, Florida

John Young, Ph.D.
Council Rock School District
Newtown, Pennsylvania

Student Reviewers

Emma Greig
Home School
Rochester, Michigan

Rebecca Irizarry
Columbia High School
Maplewood, New Jersey

Laura Stearns
Park Ridge High School
Park Ridge, New Jersey

Adam D. Stuble
Green River High School
Green River, Wyoming

Keri Ann Wolfe
Clarkstown Senior High School South
West Nyack, New York

Elizabeth Ashley Wolgemuth
Santa Margarita Catholic High School
Rancho Santa Margarita, California

Laboratory Teacher's Panel

Judith Dayner
Northern Highlands Regional High School
Allendale, New Jersey

Paul Fimbel
Northern Valley Regional High School
Old Tappan, New Jersey

Deidre Galvin
Ridgewood High School
Ridgewood, New Jersey

Patricia Anne Johnson
Ridgewood High School
Ridgewood, New Jersey

Carole Linkiewicz
Academic High School
Jersey City, New Jersey

Joan Picarelli
Leonia High School
Leonia, New Jersey

Robert Richard
Hillsborough High School
Belle Mead, New Jersey

Tom Russo
Weehawken High School
Weehawken, New Jersey

Sandy Shortt
Ridgewood High School
Ridgewood, New Jersey

Contributing Writers

Sandra Alters, Ph.D.
Salem State College
Salem, Massachusetts

John C. Kay
Iolani School
Honolulu, Hawaii

LaMoine Motz, Ph.D.
Oakland Schools
Waterford, Michigan

Sue Whitsett
L. P. Goodrich High School
Fond du Lac, Wisconsin

Reading Consultant

Laurence J. Swinburne, President
Swinburne Readability Laboratory

The Human Body

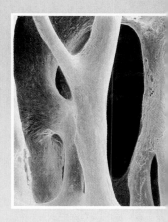

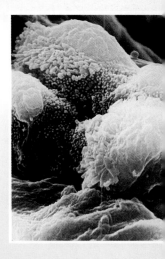

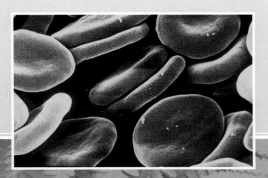

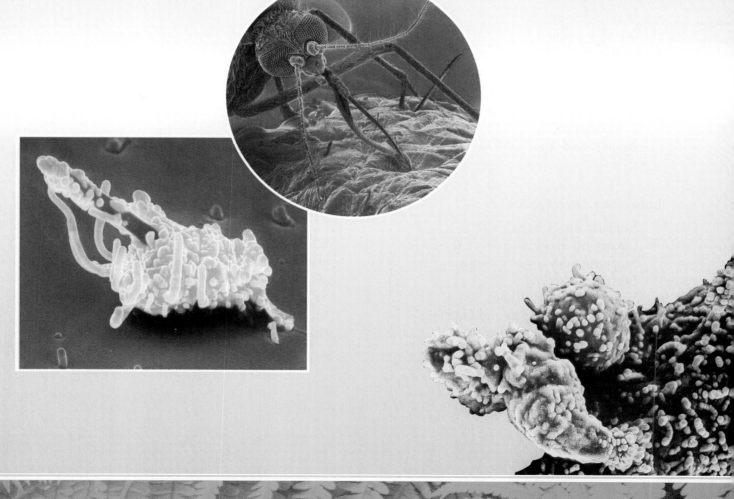

Reference Section

Features

Career Track

Connections

Laboratory Investigations

Mini Labs

Problem Solving

Visualizing . . .

YOU MAY HAVE HEARD PEOPLE SAY: "The future of our planet lies in the hands of our children." That might not mean much to you right now, but eventually the reins of power in our society, including the right to vote, will be passed to you and to your generation. As new discoveries in science and technology occur at an incredible pace, virtually every choice you make will require an understanding of science. Whether you become a scientist or an educated citizen in another career, the quality of your life, as well as the life of generations to come, will depend on how wisely you make those choices.

We wrote this book to inform, and maybe even to inspire, you about the living science of biology. We are all part of a great web of life that covers this planet, and your future depends on the survival and success of that life. The discoveries of science have greatly improved your quality of life over that of your parents and grandparents. But biology is still wide open to new discoveries that can make our world an even better place for you and your children.

The words, photographs, and illustrations in this book have been selected to help you master the basic concepts of biology in an intriguing and enjoyable manner. Many features, some of which are highlighted on these pages, have been included to help you learn and develop skills that can be used as you study biology, as well as other disciplines. We invite you to read the story of biology, to wonder and question, and to appreciate the beauty of this truly fascinating science.

The **Chapter Opener** helps you to focus on the themes and concepts that will be presented in the forthcoming pages. The **chapter-opener photograph** was selected as an interesting representation of the main ideas of the chapter.

Focusing the Chapter can be a very helpful organizational tool to use as you begin your study. All the major divisions, or sections, of the chapter are listed to help you familiarize yourself with the content of the chapter. The **theme** of the chapter helps you to make connections among the concepts presented.

You may be surprised to discover that you are already familiar with many of the concepts in the chapter. By using the **BioJournal**, you can determine what you already know and start thinking about what you would like to know.

Every section begins with a **Guide for Reading,** which highlights several of the more important ideas presented. As you read the section, you will also see **key terms** and **key ideas** presented in boldface type. This should alert you that these are important and may, indeed, be items that you will be tested on later.

Use the **visuals** and **captions** to help clarify the concepts. They have been carefully selected to visually enhance the content, as well as to relate the topic to real-world situations. Notice that the letters in the caption match the letters that identify the pictures.

In most of the chapters, you will find a feature called **Visualizing. . . .** This example shows **Visualizing Aquatic Biomes.** A lot of information is conveyed through pictures and illustrations, so you should pay close attention to these pages to ensure a complete understanding of the big ideas being presented.

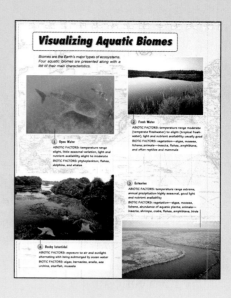

No study of biology would be complete without some kind of hands-on experience. The **Mini Labs,** as well as the **Laboratory Investigations** (not pictured), give you that opportunity—often by using materials as simple as those found in your own kitchen! They also give you the opportunity to exercise your creative thought processes as you put on a scientific hat and **design your own experiments.**

The way to an A is in large part your responsibility. By evaluating yourself and your study habits, you can discover how much you know and where you need more review. To help you assess your own progress, **Checkpoint** questions (not pictured) are integrated throughout the content. The **Section Review** questions are also designed to help you do this.

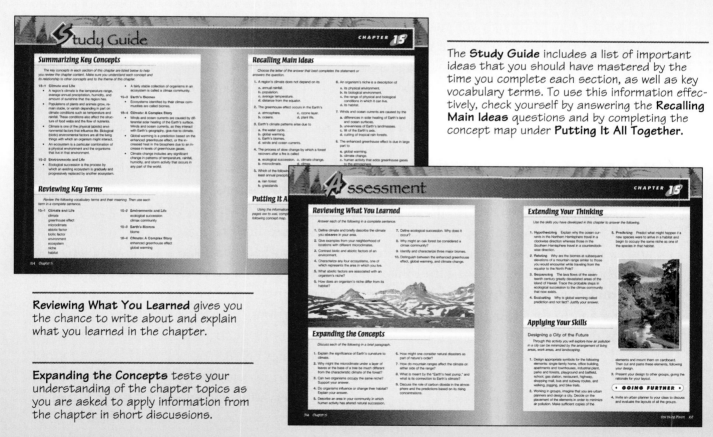

The **Study Guide** includes a list of important ideas that you should have mastered by the time you complete each section, as well as key vocabulary terms. To use this information effectively, check yourself by answering the **Recalling Main Ideas** questions and by completing the concept map under **Putting It All Together.**

Reviewing What You Learned gives you the chance to write about and explain what you learned in the chapter.

Expanding the Concepts tests your understanding of the chapter topics as you are asked to apply information from the chapter in short discussions.

Extending Your Thinking challenges your knowledge and skills as you solve the creative problems and the case studies and apply your knowledge to new situations.

Applying Your Skills allows you to put your skills to the test as you complete challenging tasks involving one or more skills.

THROUGHOUT YOUR STUDY OF science, you will learn a variety of terms, facts, and concepts. Each new topic you encounter will provide its own collection of words and ideas—which, at times, you may think seems endless. But each of the ideas within a particular topic is related in some way to the others. No concept in science is isolated. Thus, it will help you to understand the topic if you see the whole picture; that is, the interconnectedness of all the individual terms and ideas. This is a much more effective and satisfying way of learning than memorizing separate facts.

Actually, this should be a rather familiar process for you. Although you may not think about it in this way, you analyze many of the elements in your daily life by looking for relationships or connections. For example, when you look at a collection of flowers, you may divide them into groups: roses, carnations, and daisies. You may then associate colors with these flowers: red, pink, and white. The general topic is flowers. The subtopic is types of flowers. And the colors are specific terms that describe flowers. A topic makes more sense and is more easily understood if you understand how it is broken down into individual ideas and how these ideas are related to one another and to the entire topic.

It is often helpful to organize information visually so that you can see how it all fits together. One technique for describing related ideas is called a **concept map.** In a concept map, an idea is represented by a word or phrase enclosed in a box. There are several ideas in any concept map. A connection between two ideas is made with a line. A word or two that describes the connection is written on or near the line. The general topic is located at the top of the map. That topic is then broken down into subtopics, or more specific ideas, by branching lines. The most specific topics are located at the bottom of the map.

To construct a concept map, first identify the important ideas or key terms in the chapter or section. Do not try to include too much information. Use your judgment as to what is really important. Write the general topic at the top of your map. Let's use an example to help illustrate this process. Suppose you decide that the key term is Biology. Write and enclose this word in a box at the top of your map.

Now choose the subtopics that are related to the topic—Botany, Zoology, Genetics, Microbiology, Ecology. Add these words to your map. Continue this procedure until you have included all the important ideas and terms—study of plants, animals, inheritance, microscopic organisms, interactions of organisms with one another and with their environment. Then use lines to make the appropriate connections between ideas and terms. Don't forget to write a word or two on or near the connecting line to describe the nature of the connection.

Do not be concerned if you have to redraw your map before you show all the important connections clearly. If, for example, you rely on observation and experimentation as well as analysis, you may want to place these subjects next to each other so that the lines do not overlap.

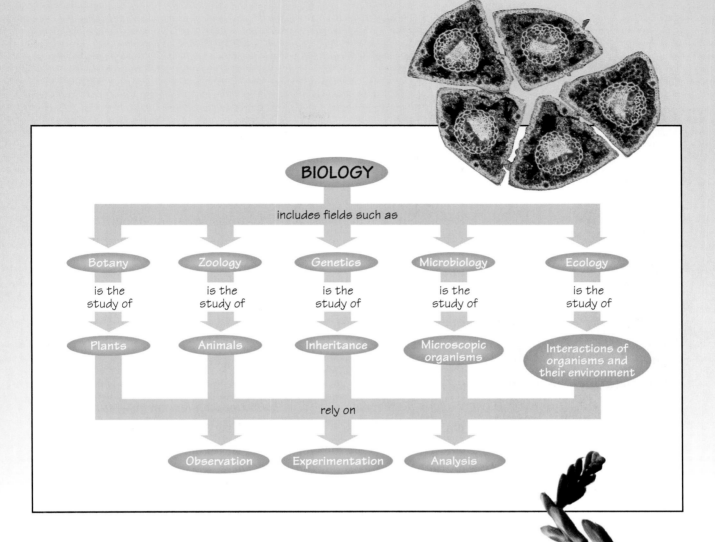

BIOLOGY

includes fields such as

Botany	Zoology	Genetics	Microbiology	Ecology
is the study of	is the study of	is the study of	is the study of	is the study of
Plants	Animals	Inheritance	Microscopic organisms	Interactions of organisms and their environment

rely on

Observation   Experimentation   Analysis

One more thing you should know about concept mapping: Concepts can be correctly mapped in many different ways. In fact, it is unlikely that any two people will draw identical concept maps for a complex topic. Thus, there is no one correct concept map for any topic. Even though your concept map may not match those of your classmates, it will be correct as long as it shows the most important concepts and the clear relationships among them. Your concept map will also be correct if it has meaning to you and if it helps you understand the material you are reading. A concept map should be so clear that if some of the terms are erased, the missing terms could easily be filled in by following the logic of the concept map.

WHEN I WAS 9 OR 10, I WANTED TO BE AN explorer. I imagined myself hiking through wild country, a hunting knife strapped to my ankle, fearlessly stepping into adventures at every turn. Growing up in suburban New Jersey, my friends and I "invented" a wilderness around the creek in a little woods at the end of our street. Almost every day we pretended to discover the place for the first time. On cool days we blazed new trails in the imaginary forest and on hot days we built dams and canals in the clay bed of the creek.

Four or five years later, when I walked into Mr. Zong's ninth-grade biology class in Rahway Junior High, I had become way too grown up to play at the creek anymore. Like most of the boys in my class, I was more interested in acting cool and learning how to do the latest dance— they called it "the twist"!

Our teacher had filled his classroom with specimens—stuffed animals, mounted bugs, pressed flowers, bones, leaves, cocoons. Everywhere you looked there was something new, something unknown, something mysterious. I began to get interested. Then one day, he asked for a volunteer. On my way to school the next morning I made a trip to the old creek. All grown up, the woods now seemed small and ordinary. I filled a jar of creek water to bring to school.

In lab that day we put a drop of the water under the microscope, and I could hardly believe my eyes. The water was teeming with life! After my last class that day, Mr. Zong let me spend another session at the microscope, and this time he helped me identify the tiny critters. We found rotifers and ciliates and a half dozen different kinds of algae. There were things that even he couldn't name for sure.

When I walked home from school that day my view of the creek had changed—and so had my view of the world. For the first time, I understood that the neighborhood I thought I knew was filled with hidden secrets, and I wanted to learn every one of them. To me, that's what biology still is like—a chance, every day, to understand a little more about the mystery of being alive.

With all my heart, I hope that this textbook, every now and then, will give you a little bit of the same feeling I had when I looked at that water under the microscope for the very first time. Life is the single most amazing thing about this remarkable little planet. I hope you will enjoy reading this textbook, but I also hope it will encourage you to study the living things outside your classroom. Who knows? Depending on what you find in that drop of water, you just might grow up to be an explorer, after all!

Ken Miller

"AH, THOSE WONDERFUL ZOO SMELLS!"

That was my reaction as a child whenever I walked into the elephant house at the Bronx Zoo. The grand old building was well-stocked with awesome animals, but it didn't have much fresh air. While my parents held their noses, I took deep breaths, enjoying the "organic" odors. My father reminded me of this a year ago, when he and I took my two-year-old son to the zoo. We had a great time. I was glad that the elephant house now has better ventilation, because my little boy thinks zoos can be "stinky."

Just weeks later, Dad lost his lifelong struggle with a disease called familial hypercholesterolemia. That jawbreaking medical term is the scientific way of saying that a defective gene left Dad's liver unable to control the amount of cholesterol in his blood. Despite surgery and medication, clogged arteries damaged his heart beyond repair while he was still a young man.

Why do I tell you this? Because finishing this textbook has made me stop to think about how biology has affected me and what it will mean to my son—and to you—in the future. As you'll learn, my brother Daniel and I each had a 50-percent chance of inheriting that bad cholesterol gene from Dad. Unfortunately, we both got it. Happily, we were diagnosed in early childhood and received treatments that Dad never had as a boy. In time, Daniel joined a biomedical team to battle heart disease with his own research. Their findings prolonged Dad's life, offered more years to many other patients, and we hope will keep us around for a while longer, too. Meanwhile, researchers elsewhere are studying a host of other disease-causing genes, including some that may affect you or your family.

But biological links between past and future involve more than genes. Why? Because some human genes enable us to learn and to teach. My father—by encouraging his sons to think for themselves, to ask questions, and to search for answers—planted seeds that grew into a lifelong love of learning. By wandering with us through zoos, in and out of museums, and along hiking trails till his legs ached, he gave us our love of nature. Whenever I take my son to the zoo, read him a book about animals, or write a book myself, I remember that love and respect for life aren't passed from generation to generation by chromosomes.

That's why my part of this textbook has a dual dedication. It is dedicated to you, in the hope that it will help to open your eyes to the joy of a science that can better all our lives, as it helps humanity survive into the future that belongs to my son and to you. And it is dedicated to the best father and grandfather anyone could have—the man who laid the foundation for everything worthwhile that I will ever do.

Joe Levine

The Human Body

CHAPTERS

"Science is part of the reality of living; it is the what, the how, and the why for everything in our experience."

— Rachel Carson

CAREER TRACK

As you explore the topics in this book, you will discover many different types of careers associated with biology. Here are a few of these careers:

- Biomedical Equipment Technician
- Electroneurodiagnostic Technologist
- Physical Therapist
- Emergency Medical Technician
- Dietician
- Physician Assistant
- Immunologist

Two dancers showing the various ranges of motion possible to the human body

Introduction to Your Body

FOCUSING THE CHAPTER
THEME: Scale and Structure

1–1 Organization of the Human Body
- **Describe** the basic organization of the human body.

1–2 Communication and Control
- **Explain** the relationship between the nervous system and the endocrine system.

BRANCHING OUT *In Action*

1–3 Physiology in Action
- **Explain** how the systems of the body work together.

LABORATORY INVESTIGATION
- **Observe** the effect of adrenaline on *Daphnia*.

Biology and Your World

BIO JOURNAL

The runners in this photograph are just starting a race. Imagine that you are one of these runners. In your journal, make a list of all the body systems that you will be using in this race. After you have read the chapter, refer back to your list and modify it if necessary.

Runners beginning a 100-meter dash

Organization of the Human Body

GUIDE FOR READING

- **Name** the four basic types of tissues.
- **List** the eleven organ systems of the body and **describe** their functions.

MINI LAB

- **Design an experiment** to observe the different types of tissue.

IT'S THE LAST INNING AND *the score is tied as the batter looks over at her coach. The coach gives a series of signals, one of which is the signal to bunt. The batter's heart beats faster, because she knows that a successful bunt will score the winning run from third base. As the pitcher winds up, the batter takes a shallow breath. Her eyes follow the release of the ball, which becomes a blur as it spins toward the plate. The batter drops the bat to waist level, catches the ball squarely, and bunts it down the base line, just inside fair territory.*

She drops the bat and runs toward first base. The runner from third sprints down the base line and slides easily across home plate. The winning run is scored!

100 Trillion Cells

A spectator watching a softball game might see this winning play as a remarkable example of teamwork between batter, base runner, and coach. As impressive as it might be, the real teamwork involves a much larger number of players—the 100 trillion cells that make up the human body. Each of these cells has a purpose of its own, but each is also part of something larger. How can so many individual cells work together? How are their activities controlled and coordinated? And how is the human body organized to use the activities of these cells to handle the everyday business of life? These are some of the questions that we will try to answer in this chapter and in those that follow.

Figure 1–1
Just as the members of a softball team work together for one common goal, so too do the organ systems in this batter's body, as she prepares to hit the ball.

Figure 1–2
The human body contains eleven major organ systems.
This chart lists each of these systems, along with its function.

SOME MAJOR BODY SYSTEMS

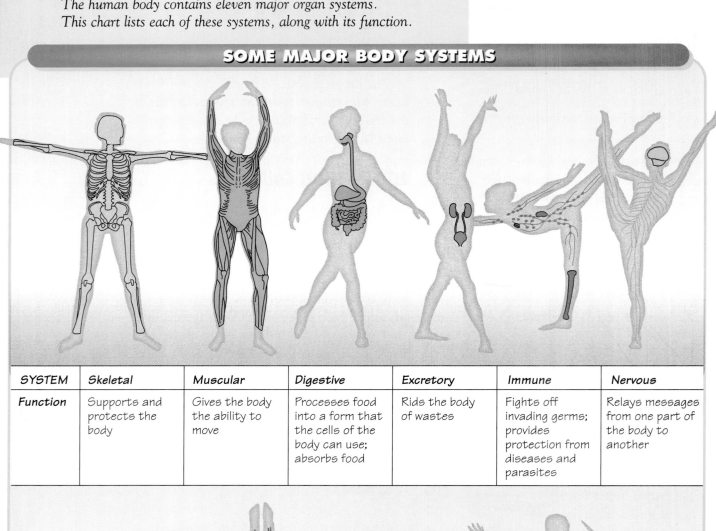

SYSTEM	Skeletal	Muscular	Digestive	Excretory	Immune	Nervous
Function	Supports and protects the body	Gives the body the ability to move	Processes food into a form that the cells of the body can use; absorbs food	Rids the body of wastes	Fights off invading germs; provides protection from diseases and parasites	Relays messages from one part of the body to another

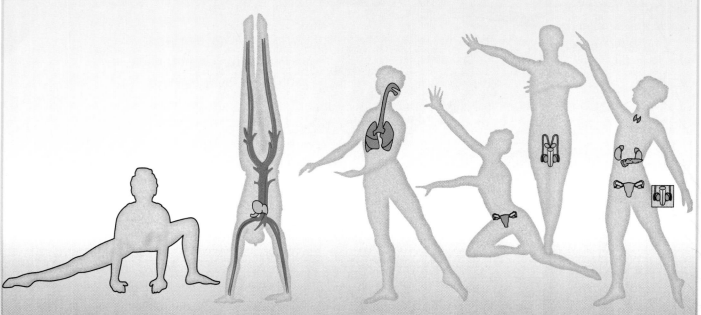

SYSTEM	Integumentary	Circulatory	Respiratory	Reproductive	Endocrine
Function	Protects the body from injury, infection, and dehydration	Brings oxygen, food, and chemical messages to cells	Brings oxygen to the body and rids the body of carbon dioxide	Produces reproductive cells; in females, nurtures and protects developing embryo	Regulates and controls the body's functions

Levels of Organization

In a country with millions of people, every person is an individual. However, people sometimes associate in groups. The most basic of these groups is the family, but there are larger groups as well. Communities, counties, and states are groups of people who work together to organize and choose governments.

Tissues

As in a human society, it's possible to classify the cells of the human body into groups. A group of similar cells that perform a single function is called a **tissue.** Your body contains many tissues. **There are four basic types—epithelial** (ehp-ih-THEE-lee-uhl), **connective, nerve, and muscle tissues.** Epithelial tissue covers interior and exterior body surfaces. Connective tissue provides support for the body and connects all its parts. Nerve tissue transmits nerve impulses through the body. And muscle tissue, along with bones, enables the body to move.

Organs

A group of tissues that work together to perform a single function is called an **organ.** The eye is an organ made up of epithelial tissue, nerve tissue, muscle tissue, and connective tissue. As different as these tissues are, they all work together for a single function—sight.

Organ Systems

An **organ system** is a group of organs that perform closely related functions. For example, the eye is one of the organs of the nervous system, which gathers information about the outside world and uses it to control many of the body's functions. *Figure 1–2* shows the eleven organ systems in the body.

Section Review   1–1

1. **Name** the four basic types of tissues.
2. **List** the eleven organ systems in the body and **describe** their functions.
3. **Critical Thinking—Relating Facts**   The eleven systems of the human body are all dependent upon one another. Explain how a virus, which affects the respiratory system, could affect the other systems of the body.
4. **MINI LAB**   What different types of tissue can you observe? **Design an experiment** to find out.

Communication and Control

GUIDE FOR READING

- **Describe** the endocrine system.
- **Explain** how negative feedback works.

IN A HUMAN SOCIETY, THERE *are many forms of communication. Every day, you communicate with your teacher and with other students by writing or speaking to them. You use this kind of communication to express your thoughts and ideas, to ask questions, and to exchange greetings.*

Communication is even more important in a large society. Think of the ways in which newspapers and magazines affect your view of the world. Remember the images that you may have seen on television last night. In many ways, these mass communications bind the people of a society together with common experiences and expose them to a range of diverse ideas. The same principle applies to the cells, tissues, organs, and organ systems of the body. Unless they communicate, they cannot act together.*

The Nervous System

Similar to a telephone network that reaches every home and office in a large city, the body contains a cellular network that carries messages from cell to cell. That network is the **nervous system.** The message-carrying cells of the nervous system are called **neurons.** Neurons can relay signals from one end of a cell to the other. They can also pass these impulses from cell to cell.

You can think of neurons as tiny wires in a vast communications network. They gather information from every region of the body and relay it to central locations. Here the information can be analyzed, then instructions and commands can be carried to organs throughout the body.

The center of this network is the brain, where impulses arrive from every part of the body. In the brain they are analyzed and compared, past information is stored and retrieved, and appropriate responses are sent back out through the network.

Figure 1–3

Communication is an important means of exchanging information. In the body, the nervous system and endocrine system are responsible for communication. (a) *Talking with your friends,* (b) *speaking on the telephone, and* (c) *reading newspapers are three common ways in which information is passed from person to person.*

The Endocrine System

If you wanted to send a message to just one or two people, you could call them on the telephone. But if you had to reach thousands of people at the same time, you might broadcast your message on radio or television.

It might not have radio or television, but your body does have a chemical "broadcasting" system that can send messages to millions of cells at the same time. This broadcasting system is the **endocrine system.** *Figure 1–4* illustrates the endocrine system. **The endocrine system is made up of a series of glands located throughout the body. Glands are organs that produce and release chemicals, and endocrine glands generally release their chemicals into the bloodstream.**

Hormones

Unlike the organs of the nervous system, the endocrine glands are not connected to one another. The endocrine glands send signals between each other and to other cells in the body.

These signals are produced by the endocrine glands in the form of **hormones**—the chemicals that travel through the bloodstream and affect the behavior of other cells. Only those cells that have **receptors**—specific chemical binding sites—for a particular hormone can respond to it. Cells that have receptors for a particular hormone are called **target cells.** Hormone receptors are similar to radios tuned to just one station. A cell that does not have receptors for a hormone cannot respond to it, just as you would miss an announcement on a jazz station if you were listening to a rock station.

☑ *Checkpoint*   What are hormones?

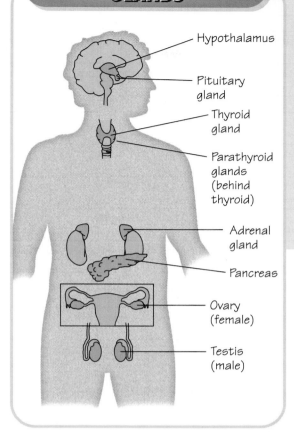

HUMAN ENDOCRINE GLANDS

- Hypothalamus
- Pituitary gland
- Thyroid gland
- Parathyroid glands (behind thyroid)
- Adrenal gland
- Pancreas
- Ovary (female)
- Testis (male)

Figure 1–4
The endocrine system consists of glands located throughout the body. Notice that in females the sex glands are called ovaries and in males they are called testes.

Pituitary Gland

A network of broadcasting stations usually has a place where the activities of individual stations are coordinated—and the endocrine system is no exception. Its headquarters is a tiny structure at the base of the brain known as the

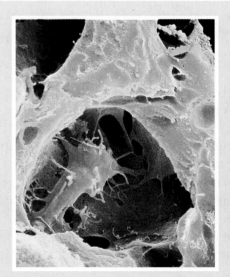

Figure 1–5
The pituitary gland, located in the brain, is responsible for secreting nine different hormones. In this scanning electron micrograph, the pituitary gland is colored a pale red-brown. The yellow objects in the center and top of the gland are large white blood cells (magnification: 2100X).

Gland	Hormone	Action
Thyroid	Thyroxine	Increases metabolic rate and body temperature; regulates growth and development
	Calcitonin	Inhibits release of calcium from bone
Parathyroid	Parathyroid hormone (PTH)	Stimulates release of calcium from bone
Pituitary	Antidiuretic hormone (ADH)	Stimulates reabsorption of water
	Oxytocin	Stimulates uterine contractions and release of milk
	Follicle-stimulating hormone (FSH)	Stimulates follicle maturation in females and sperm production in males
	Luteinizing hormone (LH)	Stimulates ovulation and growth of corpus luteum in females and testosterone secretion in males
	Thyroid-stimulating hormone (TSH)	Stimulates thyroid to release thyroxine
	Adrenocorticotropic hormone (ACTH)	Stimulates adrenal cortex to release hormones
	Growth hormone (GH) or somatropin	Stimulates growth; synthesizes protein; inhibits glucose oxidation
	Prolactin	Stimulates milk production
Adrenal	Aldosterone	Controls salt and water balance
	Cortisol, other corticosteroids	Regulate carbohydrate, protein, and fat metabolism
	Adrenaline and noradrenaline	Initiate the body's response to stress; increase blood glucose level; dilate blood vessels; increase rate and strength of heartbeat; increase metabolic rate
Pancreas	Glucagon	Stimulates conversion of glycogen to glucose, raising the blood glucose level
	Insulin	Stimulates conversion of glucose to glycogen, lowering the blood glucose level
Ovary	Estrogen	Develops and maintains female sex characteristics; initiates buildup of uterine lining
	Progesterone	Promotes continued growth of uterine lining and formation of placenta
Testis	Testosterone	Develops and maintains male sex characteristics; stimulates sperm development

Figure 1–6

Each gland of the endocrine system releases a different hormone. This chart lists the endocrine gland, the hormone or hormones it produces, as well as the action of each hormone.

pituitary gland. The hormones produced by the pituitary gland are important because many of them regulate the other endocrine glands.

Hypothalamus

What controls the pituitary gland? The pituitary gland is attached to a region of the brain known as the **hypothalamus** (high-poh-THAL-uh-muhs). Either directly or indirectly, the hypothalamus controls the release of hormones from the pituitary gland.

Some hormones released from the pituitary gland are actually made in the hypothalamus. Others are made in the pituitary gland, then released into the bloodstream only when chemical signals are received from the hypothalamus.

The link between the hypothalamus and the pituitary gland is important for two reasons. First, it explains how the pituitary gland works, controlling the activities of other endocrine glands in response to signals that it receives from the hypothalamus. Second, it shows that the nervous system and the endocrine system are interconnected. That means that input into the nervous system can influence the endocrine system by way of the connection between the hypothalamus and the pituitary gland.

☑ *Checkpoint*   Where in the body is the hypothalamus found?

Figure 1–7
CAREER TRACK
A biomedical equipment technician is responsible for the maintenance and repair of medical equipment. In this photograph, a technician is running an annual validation test for temperature and temperature uniformity on a sterilizing oven in a pharmaceutical research facility.

Endocrine System Control

To better understand how the endocrine system works, let's take a look at one of the body's most important hormones, thyroxine. Thyroxine is made by the **thyroid gland.** To make thyroxine, the thyroid gland needs the amino acid tyrosine and a small amount of iodine, which must be obtained from food.

Thyroxine affects nearly all the body's cells, increasing their metabolic rate—the rate at which they use food and oxygen. It also increases the rate at which cells grow.

Too much thyroxine in the bloodstream results in increased blood pressure, nervousness, increased pulse rate, and dangerous weight loss. Too little thyroxine results in a lowered pulse rate, lowered blood pressure, excessive sleepiness, and weight gain. How does the thyroid gland usually manage to get the level of this important hormone just right?

Control in the Hypothalamus

Like most cells in the body, the cells of the hypothalamus also have receptors for thyroxine. When levels of thyroxine drop, most cells slow down their activity, but some cells of the hypothalamus increase their activity. These cells now produce more of a thyroid-releasing hormone (TRH).

Remember how close the hypothalamus is to the pituitary? TRH travels from the hypothalamus to the pituitary gland through a network of tiny blood vessels. It then causes cells in the pituitary gland to release increased amounts of another hormone, thyroid-stimulating hormone (TSH), into the bloodstream. The target cells for TSH are the cells of the thyroid gland itself. TSH causes the thyroid gland to release more thyroxine.

Feedback Regulation

As you can see, the combination of the hypothalamus, pituitary gland, and thyroid gland automatically regulates the level of thyroxine in the bloodstream. When there is too little thyroxine in the blood, the thyroid gland is stimulated by TSH to make more. When there is too much thyroxine, TSH is not released, and the thyroid gland makes less. You could say that the activity of the thyroid gland "feeds back" to the hypothalamus. When the thyroid gland is working too fast, its own product—thyroxine—causes the hypothalamus to signal the thyroid gland to slow down. When it is working too slow, low levels of thyroxine cause the hypothalamus to signal the thyroid gland to speed up.

The relationship between the thyroid gland and the hypothalamus is an example of **negative feedback.** In humans, the release of hormones is regulated through negative feedback. **Through negative feedback, the secretion of a hormone inhibits further production of another hormone.** Negative feedback enables the conditions within the body to remain relatively constant over time.

The Salt Connection

As you have just read, thyroxine is a hormone produced by the thyroid gland and needed by the body for its cells to function properly. Thyroxine not only stimulates nerve cell growth, it is also important for brain development.

In order to produce thyroxine, the thyroid gland requires a small amount of the mineral iodine. Like all minerals, the iodine that is needed to make thyroxine must be obtained from the foods we eat. Because iodine is rarely found in soil, most foods contain very little. Fortunately, seafood is rich in iodine, and eating a small amount of seafood every now and then provides the iodine your body needs.

Iodine Deficiency

What happens if your diet does not contain the small amount of iodine your body needs? The thyroid gland attempts to compensate for the lack of iodine. It does this by increasing in size so that it can absorb as many atoms of iodine as possible. This increase in size produces a noticeable swelling of the thyroid gland, a condition called goiter.

Iodized salt

At one time, goiter was common in parts of the midwestern United States, where seafood was hard to get. Today, however, goiter is almost unheard of in the United States. Why have incidences of goiter decreased? Because in many countries, table salt is now iodized. Trace amounts of iodine are added to much of the table salt in the United States and other industrial nations. A few sprinkles of iodized salt can supply enough iodine for the body to make all the thyroxine it needs.

Severe Problems

For children, the consequences of iodine deficiency are much more severe than for adults. Because the developing brain requires thyroxine to stimulate nerve cell growth, lack of thyroxine can result in mental retardation.

Unfortunately, some parts of the world have been slow to initiate production of iodized salt to supplement the diets of people who live inland and do not eat seafood. One such place is China, and that country is experiencing a major health crisis because the diets of many Chinese people do not contain enough iodine. The Public Health Ministry of China estimates that as many as 10 million Chinese now suffer mental retardation because of iodine deficiencies during childhood.

Recently, public health authorities in China have realized the severity of the health crisis in their country. They're now rushing to ensure that iodized salt becomes available in all parts of China as soon as possible.

Making the Connection

Can you think of places other than inland China where people might not be able to get the iodine they need? Iodized salt is more expensive in China than regular salt. What solutions would you offer to solve the problem of cost versus health?

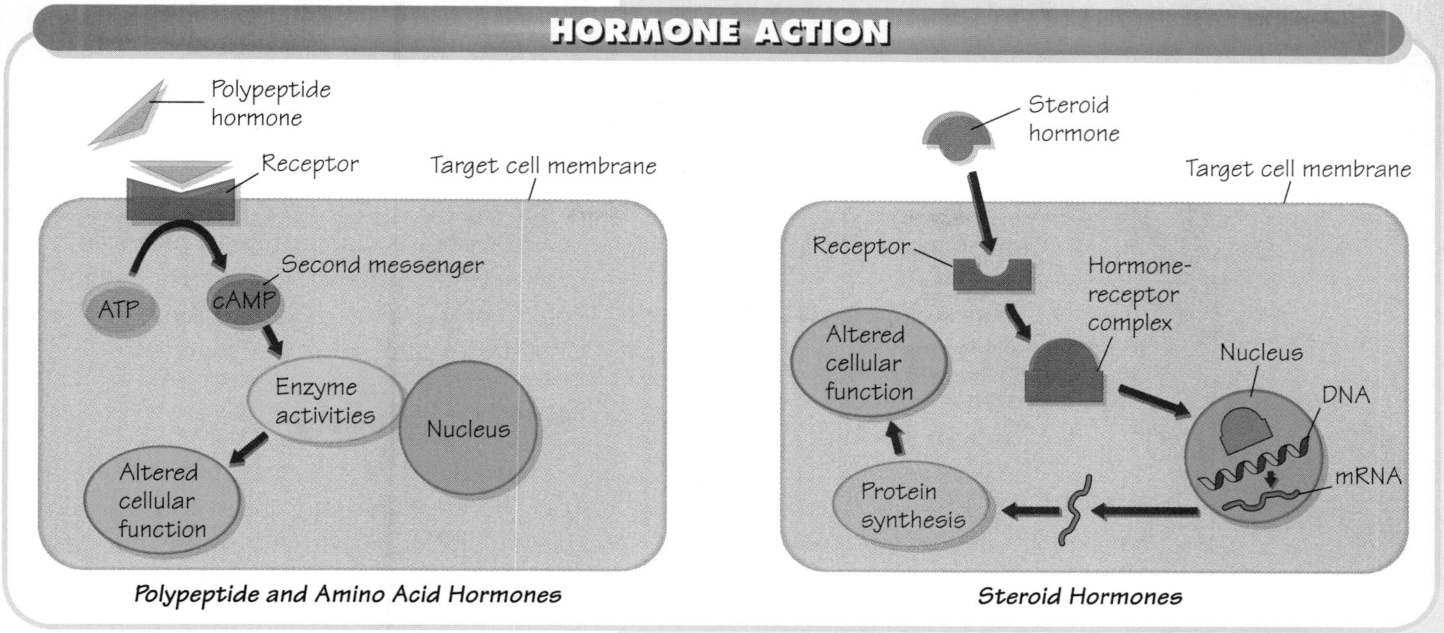

Polypeptide hormone

Receptor

Target cell membrane

Second messenger

ATP

cAMP

Enzyme activities

Nucleus

Altered cellular function

Polypeptide and Amino Acid Hormones

Steroid hormone

Target cell membrane

Receptor

Hormone-receptor complex

Altered cellular function

Nucleus

DNA

mRNA

Protein synthesis

Steroid Hormones

How Do Hormones Work?

Hormones come in many different shapes and sizes. Some are proteins, others are lipids, and still others are chemically modified amino acids. How do hormones affect their target cells?

There are two basic patterns of hormone action. Polypeptide and amino acid hormones bind to receptors on the cell surface. As *Figure 1–8* shows, when a hormone binds to a receptor on the cell surface, it activates enzymes on the inner side of the cell membrane to produce a large number of second messenger molecules. These second messengers may be ions such as Ca^{2+} or small molecules such as cyclic adenosine monophosphate, cAMP. Once released, these second messengers can activate or inhibit a wide range of other cell activities.

Figure 1–8
Polypeptide and amino acid hormones do not enter the cell, but bind to receptors on the cell membrane where they activate second messengers, such as cAMP. Steroid hormones enter the cell and bind to receptors inside it.

Unlike the polypeptide hormones, steroid hormones easily pass across the cell membrane. Steroid hormones are lipids produced from cholesterol. Target cells for these hormones have protein receptors that tightly bind to a specific steroid hormone. This hormone-receptor complex, as it is called, enters the nucleus, where it binds to a specific DNA sequence. Hormone receptor complexes work as regulators of gene expression—they can turn on or turn off whole sets of genes. Steroid hormones, which directly affect gene expression, can produce dramatic changes in cellular function.

INTEGRATING CHEMISTRY

What are polypeptides? What are amino acids? Use a chemistry textbook to find out.

Section Review 1-2

1. **Describe** the function of the endocrine system.
2. **Explain** how negative feedback works.
3. **Critical Thinking—Comparing** How do polypeptide and steroid hormones compare in terms of hormone action?

GUIDE FOR READING

- Define human physiology.

MINI LAB

- Construct a model of negative feedback in the endocrine system.

AS COMPLICATED AS IT IS, IT *sometimes seems remarkable to think that all the cells of the human body are capable of working together for a common purpose. How does this happen? To take a case in point, how did the body of the ballplayer we described at the beginning of the chapter make it possible for her to drive in the winning run?*

Human Physiology

When you think about the variety of things your body is capable of doing—including the simple things you take for granted—you realize how incredible the human body is. **The study of how the body works is called human physiology** (fihz-ee-AHL-uh-jee). Let's use the example of the softball player to see how the systems of the body work together.

Getting Ready

Two days ago, this player missed practice because she had chills and a fever. Today she feels better because her immune system fought off a cold virus.

At lunch time, she ate two slices of pizza, a salad, a glass of milk, and an apple. Her digestive system quickly broke down the complex molecules in this food so they could be absorbed into the blood of the circulatory system. The sugars from that meal were carried throughout the body, providing her with energy.

Preparing to Play

As she waited in the on-deck circle, the pressure was on her to bring home the third-base runner. Her nervous

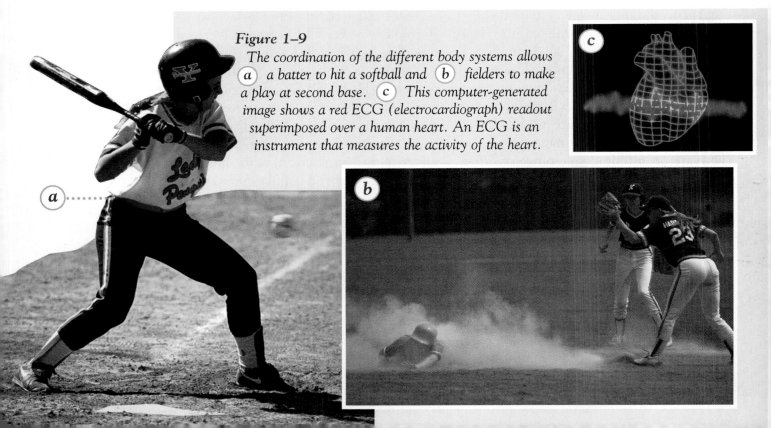

Figure 1–9

The coordination of the different body systems allows (a) *a batter to hit a softball and* (b) *fielders to make a play at second base.* (c) *This computer-generated image shows a red ECG (electrocardiograph) readout superimposed over a human heart. An ECG is an instrument that measures the activity of the heart.*

system buzzed with anxiety, and that message was passed to the endocrine system. Nerve impulses stimulated the adrenal cortex to release adrenaline into the bloodstream. Within seconds, her heart rate and blood pressure rose, and the blood supply to her muscles increased.

With a few deep breaths, her respiratory system cleared the carbon dioxide from her lungs and filled her blood with the oxygen it needed. As her coach flashed a series of signals, her nervous system searched her stored memory of pre-game plans to recall the signs.

Time for Action

As the pitcher threw the ball to the plate, the batter's eyes watched the ball. Her nervous system took less than three tenths of a second to realize that the ball was headed for the strike zone. Instantly, nerves carried the message to key muscles in her arms and legs.

After she bunted the ball, her nervous system issued a new set of commands to the muscular system. Now muscles in her legs contracted in a pattern that placed tremendous force on the long bones of the skeletal system, enabling her to run.

As she continued to run, her respiratory system provided more oxygen to the bloodstream, and her muscles quickly used the energy stored in them. Finally, as she crossed the base safely, she relaxed.

MINI LAB ··········· Modeling ·······

Dropping the Ball

PROBLEM *How can you **construct a model** of negative feedback in the endocrine system?*

PROCEDURE

1. Working with three other students, stand in a line. The first person in line will be the hypothalamus. The second person will be the pituitary gland, the third person will be the thyroid gland, and the fourth person will be the body.

2. Give the *hypothalamus* a red ball labeled TRH, the *pituitary gland* a green ball labeled TSH, and the *thyroid gland* 3 yellow balls labeled thyroxine, to be held in one hand.

3. At a signal from the *body,* the *hypothalamus* passes the TRH ball to the *pituitary gland.* The *pituitary gland* passes the TSH ball to the *thyroid gland.* The *thyroid gland* passes one thyroxine ball to the right hand of the *body* and a second thyroxine ball to the left hand of the *body.*

4. The *body* is now saturated with thyroxine. In order to accept the last thyroxine, the *body* must pass one thyroxine to the *hypothalamus.* The *body* is now able to accept the third thyroxine.

5. When the *hypothalamus* receives the thyroxine, the *thyroid gland* should drop the TSH ball.

ANALYZE AND CONCLUDE

1. What is the function of TRH? Of TSH?

2. Why did the *body* pass the thyroxine to the *hypothalamus?* What effect did this have?

3. What would happen if the *body* kept accepting thyroxine?

Section Review 1-3

1. **Define** human physiology.
2. **MINI LAB** How did you **construct a model** of negative feedback in the endocrine system?
3. **BRANCHING OUT ACTIVITY** Imagine that you are about to take a final exam. In a one-page essay, **summarize** how the systems of your body will work together to prepare you for this task and to carry it through.

Laboratory Investigation

DESIGNING AN EXPERIMENT

Daphnia and Adrenaline

Although hormones are very small molecules that are released in minute amounts, they cause very noticeable effects in an organism. Adrenaline is a hormone that prepares the body to deal with stress. It increases the heart rate and the metabolic rate. In this investigation, you will observe the heart of a small crustacean called *Daphnia*, or water flea, and you will determine the effects adrenaline has on its heart.

Problem

What can you observe about the effect adrenaline has on a *Daphnia*? **Design an experiment** to answer this question.

Suggested Materials

Daphnia culture
0.01% adrenaline solution
depression slides
medicine droppers
microscope

Suggested Procedure

1. Use the medicine dropper to transfer a single *Daphnia* from the culture to the center of the depression slide. The *Daphnia* will look like a small white dot.

2. Place the slide under the low-power objective of a microscope and observe the *Daphnia*. Locate the heart.

3. Count the number of times the heart beats in one minute. Record this information in a data table similar to Data Table 1.

4. Repeat step 3 two more times. Then average the three measurements. Record your data. Return the *Daphnia* to the culture dish.

5. Using a procedure similar to the one given in steps 1 to 4, determine the effect a 0.01% solution of adrenaline has on the *Daphnia*'s heart.

DAPHNIA

Heart

Eye

Intestine

Antennae

DATA TABLE 1

Normal Heart Rate	
Count 1	
Count 2	
Count 3	
Average	

DATA TABLE 2

Heart Rate With Adrenaline	
Time (minutes)	Heart Rate
1	
3	
5	
7	
9	

6. **Formulate a hypothesis. Make sure that you have your teacher's approval for the experiment.**

7. **Be sure to return the *Daphnia*'s heart beat to its normal rate. To do so, remove some of the adrenaline solution from the slide with a medicine dropper. Using a clean medicine dropper, replace the volume of the liquid with water from the culture. Continue observing and counting the heart rate every other minute until the heart rate returns to normal.**

8. **Carry out your experiment and record your data in a data table similar to Data Table 2.**

Observations

1. Share your observations and measurements with the rest of the class. As a class, find the average number of heartbeats for the *Daphnia* before the adrenaline solution was added and just after it was added.

2. What was the effect on the heart rate when you added the adrenaline solution?

3. How long did it take the *Daphnia* to return to a normal heart rate?

Analysis and Conclusions

1. Formulate a hypothesis to explain the results of your experiment. Could a different hypothesis also explain the results? Discuss this possibility.

2. How do you think the *Daphnia* adjusted its heart rate to the adrenaline solution?

3. Why might it be a good idea to take an average of the class data in this experiment?

4. Why do you think that *Daphnia* are useful organisms in an experiment such as this? Explain your answer.

More to Explore

Design an experiment to determine the effects of various concentrations of adrenaline solution on a Daphnia.

Study Guide

Summarizing Key Concepts

The key concepts in each section of this chapter are listed below to help you review the chapter content. Make sure you understand each concept and its relationship to other concepts and to the theme of this chapter.

1–1 Organization of the Human Body

- There are four basic types of tissue—epithelial, connective, nerve, and muscle.

- The eleven systems of the body include the skeletal system, muscular system, digestive system, excretory system, immune system, nervous system, integumentary system, circulatory system, respiratory system, reproductive system, and endocrine system.

1–2 Communication and Control

- The endocrine system is made up of a series of glands located throughout the body. Glands are organs that produce and release chemicals, and endocrine glands generally release their chemicals into the bloodstream.

- Hormones are chemicals that travel through the bloodstream and affect the behavior of other cells.

- During negative feedback, the secretion of a hormone inhibits further production of another hormone.

1–3 Physiology in Action

- The study of how the body works is called human physiology.

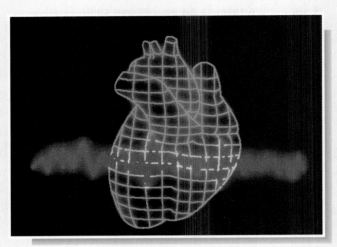

Reviewing Key Terms

Review the following vocabulary terms and their meaning. Then use each term in a complete sentence.

1–1 Organization of the Human Body

tissue
organ
organ system

1–2 Communication and Control

nervous system
neuron

endocrine system
hormone
receptor
target cell
pituitary gland
hypothalamus
thyroid gland
negative feedback

Recalling Main Ideas

Choose the letter of the answer that best completes the statement or answers the question.

1. A group of similar cells that perform a similar function is called a(an)

   a. organism.   **c.** tissue.
   b. organ.   **d.** organ system.

2. Which type of tissue covers interior and exterior surfaces?

   a. epithelial   **c.** connective
   b. muscle   **d.** nerve

3. The body system that relays messages from one part of the body to another is the

   a. immune system.   **c.** excretory system.
   b. nervous system.   **d.** digestive system.

4. Organs that produce and release substances are called

   a. hormones.   **c.** glands.
   b. receptors.   **d.** target cells.

5. What controls the release of hormones from the pituitary gland?

   a. hypothalamus   **c.** thyroid
   b. adrenal glands   **d.** pancreas

6. Which endocrine gland produces estrogen?

   a. testes   **c.** adrenal gland
   b. ovaries   **d.** pituitary gland

7. Which system is responsible for clearing the blood of carbon dioxide and replacing it with oxygen?

   a. circulatory   **c.** excretory
   b. digestive   **d.** respiratory

Putting It All Together

Using the information on pages xii to xiii, complete the following concept map.

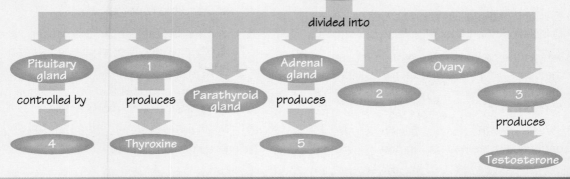

ENDOCRINE SYSTEM

divided into

Pituitary gland	1		Adrenal gland		Ovary	
controlled by	produces	Parathyroid gland	produces	2		3
						produces
4	Thyroxine		5			Testosterone

Reviewing What You Learned

Answer each of the following in a complete sentence.

1. Explain the function of muscle tissue.
2. What is a tissue?
3. What is an organ system?
4. Explain the function of the excretory system.
5. What are neurons?
6. How does the endocrine system work?
7. What are glands?
8. What are hormones? In which system are they produced?
9. How does the integumentary system work?
10. What are receptors?
11. What are target cells?
12. Where is the pituitary gland located?
13. Where is the hypothalamus located?
14. Which gland produces thyroxine?

15. What kinds of chemicals are hormones usually made of?
16. Explain the purpose of the second messenger hormone.
17. Why is negative feedback important?

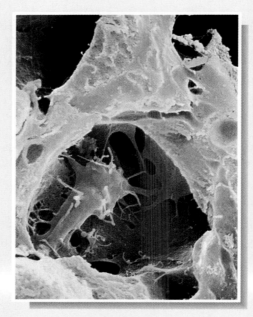

Expanding the Concepts

Discuss each of the following in a brief paragraph.

1. What is the function of each of the four types of tissue?
2. Compare tissues with organs.
3. Can any of the eleven body systems work in isolation of another? Explain your answer.
4. Why is the nervous system often referred to as the coarse control of the human system while the endocrine system is considered the fine control?
5. Explain how the nervous system and the endocrine system work together.

6. Explain how glucagon and insulin have opposite effects on the body.
7. What is the relationship between the pituitary gland and the hypothalamus?
8. Using the hypothalamus, the pituitary gland, and the thyroid gland, explain how negative feedback works.
9. **Construct a model** that illustrates the two basic patterns of hormone action.
10. Explain the action of a polypeptide hormone and a steroid hormone.

Extending Your Thinking

Use the skills you have developed in this chapter to answer the following.

1. **Analyzing**   Explain how the negative-feedback mechanism works in a way similar to a thermostat that maintains the temperature of a room.

2. **Making judgments**   With the advent of genetic engineering, many techniques have led to bacterially produced hormones. One of these hormones—human growth hormone (GH)—is now readily available. Consider the advantages and disadvantages of administering this hormone over an extended period of time to adjust the size of a patient.

3. **Designing an experiment**   A person driving a car is maintaining a constant speed at the speed limit. How could you design an experiment to illustrate how this is an example of negative feedback?

4. **Hypothesizing**   You have probably heard stories of people who had incredible strength when placed in an extremely dangerous situation. How might a person be able to summon such strength for a short period of time?

5. **Making judgments**   Anabolic steroids are synthetic drugs produced from the hormone testosterone. Although anabolic steroids are used for medical purposes to reduce swelling and promote healing, they are sometimes misused to develop muscle mass and muscle strength. Whatever the case, the long-term effects of steroid use are serious and dangerous. Should anabolic steroids be reclassified as an illegal substance? Why or why not?

Applying Your Skills

The Squeeze Play

In order to do things effectively, the systems of the body must all work together. As a class, conduct the following activity, which involves reaction time.

1. In groups of 8 to 10 students, stand in line holding hands. Identify the first person in line as the timekeeper. He or she will need a stopwatch or clock with a second hand. All students but the timekeeper should close their eyes.

2. When everyone in the group is ready, the timekeeper begins timing and, at the same time, squeezes his or her neighbor's hand. As soon as the neighbor feels the squeeze, he or she squeezes the hand of the next person. Each person does this in turn. When the last person feels the squeeze, he or she yells "stop." This is the signal to stop timing and note the time. Record your group's reaction time.

3. Repeat steps 1 and 2 two more times, recording your data each time. Calculate a class average for reaction time.

• GOING FURTHER •

4. Do you think you react faster earlier in the day than you do later in the day?

5. Will practice doing this activity decrease your reaction time? Explain your answer.

Nervous System

FOCUSING THE CHAPTER
THEME: Stability

2–1 The Human Nervous System
- **Describe** the basic structures of the nervous system.

2–2 Organization of the Nervous System
- **Explain** how the nervous system is organized.

2–3 The Senses
- **Describe** each of the five senses.

BRANCHING OUT *In Depth*

2–4 Nerve Impulses and Drugs
- **Explain** the effects various drugs have on nerve impulses.

LABORATORY INVESTIGATION
- **Identify** the parts of a sheep brain.

Biology and Your World

BIO JOURNAL

The gymnast in this photograph relies on her nervous system for balance and coordination. Pick a favorite sport or activity. In your journal, explain how you rely on your nervous system to perform that sport or activity. Remember to include your five senses as well.

Gymnast on balance beam

The Human Nervous System

SECTION

2–1

GUIDE FOR READING

- **Name** the three parts of a neuron.
- **Describe** the way in which a nerve impulse begins.

A COMPUTER CAN DELIVER A *page of text, graphics, and even a video in a few seconds. However, there is another "machine" less than a meter away from the computer that can perform equally astonishing feats. In a fraction of a second, this machine can take in everything on the computer screen; scan the area around the computer; monitor the sound, light, and heat in the room; and automatically regulate the activities of hundreds of devices running at the same time. What kind of information-processing system can do all this? The answer is inside you—the human nervous system.*

Neurons

To understand a computer, you start with the basics—with electricity, wires, and switches. Gradually, you see how thousands of individual components are wired together to form a functional unit. We can do almost the same thing with the nervous system. The basic units of the nervous system are cells called **neurons.** These cells carry messages in the form of electrical signals known as **impulses.**

Some features of a typical neuron are shown in *Figure 2–2* on the next page. **A neuron is made up of a cell body, dendrites, and an axon.** The largest part of the neuron is its **cell body.** Most of the metabolic activity of the cell takes place there. In addition, the cell body collects information from the **dendrites**—small branched extensions that spread out from the cell body. Dendrites carry impulses toward the cell body. And the long

Cell body cyton

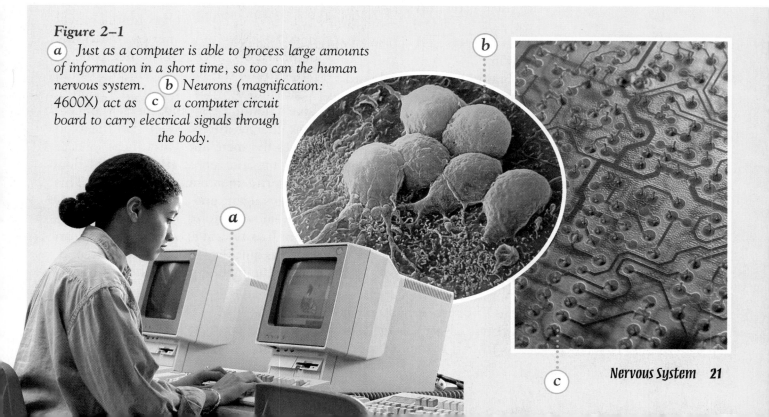

Figure 2–1

(a) *Just as a computer is able to process large amounts of information in a short time, so too can the human nervous system.* (b) *Neurons (magnification: 4600X) act as* (c) *a computer circuit board to carry electrical signals through the body.*

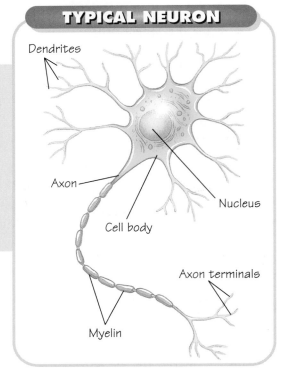

TYPICAL NEURON

Dendrites

Axon

Cell body

Nucleus

Axon terminals

Myelin

Figure 2–2
The main structures of a typical neuron include the dendrites, the cell body, and the axon.

branch that carries impulses away from the cell body is called an **axon.** A neuron may have many dendrites, but it usually has only one axon.

In most animals, neurons are clustered into bundles of fibers called **nerves.** Some nerves contain only a few neurons, but many others have hundreds or even thousands of neurons.

There are three general types of neurons, distinguished by the directions in which they carry impulses. The **sensory neurons** carry impulses from the sense organs to the brain and the spinal cord. **Motor neurons** carry impulses in the opposite direction—from the brain or spinal cord to muscles or other organs. **Interneurons** connect sensory and motor neurons, and carry impulses between them.

☑ *Checkpoint*   What are the three types of neurons?

The Nerve Impulse

A neuron not carrying an impulse is said to be at rest. The resting neuron has an electrical potential—a charge difference—across its cell membrane. The inside of the cell is negatively charged and the outside is positively charged.

This difference in electrical charges is called the **resting potential.** Although negative and positive ions are found on both sides of the membrane, there is a net excess of negative charges on the inside of the membrane, and that's what produces the resting potential.

An impulse begins when a neuron is stimulated by another neuron or by the environment. Once it begins, the impulse travels rapidly down the axon away from the cell body. As *Fig. 2–3* shows, the impulse is a sudden reversal of the membrane potential. For a few milliseconds, positive ions rush across the cell membrane, reversing the charge difference. For that brief instant, the inside of the membrane is more positive than the outside. In less than 10 milliseconds, the potential reverses itself again, and the resting potential is restored.

This rapid change in voltage on the inside of the axon—negative to positive and back to negative—is called an **action potential.** A nerve impulse is an action potential traveling down an axon.

How does the action potential move? Imagine a row of dominoes. When one domino falls, it causes the next one to fall, causing the next to fall, and so on. That's almost what happens in a neuron. Like a domino toppling, the flow of positive charges into one region of the axon causes the membrane just ahead of it to open up and let positive charges flow across the membrane there, too. This happens again and again, until the impulse moves along the length of the axon. In a typical axon, the impulse can move as quickly as one meter per second. Once the impulse passes, the resting potential is restored, and the neuron is ready to conduct another impulse.

☑ *Checkpoint*   What is an action potential?

Myelin

As you know, most electrical wires are insulated—that is, they are covered with rubber or plastic to prevent a short circuit. The nervous system has a kind of insulation, too. In some nerve cells, Schwann cells surround the axons of certain neurons. As Schwann cells grow around an axon, they wrap it in layers of their own cell membrane, forming a material known as **myelin** (MIGH-uh-lihn). The Schwann cells that surround a single long axon leave many gaps—called nodes—between themselves where the axon membrane is exposed.

When an impulse moves down an axon covered with myelin, the action potential jumps from one node to the next. This happens because electrical current flows from one node to the next, which greatly speeds up the rate at which the impulse moves. A large axon with myelin can carry messages at speeds as great as 200 meters per second!

☑ *Checkpoint* What are Schwann cells?

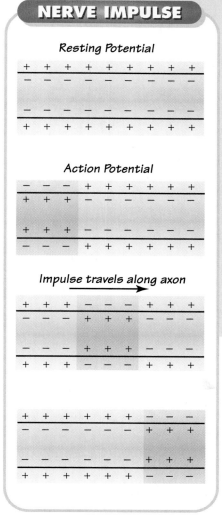

NERVE IMPULSE

Resting Potential

Action Potential

Impulse travels along axon →

Figure 2–3
At rest, the outside of the neuron's membrane is more positively charged than is the inside. If a stimulus is applied, causing an impulse, the electrical charges become reversed. The reversal of electrical charges continues as the action potential moves down the axon.

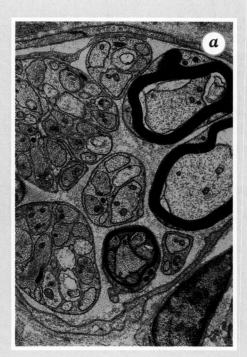

Figure 2–4
ⓐ *This transmission electron micrograph of the cross section of nerve tissue shows both myelinated and unmyelinated axons. The axons that are covered with myelin are those that seem to have black rings around them (magnification: 47,000X).* **ⓑ** *An action potential can move much faster along a myelinated axon because it can jump from node to node, rather than moving continuously along the membrane.*

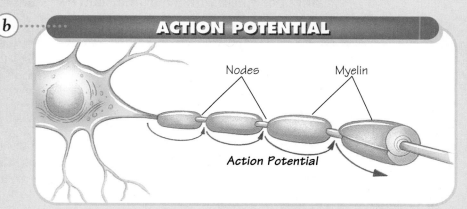

ACTION POTENTIAL

Nodes   Myelin

Action Potential

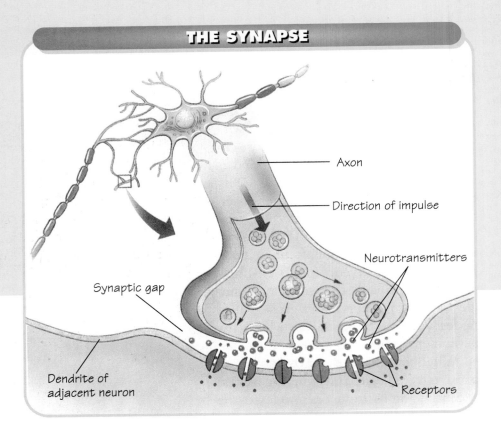

Figure 2–5
When an impulse reaches the end of the axon of one neuron, neurotransmitters are released into the synaptic gap. The neurotransmitters bind to the receptors on the membrane of an adjacent neuron. As a result, the nerve impulse continues to the next neuron.

Axon

Direction of impulse

Neurotransmitters

Synaptic gap

Dendrite of adjacent neuron

Receptors

The Synapse

Even though some neurons are among the longest cells in your body, there comes a point when an impulse reaches the end of an axon. Usually the neuron then makes contact with another cell, and it may even pass the impulse to this cell. Motor neurons, for example, pass their impulses to muscle cells.

The point at which a neuron can transfer an impulse to another cell is called the **synapse** (SIHN-aps). The synapse is a small space between the axon of one neuron and the dendrites of the next neuron. The synapse contains tiny sacs filled with **neurotransmitters** (NOO-roh-trans-miht-erz). Neurotransmitters are chemicals used by one neuron to signal another cell.

When an action potential arrives at the end of an axon, the sacs release the neurotransmitters into the synapse between the two cells. The neurotransmitter molecules attach to receptors on the neighboring cell. This causes positive ions to rush across the cell membrane, stimulating that cell. If the stimulation is great enough, a new impulse begins.

A fraction of a second after binding to their receptor, the neurotransmitter molecules are released from the cell surface. They may then be broken down by enzymes or recycled by the axon.

Section Review 2–1

1. **Name** the three parts of a neuron.
2. **Describe** the way in which a nerve impulse begins.
3. **Critical Thinking—Relating Concepts** Your "funny bone" is actually a nerve in your arm. How does this explain your reaction when you "hit" it?

Organization of the Nervous System

GUIDE FOR READING

- **Describe** the two major divisions of the nervous system.

THE HUMAN NERVOUS SYSTEM is similar to a complex telephone network in a large city. In a telephone network, telephone lines and wires connect homes, businesses, and schools through a central telephone switching station. The nervous system has connecting wires as well—the neurons. The nervous system itself works like the central switching station of the body. It receives, compares, and analyzes information, then it sends messages and commands to the rest of the body.

The Central Nervous System

The human nervous system is divided into two main parts—the central nervous system and the peripheral nervous system. **The central nervous system consists of the brain and the spinal cord.** The brain and spinal cord share many structural similarities. The brain is protected by the bones of the skull, and the spinal cord is protected by the vertebrae of the backbone. Both are cushioned by three layers of tough, elastic tissue called **meninges** (muh-NIHN-jeez). Between the meninges is a space filled with **cerebrospinal** (ser-uh-broh-SPIGH-nuhl) **fluid,** which cushions the brain and spinal cord. These three means of protection help to prevent many injuries to the central nervous system.

The Brain

The brain contains about 100 billion cells—a far greater number than the number of people in the world! That fact alone should prepare you for how complicated this organ is. Although the brain represents only about 2 percent of the mass of the body, it is so active that it may use as much as 25 percent of the body's energy. To supply the food and oxygen needed to support that activity, the brain has a rich blood supply. ✺ If that blood supply is interrupted—even for just a few minutes—the brain may suffer damage serious enough to cause death. ●

INTEGRATING
HEALTH

Refer to a health book to find out what causes a stroke.

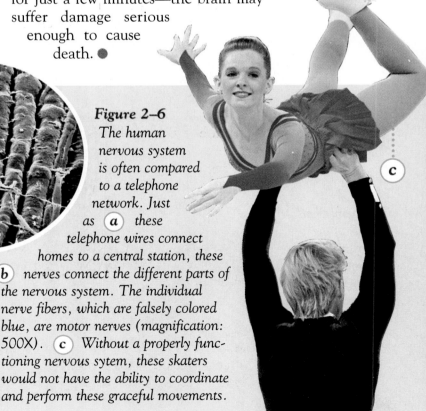

Figure 2–6
The human nervous system is often compared to a telephone network. Just as (a) *these telephone wires connect homes to a central station, these* (b) *nerves connect the different parts of the nervous system. The individual nerve fibers, which are falsely colored blue, are motor nerves (magnification: 500X).* (c) *Without a properly functioning nervous sytem, these skaters would not have the ability to coordinate and perform these graceful movements.*

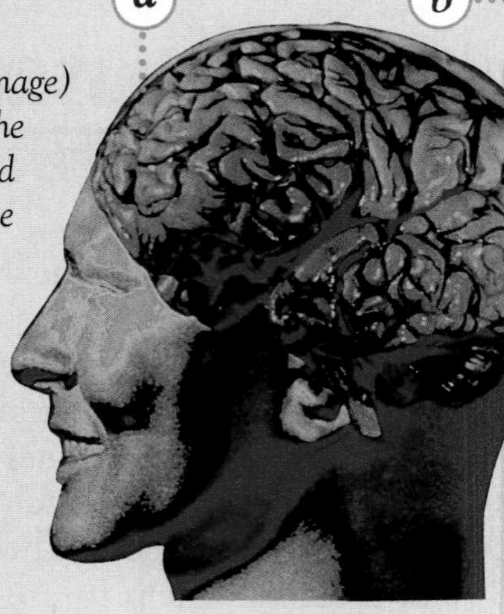

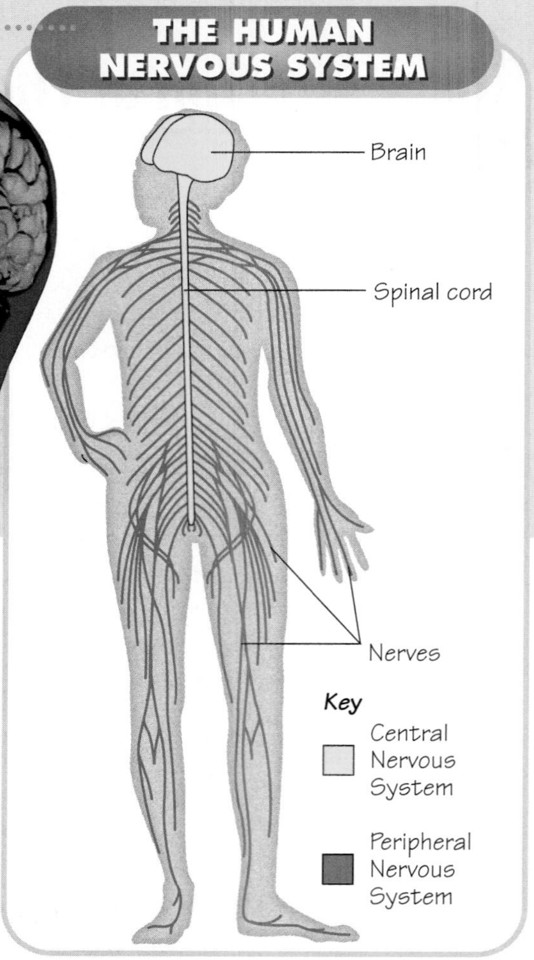

Figure 2–7

(a) An MRI (magnetic resonance image) of the brain—the control center of the human body—has been superimposed over an image of the head. (b) The human nervous system consists of two main divisions. The central nervous system, colored yellow, consists of the brain and the spinal cord. The peripheral nervous system, colored red, consists of all the nerves that carry information to and from the spinal cord.

THE HUMAN NERVOUS SYSTEM

Brain

Spinal cord

Nerves

Key

Central Nervous System

Peripheral Nervous System

The **cerebrum** (SER-uh-bruhm) is the largest part of the human brain. It is responsible for functions such as learning, intelligence, and judgment. The cerebrum is divided into a left and a right hemisphere by a deep groove. These two hemispheres are connected at the corpus callosum (KOR-puhs kuh-LOW-suhm).

The surface of the cerebrum, the **cerebral cortex,** is deeply creased. The creasing enlarges its surface area and increases the number of cells that can be packed into this layer. The cerebral cortex processes information from the senses and controls body movements.

The **cerebellum** (ser-uh-BEHL-uhm), the second-largest part of the brain, is located just below the cerebrum at the base of the skull. When the cerebral cortex commands a muscle group to move, that message is routed through the cerebellum. The cerebellum coordinates and balances the actions of muscles so the body moves gracefully and efficiently.

The **brainstem** connects the brain to the spinal cord. The brainstem includes regions called the **medulla oblongata** (mih-DUHL-uh ahb-lahn-GAHT-uh) and the **pons.** Some of the body's most important functions—including blood pressure, heart rate, breathing, and swallowing—are controlled in this part of the brain.

The thalamus is located just beneath the cerebrum. The thalamus receives messages from sense organs, including the eyes and the nose, before they are relayed to the cerebral cortex. Just beneath the thalamus is the hypothalamus, a small region that is linked to the pituitary gland.

LOBES OF THE BRAIN

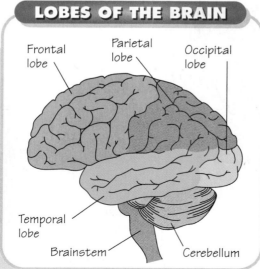

Frontal lobe

Parietal lobe

Occipital lobe

Temporal lobe

Brainstem

Cerebellum

Figure 2–8

Each hemisphere, or half, of the cerebrum contains the same four lobes—frontal lobe, parietal lobe, occipital lobe, and temporal lobe.

Figure 2–9
The spinal cord is surrounded by three layers of meninges. In the upper right, the cross section of the spinal cord shows both the gray matter and the white matter. The gray matter gets its color from the color of the cell bodies, of which it is mostly made. The white matter consists mainly of long axons, which get their color from myelin sheaths.

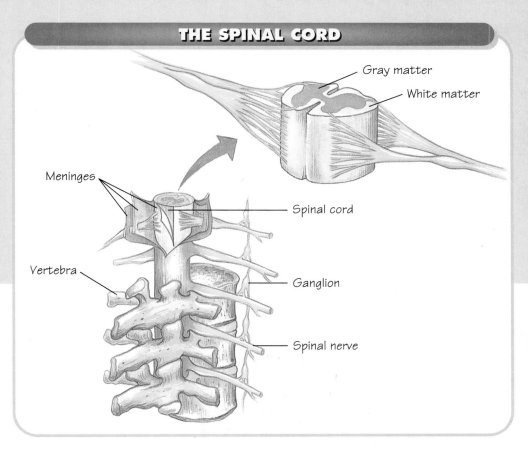

THE SPINAL CORD

Gray matter

White matter

Meninges

Spinal cord

Vertebra

Ganglion

Spinal nerve

The Spinal Cord

The spinal cord is the primary link between the brain and the rest of the body. Thirty-one pairs of spinal nerves branch out from the spinal cord, connecting the brain to all parts of the body. Certain kinds of information are processed directly in the spinal cord. One example is the well-known knee-jerk reflex. A **reflex** is a quick, automatic response to a stimulus. As shown in *Figure 2–10,* a tap on the knee stimulates a reflex. The nerve impulses travel through sensory neurons to the spinal cord. There the impulse synapses with motor neurons, which sends the message back to the leg muscle to contract.

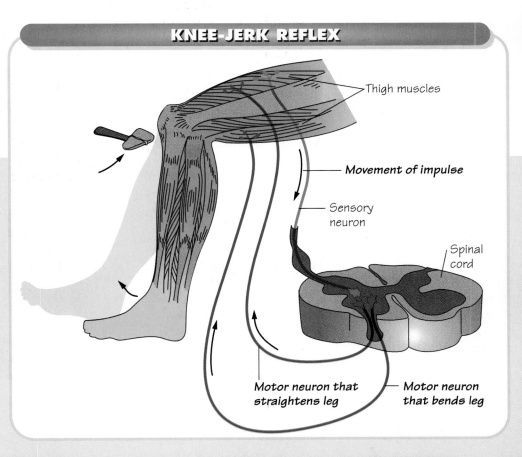

KNEE-JERK REFLEX

Thigh muscles

Movement of impulse

Sensory neuron

Spinal cord

Motor neuron that straightens leg

Motor neuron that bends leg

Figure 2–10
The knee-jerk reflex is one of the simplest neural circuits in the body. Tapping the kneecap causes a sensory neuron to send a signal to the spinal cord, where it stimulates an interneuron. The interneuron stimulates a motor neuron, which sends the signal back to the leg "telling" the leg muscles to contract, thereby straightening the leg.

Informed Consent

Whenever Kim came home from work lately, all she wanted to do was lie down and take a nap. At first, she didn't think too much of it, even though she usually liked to go for a run before dinner.

When her husband became concerned and asked her about her lack of energy, she would say, "It's nothing. I just have a headache."

Strange Symptoms

Then one day, Kim noticed a strange metallic taste in her mouth. She also began smelling perfume, even though she did not usually wear it. Finally, Kim decided to go to see her doctor.

The doctor suggested that Kim undergo a few tests. One test was called an MRI, or Magnetic Resonance Imaging, which was able to take a "snapshot" of Kim's brain.

Test Results

Unfortunately, the results of Kim's MRI showed a small brain tumor. And although the tumor was not cancerous, Kim would probably need surgery to avoid further, more serious, complications. Specifically, the tumor might eventually lead to blindness if left untreated. Kim agreed to the operation.

Possible Side Effects

The night before Kim was to have surgery, her doctor visited her in her hospital room. Before proceeding with the operation, the doctor wanted to discuss all the possible side effects—which might include infection, paralysis, or loss of speech—so that Kim could make a final decision based on the best possible information. This is called informed consent.

One of the problems doctors often face is just how much (or how little) to tell a patient. On the one hand, patients like Kim need to know certain information before they can consent to surgery or other procedures that might have serious side effects. In fact, there are laws that make it mandatory for doctors to keep their patients informed of all possible outcomes. On the other hand, how much information is too much information, which might only cause more fear in the patient? How much knowledge does a patient need in order to give informed consent? There is a fine line between knowing enough and knowing too much.

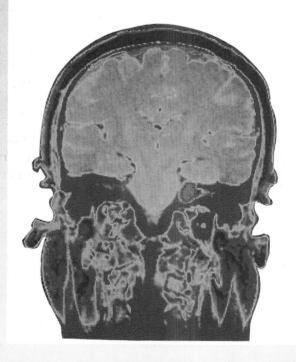

An MRI scan of the back of the head showing a noncancerous tumor (green area)

Making the Connection

If you were facing a serious operation, what kinds of questions would you ask your doctor? How would the answers to those questions help you to make an informed decision?

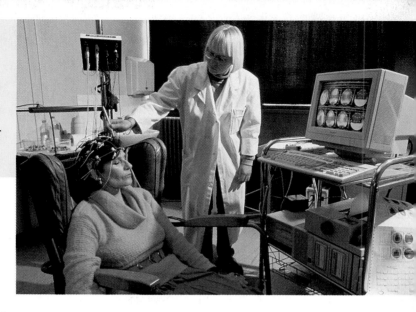

Figure 2–11
CAREER TRACK

An electroneurodiagnostic technologist is responsible for taking electroencephalogram (EEG) images of the brain. EEGs show the average electrical activity of the brain and are useful in studying the process of sleep and in diagnosing some brain abnormalities.

The Peripheral Nervous System

The peripheral nervous system includes all the nerves and associated cells that connect the brain and spinal cord to the rest of the body. The peripheral nervous system receives information from the environment and relays commands from the central nervous system to organs throughout the body.

There are two divisions in the peripheral nervous system—the sensory division and the motor division. The sensory division carries information from the sense organs to the central nervous system. The motor division transmits messages in the other direction—from the central nervous system to the rest of the body. The motor division is further divided into the **somatic nervous system** and the **autonomic nervous system.**

The Somatic Nervous System

The somatic nervous system controls voluntary movements. Every time you turn a page of this book, you are using the somatic nervous system to command the movements of your hand. Some somatic nerves are also part of reflexes and act with or without conscious control.

The Autonomic Nervous System

The autonomic nervous system regulates activities that are not under conscious control, including the beating of the heart and the contraction of muscles surrounding the digestive system. This system regulates the activities of many organs throughout the body. The autonomic nervous system consists of two distinct parts—the sympathetic nervous system and the parasympathetic nervous system. In nearly every case, nerves from both systems regulate each organ.

Why is each organ regulated by both nervous systems? The answer is that the effects of each system are different. For example, sympathetic nerves cause the heart rate to speed up, but parasympathetic nerves cause it to slow down—like the gas pedal and the brake of a car. Therefore, the autonomic nervous system can quickly speed up the activities of important organs or slam on the brakes—whichever is necessary.

Section Review 2–2

1. **Describe** the two major divisions of the nervous system.
2. **Critical Thinking—Making Inferences** Each hemisphere of the cerebrum receives sensory information and controls movement on the opposite side of the body. In a right-handed person, which hemisphere is dominant? In a left-handed person?

The Senses

- List the five senses.

MINI LAB

- Design an experiment to determine your threshold for taste.

HOW DO YOU KNOW THAT there is a world around you? That might seem to be an obvious question, but philosophers have wondered about this for thousands of years. Many of them have come to an interesting conclusion—that what we know of the world depends entirely on our senses. In this very important way, we are at the mercy of our sensory systems.

The Five Senses

Our five senses—vision, hearing, smell, taste, and touch—each begins with specialized sense organs that respond to the environment. Sensory neurons carry impulses from these sense organs back to the central nervous system, where they form the basis for our understanding of the world.

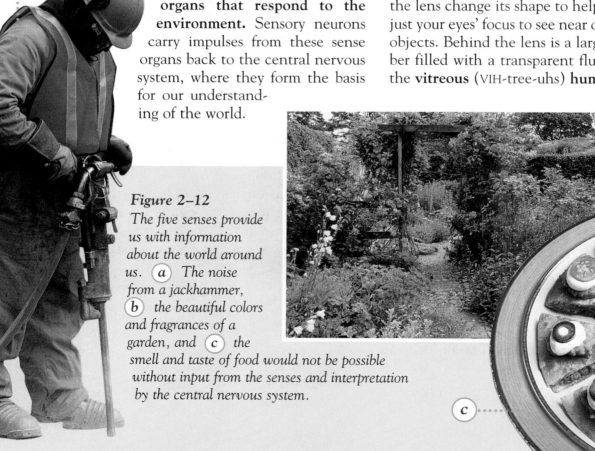

Figure 2-12
The five senses provide us with information about the world around us. (a) The noise from a jackhammer, (b) the beautiful colors and fragrances of a garden, and (c) the smell and taste of food would not be possible without input from the senses and interpretation by the central nervous system.

Vision

Similar to other primates, humans have exceptionally good eyesight. In a world that is filled with sunlight, our vision, more than any other sense, shapes our understanding of everything around us.

Light enters the eye through the **cornea,** a tough transparent layer at the surface of the eye. The cornea focuses the entering light, which then passes through a fluid-filled chamber. At the back of this chamber is a disk of tissue called the **iris.** Tiny muscles adjust the size of the opening in the iris, called the **pupil,** to regulate the amount of light that enters the eye. Pigments in the iris give your eye its color, making it appear blue, brown, or green.

Just behind the pupil is the **lens,** a flexible structure filled with a transparent protein. Small muscles attached to the lens change its shape to help you adjust your eyes' focus to see near or distant objects. Behind the lens is a large chamber filled with a transparent fluid called the **vitreous** (VIH-tree-uhs) **humor.**

Figure 2-13

The human eye is a complicated organ responsible for the sense of vision. The area on the retina that contains no rods or cones is called the blind spot.

Similar to a miniature slide projector, the lens and cornea project an image of the scene in front of your eyes directly onto the **retina,** the layer of cells at the back of the eye. The light-sensitive photoreceptor cells in the retina come in two kinds—rods and cones. Rods are extremely sensitive to light, but they cannot detect color. Cones can detect color, but they need more light than rods to work properly.

Rods and cones are wired directly to a series of interneurons that are part of the retina itself. These cells help to analyze the pattern of cells stimulated by light and then relay that information to the brain through the optic nerve. A major portion of the human brain is devoted to receiving and analyzing signals from the optic nerve.

☑ *Checkpoint*   What are rods and cones?

THE EYE

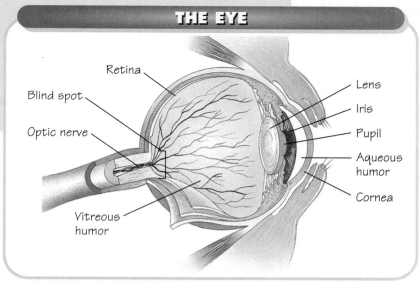

Hearing and Balance

Sound is nothing more than vibrations in the air around us. Slow vibrations—those that shake the air 100 to 500 times a second—produce deep, low-pitched sounds. Higher pitches result from faster vibrations—1000 to 5000 times per second. Our ears allow us to sense the pitch and determine its loudness—how strong the vibration is.

Vibrations enter the ear through the **auditory canal,** causing the **tympanum,** the eardrum, to vibrate. The vibrations are picked up by three tiny bones, the

THE EAR

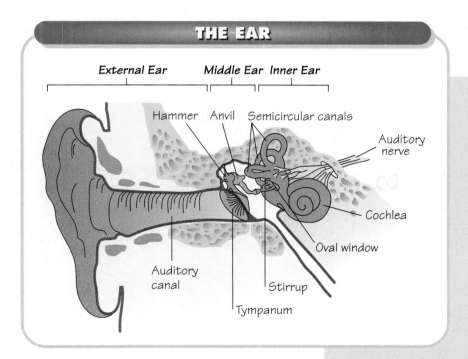

Figure 2-14

The human ear is divided into three parts—the outer ear, the middle ear, and the inner ear. Each of the structures within the ear is responsible for either hearing or maintaining balance.

THE NOSE

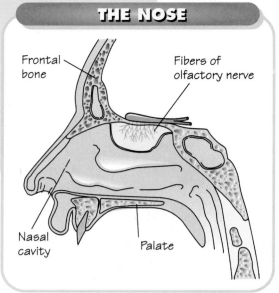

Frontal bone

Fibers of olfactory nerve

Nasal cavity

Palate

Figure 2–15
Nerve cells located in tissues lining the upper part of the nasal cavity are responsible for the sense of smell.

hammer, the anvil, and the stirrup. These bones transmit the vibrations to a thin membrane called the oval window. The oval window covers the opening for the inner ear. Vibrations of the oval window create pressure waves in the fluid-filled **cochlea** (KAHK-lee-uh) of the inner ear.

The cochlea is lined with tiny hair cells that are pushed back and forth by these pressure waves. In response to these movements, the hair cells produce nerve impulses that are sent to the brain through the auditory nerve.

The ear also contains a tiny organ that helps you to sense your position in space and maintain your balance. Three fluid-filled **semicircular canals** enable the nervous system to sense changes in the position of the head. When the head is moved quickly in any direction, pressure is developed in one or more of the canals, and tiny hairs near the ends of the canals sense these pressures.

Two tiny sacs located below the semicircular canals are embedded in a gelatinlike substance that contains tiny grains of calcium carbonate. The downward pressure produced by these tiny grains enables you to sense the pull of gravity. Together, the semicircular canals and these sacs enable you to sense your body's position and keep your balance steady.

☑ *Checkpoint* What is the function of the semicircular canals?

ⓐ **THE TONGUE**

Bitter

Sour

Salty

Sweet

Figure 2–16
ⓐ *Although the tongue is covered with taste buds, the taste buds are grouped into four regions, depending on the "taste" they perceive.* **ⓑ** *This scanning electron micrograph shows what the surface of the tongue really looks like. The large disk-shaped objects are the taste buds (magnification: 240X).*

ⓑ

Smell

You may never have thought of it this way, but your sense of smell is actually the ability to detect chemicals. Special cells in the upper part of the nasal passageway act as receptors for a variety of chemicals. When stimulated, these cells produce the nerve impulses that travel to the central nervous system.

Your sense of smell is capable of producing thousands of different sensations. In fact, much of what is commonly called the "taste" of food actually depends on your sense of smell. To prove this, eat a few bites of food while holding your nose. You'll discover that the food doesn't have much taste until you open your nose and breathe freely.

Taste

Your mouth contains chemical receptors called **taste buds,** which are located on the tongue. Although you are able to perceive hundreds of tastes, there are only four types of taste receptors—sweet, sour, salty, and bitter. Sensitivity to these different tastes varies on different parts of the tongue, as shown by the drawing in *Figure 2–16.*

Touch and Related Senses

The largest sense organ in your body is the skin, which contains different receptors for touch, pain, heat, and cold. Each receptor responds to its particular stimulus and produces nerve impulses that signal the central nervous system.

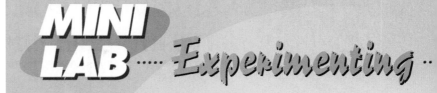

MINI LAB ····· Experimenting ··

How Tasty Is It?

PROBLEM   *How can you determine your threshold for taste?* ***Design an experiment*** *to answer this question.*

SUGGESTED PROCEDURE

1. Rinse your mouth with water.
2. Using a clean cotton swab, place a drop of sugar solution on the tip of your tongue. Record your observations. Rinse your mouth with water.
3. Using a procedure similar to the one used in steps 1 and 2, design an experiment to determine the effects of two different concentrations of sugar solution on the tip of your tongue. Have your teacher check your procedure before carrying out your experiment.

ANALYZE AND CONCLUDE

1. Which sugar solutions were you able to taste? Explain why.
2. What do you think the word "threshold" means with regard to taste?
3. Why was it important for you to rinse your mouth between tastings?

Not all parts of the body are equally sensitive to touch, because not all parts have the same number of receptors. The greatest densities of touch receptors, for example, are found on your fingers, toes, and lips.

Section Review 2-3

1. **List** the five senses.
2. **Critical Thinking—Drawing Conclusions**   Why do you think you feel dizzy after spinning around for a few seconds?
3. **MINI LAB**   **Design an experiment** to determine your threshold for taste.

GUIDE FOR READING

- **Describe** the function of the sodium-potassium pump.
- **Describe** the effects of drugs on the nervous system.

MINI LAB

- **Predict** how the nervous system will respond to a stimulus.

AS YOU HAVE READ, IN THE *nervous system, neurons are similar to telephone connecting wires carrying coded messages and passing signals from one cell to the next. How, exactly, do neurons do this? What produces the electrical potential across the neuron cell membrane? What happens when an impulse moves along an axon? And what happens when chemical substances alter the nervous system? To answer these questions in depth, we have to look closely at the cell membrane and at the point of synapse between two nerves.*

The Resting Potential

As you have learned, there is a difference in electrical charge in a neuron's membrane, called the resting potential. There are two forces that produce this potential, both of which depend upon the special properties of the neuron cell membrane.

The first force is an active-transport protein built into the membrane, the **sodium-potassium pump.** What does this pump do? **The sodium-potassium pump uses the energy from ATP to pump sodium ions (Na^+) out of the cell while at the same time pumping potassium ions (K^+) into the cell.**

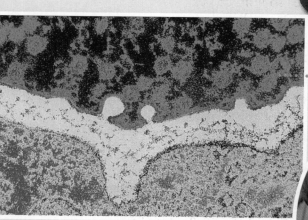

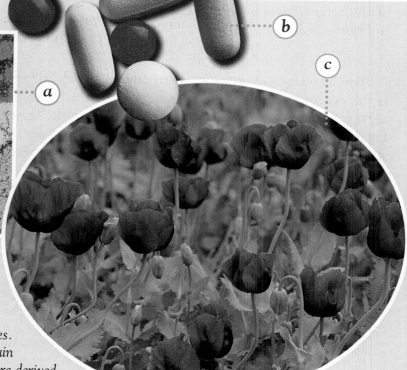

Figure 2–17

(**a**) *The color-enhanced transmission electron micrograph shows the synapse between two neurons.* (**b**) *Drugs can cause changes in the synapse, which, in turn, can affect nerve impulses.* (**c**) *The centers of the opium poppy flowers contain pods from which opiates, the pain-killing drugs, are derived.*

Figure 2–18

At resting potential, sodium ions (Na⁺) are outside the cell membrane. As the action potential begins, the sodium gates open and Na⁺ ions rush across the membrane. In a few milliseconds, the sodium gates close and the potassium gates open. This allows potassium ions (K⁺) to cross the membrane. So many K⁺ ions rush across the membrane that the outside of the membrane becomes more positive than the inside, thus restoring the resting potential.

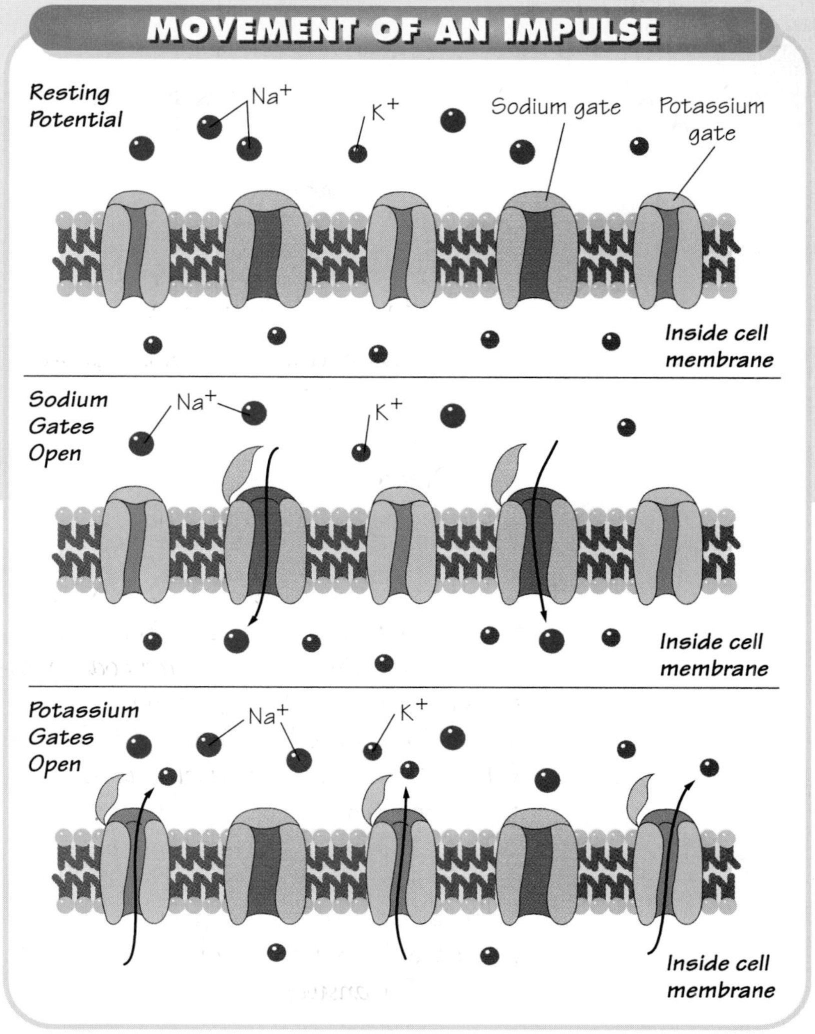

MOVEMENT OF AN IMPULSE

The difference in sodium and potassium ions on the two sides of the membrane is important because sodium and potassium are both positive ions. Ions do not move across most cell membranes very easily, and once the sodium ions are pumped out of the cell, they tend to stay out. However, significant numbers of potassium ions do manage to leak across the membrane. Remember, potassium ions are located mostly inside the cell. This means that large numbers of positive ions leak out of the cell but few leak into it.

What is the result of positive charges leaking out of the cell? As you might expect, this leaves fewer positive ions inside the cell, meaning that it is negatively charged compared with the outside. The great difference in charges between the two sides of the membrane produces the resting potential.

The Action Potential

A nerve impulse consists of an action potential that rapidly moves down the axon. How does this happen? Remember that an impulse can be started by the environment, by another neuron, or by an electrical stimulus.

The cell membrane of a neuron contains thousands of tiny protein channels known as **voltage-sensitive gates,** which can allow either sodium or potassium to pass through. Generally, the gates are closed. However, when the voltage across the membrane changes—as it does when a stimulus is present—the sodium gates open, allowing Na⁺ ions to rush across the membrane.

So many Na⁺ ions rush across the membrane that for a few milliseconds, the inside of the membrane becomes more positive than the outside! As you might expect, the inward rush of positive charges in one region of the membrane causes the sodium gates just ahead of it to respond to the voltage change, and these gates open, too. Very quickly, the impulse spreads along the axon.

However, almost as rapidly as they open, the sodium gates close, and the

MINI LAB — Predicting

Face to Face

PROBLEM **Predict** how the nervous system will respond to a stimulus.

PROCEDURE

1. Have two members of your group stand a few meters away from each other. They should be facing each other.

2. Have one group member hold a piece of screening or a sheet of clear plastic in front of his or her face.

3. Have the second group member toss a crumpled piece of paper at the screening or plastic. Observe the eyes of the group member behind the screening.

4. Repeat steps 1 to 3, but this time have the group member behind the screening try not to respond to the tossed paper. Predict what will happen.

ANALYZE AND CONCLUDE

1. What response did the group member have when the paper was tossed?

2. Was your prediction correct about the group member being successful in stopping the response to the stimulus (tossed paper)? Why or why not?

3. What is the advantage of having this quick response?

4. Which part of the central nervous system is responsible for this response? What is this response called?

movement of sodium stops. A few milliseconds after the sodium gates open, the potassium gates open, allowing K^+ ions to rush out of the cell. Within a few milliseconds, the inside of the membrane is negative once again.

The rapid opening and closing of sodium and potassium gates makes the impulse possible. The small amounts of sodium and potassium that cross the cell membrane during an impulse are quickly pumped back by the sodium-potassium pump, and the neuron is ready for another impulse.

When an action potential reaches the synapse, it triggers the release of a neurotransmitter. The neurotransmitter molecules diffuse across the gap and bind to receptors in the dendrites of the next neuron. The receptors cause the ion gates to open, and the impulse continues.

☑ **Checkpoint** What are voltage-sensitive gates?

Drugs and the Synapse

The nervous system depends on neurotransmitters to relay information about the world from cell to cell. This means that the synapse—the connection from one neuron to the next—is one of the body's most important relay stations.

What might happen if a chemical such as a **drug** that affected the synapse was introduced into the body? The nervous system could malfunction. A drug is any substance that causes a change in the body. **Drugs can affect the body in a variety of ways, causing changes in the brain, the nervous system, and the synapses between nerves.**

Stimulants

Some drugs, such as **stimulants,** increase the release of neurotransmitters at some synapses in the brain. This speeds up the nervous system, leading to a feeling of energy and well-being. When the effects of stimulants wear off, however, the brain's supply of neurotransmitters has been depleted. The user quickly falls into fatigue and depression. Long-term use causes hallucinations, circulatory problems, and psychological depression.

Even stronger effects are produced by drugs, such as **cocaine,** that act on neurons in what are known as the pleasure centers of the brain. The effects of cocaine are so strong that they produce **addiction**—an uncontrollable craving for more of the drug.

Cocaine causes the sudden release of a neurotransmitter called dopamine. Normally, dopamine is released when a basic need, such as hunger or thirst, is fulfilled. By fooling the brain into releasing dopamine, cocaine produces intense feelings of pleasure and satisfaction.

Cocaine is a powerful stimulant that increases the heart rate and blood pressure. For many first-time users, this stimulation is just too much—cocaine can damage the heart and has produced heart attacks, even in young people. In the United States, an inexpensive form of cocaine called crack has become one of the most dangerous drugs on the street. The intense high produced by crack wears off quickly and leaves the brain with too little dopamine. As a result, the user suddenly feels sad and depressed and quickly seeks another dose.

Depressants

Other drugs, called **depressants,** decrease the rate of brain activity. Some depressants, such as alcohol, enhance the effects of neurotransmitters that prevent some nerve cells from starting action potentials. This calms some parts of the brain that sense fear and relaxes the individual. However, long-term use of this type of drug can also cause problems. Depressant drugs reduce the effects of natural inhibitors of these neurons. As a result, the user comes to depend on the

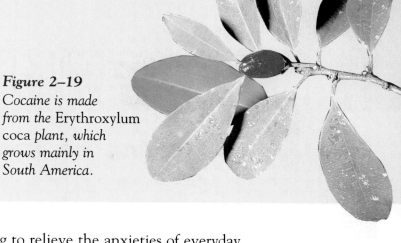

Figure 2–19
Cocaine is made from the Erythroxylum coca *plant, which grows mainly in South America.*

drug to relieve the anxieties of everyday life, which may seem unbearable without the drug.

☑ *Checkpoint*   What are depressants?

Opiates

The opium poppy produces a powerful class of pain-killing drugs called **opiates.** These include chemical derivatives of opium, such as morphine and heroin. Opiates mimic natural chemicals in the brain known as endorphins, which normally help to overcome sensations of pain. The first few doses of these drugs produce strong feelings of pleasure and security, but the body quickly adjusts to the higher levels of endorphins. Once this happens, the body literally cannot do without them. If the user attempts to stop taking these drugs, the body cannot produce enough of the natural endorphins that are needed to prevent the user from the uncontrollable pain and sickness that accompany withdrawal from the drug.

Section Review   2-4

1. **Describe** the function of the sodium-potassium pump.
2. **Describe** the effects of drugs on the nervous system.
3. **MINI LAB**   **Predict** how the nervous system will respond to a stimulus.
4. **BRANCHING OUT ACTIVITY**   Use library references to make a chart of the following groups of drugs—stimulants, depressants, hallucinogens, opiates, cocaine, marijuana, alcohol, and tobacco. **Summarize** their long- and short-term effects on the nervous system.

Laboratory Investigation

Observing the Structures of the Brain

In structure, the brain of a sheep is similar to the brain of a human. Most of the parts are located in identical areas. In this investigation, you will use the sheep brain to illustrate the anatomy of the human brain.

Problem

How can you **identify** the parts of the sheep brain?

Materials (per group)

dissecting pan
scalpel
probe
gloves
sheep brain

Procedure

1. Put on the pair of gloves provided. Place the sheep brain in a dissecting pan so that the raised side (dorsal) is up and the flat side (ventral) is resting on the pan.

2. Notice the large anterior section, the cerebrum. The cerebral cortex has many convolutions, or gyri (singular: gyrus), and grooves, called sulci (singular: sulcus). Each sulcus separates the cerebrum into lobes.

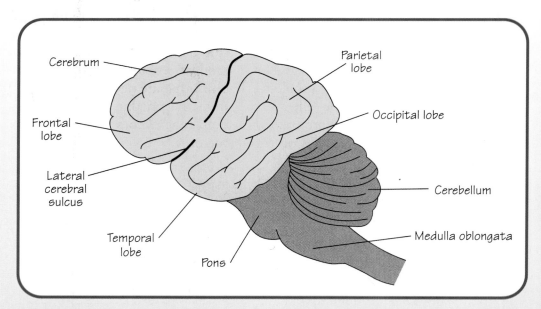

3. Locate the central sulcus that runs down from the top to the bottom of the cerebrum, midway between the front (anterior) and the back (posterior). In front of the central sulcus, you will find the frontal lobe. Behind the central sulcus is the parietal lobe.

4. Locate the lateral cerebral sulcus, a groove that runs horizontally along the cerebrum, separating the frontal lobe (above) from the temporal lobe (below).

5. Locate the occipital lobe, which is found posterior to the parietal lobe.

6. Posterior to the cerebrum is a smaller lobed structure called the cerebellum. Holding the brain in your hand, gently bend the cerebellum down. Although in the sheep the cerebellum is directly behind the cerebrum, in humans it is positioned similarly to where it is located when you bend the sheep's brain downward.

7. Posterior to the cerebellum, you will find the medulla oblongata, which forms a triangular shape. This part of the brain narrows into and becomes the spinal cord.

8. The midbrain section is more visible on the ventral (underneath) side. Locate the pons— a bridgelike, raised area in the cerebellum region. The pons is in front of the medulla oblongata.

9. With a scalpel, carefully cut the brain in half lengthwise. **CAUTION:** *Be very careful when using a sharp instrument.*

10. Distinguish between the outer gray cortex area of the cerebellum and its inner white matter. The gray matter is slightly darker than the white and not really gray at all.

11. Dispose of the brain as directed by your teacher. Clean your dissecting pan and scalpel and probe. Remove your gloves and wash your hands thoroughly.

Observations

1. Compare the sheep brain to the human brain.

2. Compare the size of the cerebrum with the other parts of the brain. What significance does the size of the cerebrum have?

3. Describe the location of the "gray" matter and the "white" matter in the brain. Other than by color, how do they differ?

Analysis and Conclusions

1. Were you able to identify the four lobes of the brain? Why or why not?

2. The hypothalamus is connected to the pituitary gland. What is the relationship between the hypothalamus and the pituitary gland?

3. What is the function of the medulla oblongata? Of the cerebellum?

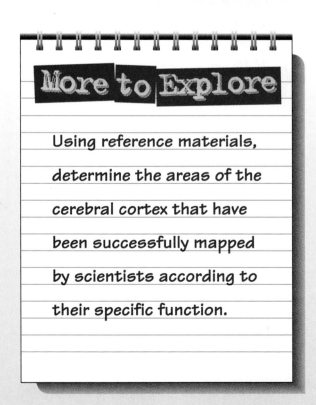

More to Explore

Using reference materials, determine the areas of the cerebral cortex that have been successfully mapped by scientists according to their specific function.

Study Guide

Summarizing Key Concepts

The key concepts in each section of this chapter are listed below to help you review the chapter content. Make sure you understand each concept and its relationship to other concepts and to the theme of this chapter.

2–1   The Human Nervous System

- A neuron is made up of a cell body, dendrites, and an axon.

- An impulse begins when a neuron is stimulated by another neuron or by the environment. Once it begins, the impulse travels rapidly down the axon away from the cell body.

2–2   Organization of the Nervous System

- The central nervous system consists of the brain and the spinal cord.

- The peripheral nervous system includes all the nerves and associated cells that connect the brain and spinal cord to the rest of the body.

2–3   The Senses

- Our five senses—vision, hearing, smell, taste, and touch—each begins with specialized sense organs that respond to the environment.

2–4   Nerve Impulses and Drugs

- The sodium-potassium pump uses the energy from ATP to pump sodium ions out of the cell while at the same time pumping potassium ions into the cell.

- Drugs can affect the body in a variety of ways, causing changes in the brain, the nervous system, and the synapses between nerves.

Reviewing Key Terms

Review the following vocabulary terms and their meaning. Then use each term in a complete sentence.

2–1   The Human Nervous System

neuron	motor neuron
impulse	interneuron
cell body	resting potential
dendrite	action potential
axon	myelin
nerve	synapse
sensory neuron	neurotransmitter

2–2   Organization of the Nervous System

meninges	medulla oblongata
cerebrospinal fluid	pons
cerebrum	reflex
cerebral cortex	somatic nervous system
cerebellum	autonomic nervous system
brainstem	

2–3   The Senses

cornea	auditory canal
iris	tympanum
pupil	cochlea
lens	semicircular canal
vitreous humor	taste bud
retina	

2–4   Nerve Impulses and Drugs

sodium-potassium pump	stimulant
	cocaine
voltage-sensitive gate	addiction
	depressant
drug	opiate

Recalling Main Ideas

Choose the letter of the answer that best completes the statement or answers the question.

1. Axons connect with other nerve cells at
   a. synapses.
   b. nodes.
   c. the brainstem.
   d. Schwann cells.

2. Dendrites
   a. transmit impulses away from the cell body.
   b. contain nuclei.
   c. are specialized to receive impulses from other cells.
   d. are surrounded by Schwann cells.

3. Which type of neuron is responsible for transmitting impulses to a muscle?
   a. sensory
   b. myelinated
   c. interneuron
   d. motor

4. What is the space between two neurons called?
   a. dendrite
   b. neurotransmitter
   c. synapse
   d. axon

5. In which function is the cerebral cortex not involved?
   a. sensory
   b. motor
   c. associative
   d. involuntary

6. A loss of balance might result from a disease of the
   a. cerebellum.
   b. cerebrum.
   c. pons.
   d. cranium.

7. The brain and the spinal cord are cushioned by layers of tough, elastic tissue called
   a. myelins.
   b. meninges.
   c. corneas.
   d. synapses.

8. Which of these is an active-transport protein located in a neuron's membrane?
   a. neurotransmitter
   b. myelin
   c. sodium-potassium pump
   d. vitreous humor

9. Substances that cause a change in the body are known as
   a. myelins.
   b. drugs.
   c. neurotransmitters.
   d. meninges.

Putting It All Together

Using the information on pages xii to xiii, complete the following concept map.

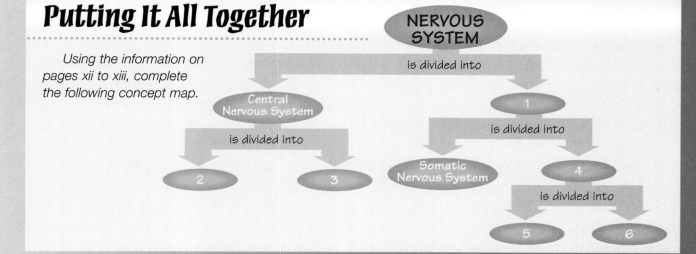

Reviewing What You Learned

Answer each of the following in a complete sentence.

1. What is a neuron?

2. List the three types of neurons.

3. What is a resting potential? An action potential?

4. What is myelin?

5. What is a synapse?

6. Explain the difference between a sensory neuron and a motor neuron.

7. Describe the two parts of the human nervous system.

8. Give the function of the meninges and the cerebrospinal fluid.

9. List the functions of the three parts of the brain.

10. Which area of the brain is linked to the pituitary gland?

11. What is a reflex?

12. How many divisions are there in the peripheral nervous system? Name them.

13. Describe the functions of the sympathetic and parasympathetic nervous systems.

14. Which organs are associated with the five senses?

15. What is the sodium-potassium pump?

16. List three types of drugs and their effects on the body.

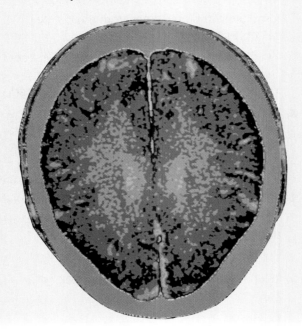

Expanding the Concepts

Discuss each of the following in a brief paragraph.

1. Describe the advantage of having an axon covered with myelin.

2. Describe how an action potential is carried from one neuron to the next.

3. Compare the central nervous system and the peripheral nervous system.

4. Describe the electrical state of the resting neuron.

5. Explain the sequences of changes associated with the passage of an impulse along the axon.

6. What are two factors that affect the rate at which impulses are transmitted along an axon?

7. Which parts of your nervous system are involved in reading and answering this question?

8. What changes in ion distribution occur in the area of an impulse?

9. Describe the function of the sodium-potassium pump.

10. How do the different types of drugs affect the nervous system?

Extending Your Thinking

Use the skills you have developed in this chapter to answer the following.

1. **Relating concepts**   The effects of the two divisions of the autonomic nervous system are said to be antagonistic. What does this mean? What is the advantage of this relationship?

2. **Applying concepts**   When you go snorkeling with a face mask, you can see very clearly in the water. But if you remove the face mask, things become blurry. Why is this so?

3. **Predicting**   Multiple sclerosis (MS) is characterized by the patchy destruction of myelin. Predict the symptoms that might be produced.

4. **Interpreting**   Heat receptors of mammals are particularly concentrated on the tongue. These receptors keep humans from burning the mouth with hot food. What advantage is it for a wild mammal that doesn't cook its food to have so many heat receptors on its tongue?

5. **Designing an experiment**   Design an experiment to determine the effects of fatigue on reaction time. Formulate a hypothesis and write up a procedure. Have your teacher check your experimental plan before you begin.

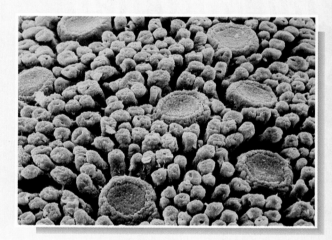

Applying Your Skills

Sensing Trouble

We respond to many stimuli in our environment every day. Through the use of our sense organs, we react to the stimuli, process the information, and respond very quickly. How does this happen?

1. Choose any two of the following situations:

   a. Seeing an approaching ambulance in the rear-view mirror of a car, then pulling over to the side to get out of the way

   b. Hearing a telephone ringing, then running to answer it

   c. Eating a vegetable you don't like, then deciding to take a drink of water

   d. Feeling chilly in a swimming pool, then deciding to get out of the water

2. Diagram the path taken when the sense organ first reacts to the stimulus in each situation to when the impulse is processed as a response.

3. Label the various neurons as well as the parts of one neuron.

• GOING FURTHER •

4. Determine the time it takes you to react to smelling a pizza burning and getting up to turn off the oven.

Integumentary, Skeletal, and Muscular Systems

FOCUSING THE CHAPTER
THEME: *Scale and Structure*

Biology and Your World

BIO JOURNAL

Support and movement are the basic functions of the integumentary, skeletal, and muscular systems. In your journal, compare these three body systems to a building being constructed. What are the girders? What are the walls? How are they similar? How are they different?

Teens playing soccer

GUIDE FOR READING

- **Identify** the basic structures of the integumentary system.

WHEN YOU LOOK AT YOURSELF in the mirror, what do you notice first? Maybe you notice your hair or your skin— or another freckle. Did you know that one system of the body is responsible for the shade of your skin, your hair, and even your nails? This body system is the integumentary system. Your integumentary system acts like a protective covering for the rest of your body. In this section, we will examine the structures of the integumentary system.

Layers of Skin

The largest organ of the body— the **skin**—is part of the integumentary (ihn-tehg-yoo-MEHN-ter-ee) system. **The integumentary system includes your skin, hair, nails, and a number of important glands in the skin.** The skin itself is made up of two layers. The outer layer is called the **epidermis,** whereas the inner layer is called the **dermis.**

Epidermis

The epidermis is made up of layers of epithelial cells. Deep in the epidermis, these cells grow and divide rapidly, producing new cells that are gradually pushed toward the surface of the skin. As they move upward, the cells begin making **keratin,** a tough, flexible protein. In humans, keratin is the major protein found in hair and fingernails.

INTEGRATING LANGUAGE ARTS

The word integere *is a Latin verb meaning "to cover." How does this explain how the integumentary system got its name?*

Figure 3–1
The skin—the single largest organ of the body—is part of the integumentary system. **(a)** *The small dark granules within this melanocyte are responsible for protecting the skin from the harmful ultraviolet rays of the sun.* **(b)** *Sweating is one way the body regulates temperature.* **(c)** *This sweat gland, which is one of about 3 million in the skin, helps to regulate body temperature. The green spheres inside the sweat gland are bacteria (magnification: 10,000X).*

CROSS SECTION OF SKIN

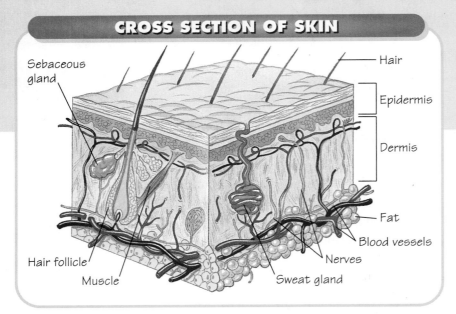

Sebaceous gland

Hair

Epidermis

Dermis

Fat

Blood vessels

Nerves

Sweat gland

Hair follicle

Muscle

Figure 3–2
The skin consists of two layers—the epidermis and the dermis. The layer of fat in the dermis provides insulation.

As they near the surface, these cells die, but the keratin within remains, forming a tough, waterproof layer on the surface of the skin. As you walk, work, and bathe, you wash and scrape off millions of these dead cells every day. But don't worry, your skin produces more than enough new cells to take their place.

Cells that produce pigments, called melanocytes, are also found in the epidermis. They contain granules of **melanin,** a dark-brown pigment that gives skin its color. Most people have the same number of melanocytes in their skin, but dark-skinned people produce more melanin than people with light skin.

Dermis

The dermis supports the epidermis and contains cells such as nerve endings, blood vessels, and smooth muscles. When you feel something by touching it with your fingers, touch receptors in your dermis are picking up the sensation.

The dermis reacts to the body's needs in a number of ways. For example, on cold days—when you need to conserve heat—blood vessels in the dermis narrow, limiting the loss of heat. When the body is hot, the same vessels widen, bringing more blood to the skin. This warms the skin, causing the loss of heat.

The dermis also contains two types of glands—sweat glands and sebaceous (suh-BAY-shuhs), or oil, glands. Sweat glands produce a watery secretion that contains ammonia, salt, and other compounds. These glands are controlled by the nervous system, which activates them to cool the body when it gets too hot. Sebaceous glands produce an oily secretion that helps keep the epidermis flexible and waterproof.

Hair and Nails

Hair is produced from columns of cells that are filled with keratin and then die. Clusters of such cells make up **hair follicles,** which are anchored in the dermis. Cells multiply in the base of the follicle, causing the hair to grow longer.

Toenails and fingernails are formed in almost the same way, except that the keratin-forming cells in these tissues form a flattened plate. Nails cover and protect the tips of your fingers and toes.

Section Review 3–1

1. **Identify** the basic structures of the integumentary system.
2. **Critical Thinking—Inferring** Some scientists are concerned about the destruction of the ozone layer, which prevents the sun's ultraviolet radiation from reaching the Earth. Why might this be of concern for humans?

The Skeletal System

GUIDE FOR READING

- **List** the functions of an internal skeleton.
- **Compare** the three main kinds of joints.

MINI LAB
- **Classify** your joints based on the motions they make.

LIKE THE FRAMEWORK OF A tall building, the human skeleton contains important clues as to the kind of organisms we are. The shape of our hip bones shows that we walk on two legs. The structure of the bones in our hands, especially our thumbs, gives us the ability to hold and grasp objects. And the size and shape of our skull indicate that we have a well-developed nervous system.

Bones

All vertebrates, humans included, have an internal skeletal system. **An internal skeleton provides support for the body, attachment sites for muscles, and protection for internal organs.** The skull protects the brain, and the ribs protect the heart and lungs. Bones store supplies of calcium and phosphorus that can be used by other tissues, and they also produce blood cells.

Bone Structure

Bones are surrounded by a tough membrane called the **periosteum** (per-ee-AHS-tee-uhm). Just inside the periosteum is a dense layer of **compact bone.** Compact bone appears to be solid, but a series of **Haversian** (huh-VER-zhuhn) **canals** containing nerves and blood vessels runs through it. A region of **spongy bone** is usually located just inside the compact bone. Although it is less dense than compact bone, spongy bone is strong and resilient.

Figure 3–3
The human skeleton is made up of four types of connective tissue—bone, cartilage, ligament, and tendon. (a) *This electron micrograph shows a mature bone cell, or osteocyte, that makes up normal bone tissue.* (b) *Like the skeletal system,* (c) *the framework of this building provides structure and support.*

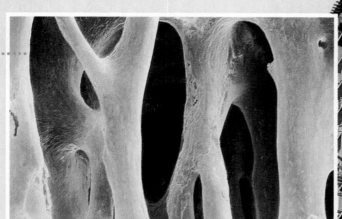

Figure 3–4

The human skeleton is made up of 206 bones. The axial skeleton, colored blue, includes the skull, the vertebral column, and the rib cage. The appendicular skeleton, colored beige, includes the bones of the arms, legs, hands, and feet.

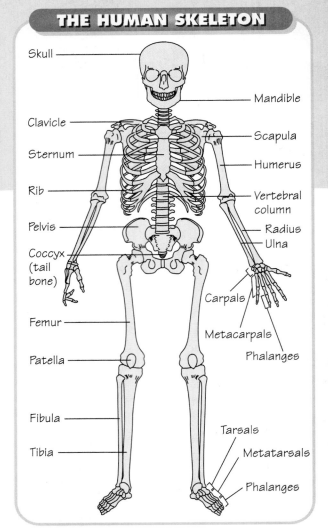

THE HUMAN SKELETON

Skull
Mandible
Clavicle
Scapula
Sternum
Humerus
Rib
Vertebral column
Pelvis
Radius
Coccyx (tail bone)
Ulna
Femur
Carpals
Metacarpals
Phalanges
Patella
Fibula
Tibia
Tarsals
Metatarsals
Phalanges

Embedded in both compact and spongy bone are cells called **osteocytes** (AHS-tee-oh-sights). Osteocytes help to build and maintain bones. They deposit the minerals that make up bone and can reabsorb them when the body needs them elsewhere.

As you can see in **Figure 3–6,** inside many larger bones is a region of blood-forming tissue called **bone marrow.** White and red blood cells are produced in the bone marrow. The marrow also plays an important role in the immune response.

a

Figure 3–5

a *This illustration shows the structures of compact and spongy bone. Running through compact bone is a network of tubes called Haversian canals, which contain blood vessels and nerves.* **b** *In this scanning electron micrograph of compact bone, some blood vessels can be seen in a Haversian canal (magnification: 315X).*

b

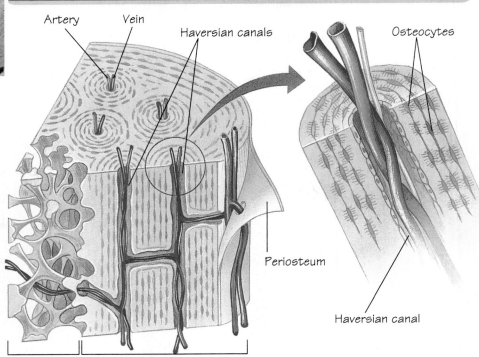

STRUCTURES OF COMPACT AND SPONGY BONE

Artery
Vein
Haversian canals
Osteocytes
Periosteum
Haversian canal
Spongy Bone
Compact Bone

Bone Growth

Bones are produced from cartilage. During embryonic development, the human skeleton first appears almost as a cartilage "scale model." Gradually, this cartilage "model" is replaced by bone.

Osteocytes near the surface of the bone begin this process, gradually moving inward, depositing minerals that replace the cartilage with bone. The long bones of the arms and legs, for example, have growing points at either end called growth plates. Cartilage is produced at these plates and then is gradually replaced by bone as the skeleton enlarges. By the time you have stopped increasing in height—usually between the ages of 18 and 20—the growth plates have disappeared and the bone has reached its final size and shape.

Joints

Joints are the places where two bones meet. Your ability to move depends not only on your muscles, but also on the joints that must allow bones to move smoothly past each other. There are three kinds of joints—**fixed, slightly movable,** and **freely movable.**

Fixed joints allow little or no movement between bones. Some of the most important fixed joints are those located in the skull. Skull

All the Right Moves

PROBLEM *How can the motions you make be used to* **classify** *your joints?*

PROCEDURE

1. Try each of the actions listed below. Notice which freely movable joints are used and the kind of motion in each joint:
   - waving a paper fan
   - looking behind yourself
   - shrugging your shoulders
   - rotating your index finger
   - pushing open a door
   - lifting a backpack

2. Compare the motion in each joint with the illustration on page 50.

ANALYZE AND CONCLUDE

1. Which type of freely movable joint did you use in each action? Construct a table to record your answer.

2. Which joint was the easiest to classify? Which was the hardest? Why do you think this is so?

Figure 3–6
In a typical bone, such as the femur, blood vessels pass through the periosteum, carrying oxygen and nutrients to the bone. In addition to red marrow, most bones also contain yellow marrow, which is made up of blood vessels, nerve cells, and fat.

THE STRUCTURE OF BONE

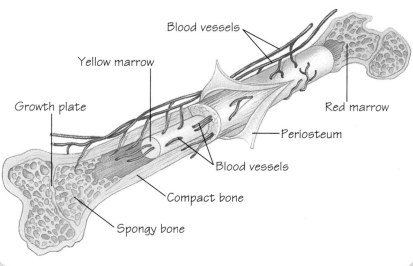

Blood vessels

Yellow marrow

Growth plate

Red marrow

Periosteum

Blood vessels

Compact bone

Spongy bone

First two cervical vertebrae   Elbow   Base of fingers   Base of thumb   Shoulder   Toes

Pivot   Hinge   Ellipsoid   Saddle   Ball-and-socket   Gliding

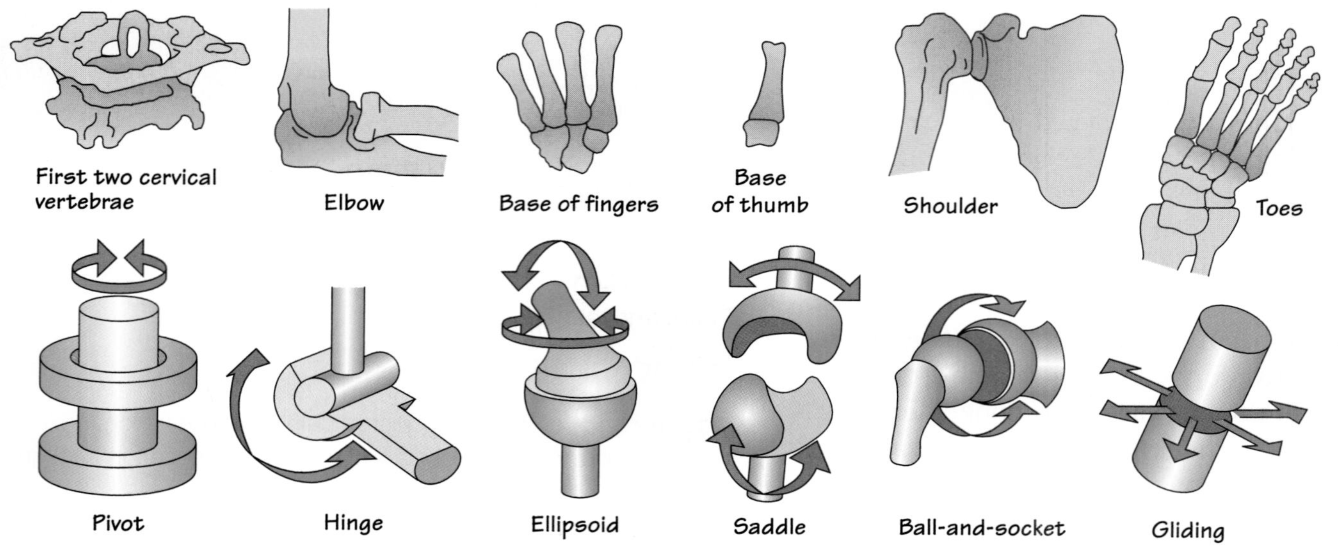

Figure 3–7

The six types of freely movable joints allow a wide range of motion. A pivot joint allows for rotation of one joint around another; a hinge joint permits back-and-forth motion; an ellipsoid joint allows for a hinge-type movement in two directions; a saddle joint allows for movement in two planes; a ball-and-socket joint permits circular movement; and a gliding joint permits a sliding motion of one bone over another.

bones do not move because their purpose is to protect the brain and sense organs in the head.

Slightly movable joints allow a small amount of movement. The bones of the spinal column as well as the ribs are slightly movable joints. The bones of the spinal column are separated from each other by pads of cartilage, called disks. Cartilage is extremely flexible and absorbs most of the shocks and strains of everyday activity.

Freely movable joints allow a wide range of movement. Ball-and-socket joints, located in the shoulders and hips, allow the widest range of movement. The other types of freely movable joints are shown in *Figure 3–7.*

The ends of bones in freely movable joints are covered with layers of cartilage, providing a smooth surface at the point of contact. The joint itself is enclosed by a joint capsule. The capsule may include **ligaments**—tissues that connect the bones of the joint—and **tendons,** which connect muscles and bones. Inside the capsule is **synovial** (sih-NOH-vee-uhl) **fluid,** a natural lubricant that reduces friction and allows the cartilage-coated bones to slip past each other easily.

Section Review 3–2

1. **List** the functions of an internal skeleton.
2. **Compare** the three main kinds of joints.
3. **Critical Thinking—Inferring**   Why do you think that the amount of cartilage as compared to bone decreases as a person develops?
4. **MINI LAB**   How can your motions be used to **classify** your joints?

The Muscular System

GUIDE FOR READING

- **Compare** the three types of muscle tissue.
- **Describe** the process of muscle contraction.

MINI LAB
- **Compare** the actions of the muscles of your left hand with those of your right hand.

DESPITE THE FANTASIES OF *Hollywood horror films, the skeleton cannot move by itself. Muscles provide the forces that put the body into motion. More than 40 percent of the mass of the human body is muscle—making it the most common tissue in the body. The muscular system includes the large muscles, which athletes proudly display as signs of physical* development. *But it also includes thousands of tiny muscles throughout the body that regulate blood pressure, move food through the digestive system, and power every movement of the body—from the blink of an eye to the hint of a smile.*

Muscle Tissue

There are three types of muscle tissue—**skeletal, cardiac,** and **smooth**—that are specialized for a different job in the body. Each of these three types of muscle has a different cellular structure.

Skeletal Muscle Tissue

Skeletal muscle tissue is generally attached to the bones of the skeleton and is usually under voluntary control.

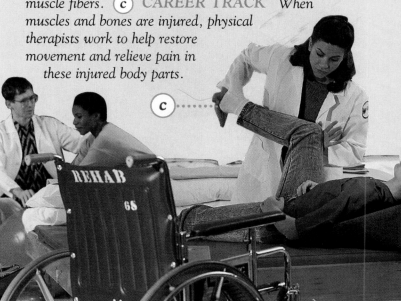

Figure 3–8
Muscle tissue is found everywhere within the body—from beneath the skin to deep within the body. (**a**) *Skeletal muscles are generally connected to bones and are at work every time we move.* (**b**) *This transmission electron micrograph of skeletal muscle shows the banding pattern of the myofibrils—the units that make up muscle fibers.* (**c**) CAREER TRACK *When muscles and bones are injured, physical therapists work to help restore movement and relieve pain in these injured body parts.*

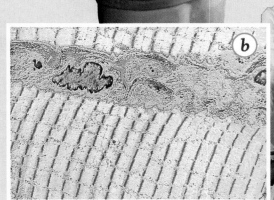

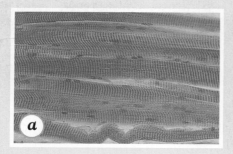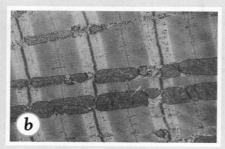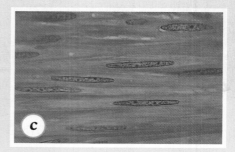

Figure 3–9

There are three types of muscle tissue—skeletal, cardiac, and smooth. **(a)** *Because skeletal, or striated, muscle cells are long and slender, they are often called muscle fibers rather than muscle cells (magnification: 140X).* **(b)** *Unlike skeletal muscle tissue, cardiac muscle tissue contracts without direct stimulation by the nervous system (magnification: 200X).* **(c)** *Smooth muscle tissue is found in many internal organs and in the walls of many blood vessels. Their contractions move food through the digestive system and control the flow of blood through the circulatory system (magnification: 360X).*

Skeletal muscle tissue is behind every conscious movement you make, whether you are lifting a weight or tying your shoelaces. This is because most skeletal muscle tissue is controlled directly by the nervous system. Skeletal muscle cells have many nuclei because they form during development from the fusion of scores of individual cells.

Skeletal muscle cells can be very large—as long as 60 centimeters in the cells in the large muscles of your arms and legs! Under the light microscope, skeletal muscle cells appear striated, or striped. For this reason, skeletal muscle tissue is often called striated muscle tissue.

Figure 3–10

Skeletal muscles are made up of densely packed muscle fibers. Each muscle fiber is made up of many thin fibers called myofibrils. Each myofibril, in turn, is made up of both thick contractile filaments—myosin—and thin contractile filaments—actin.

ANATOMY OF A MUSCLE

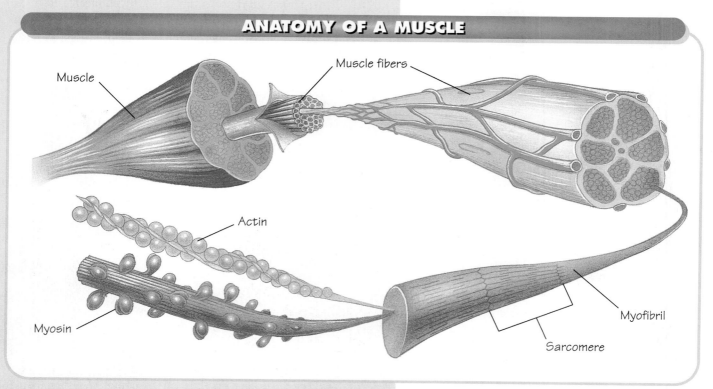

Muscle

Muscle fibers

Actin

Myosin

Myofibril

Sarcomere

A Stimulating Situation

Your class is discussing the muscular system and muscular contraction. One of the students asks what causes a muscle twitch. The teacher responds by saying that a muscle twitch is a quick contraction of the muscle followed by immediate relaxation.

Another student wonders how you can maintain a muscle contraction over a length of time. The teacher explains that when there is a continuous stream of nerve impulses, the muscle fibers receive new stimulation before they are able to relax. The individual muscle twitches together form a smooth, continuous contraction called tetanization. If the muscle is continuously stimulated for a long period of time, however, it would be unable to respond to further stimulation and fatigue would set in.

The teacher shows the class the following graph to further explain muscular contraction. Look at the graph and answer the questions that follow.

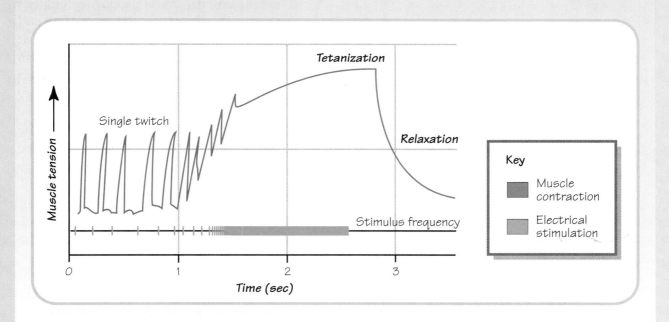

• THINK ABOUT IT •

1. Describe what happens when the stimulus frequency is slow.

2. Describe what happens when the stimulus frequency increases.

3. According to this graph, when does tetanization occur?

4. Fatigue can occur only in skeletal muscles. Can you explain why this is so?

Figure 3–11
When a muscle is stimulated to contract, the myosin and actin filaments slide past each other, causing the muscle cells to shorten and the muscle to contract.

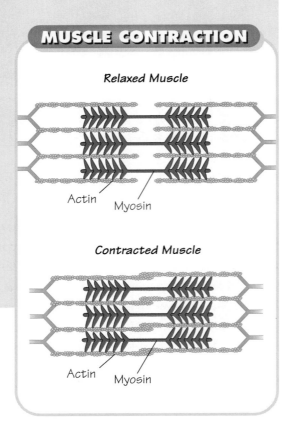

Relaxed Muscle

Actin   Myosin

Contracted Muscle

Actin   Myosin

Cardiac Muscle Tissue

Cardiac muscle tissue is found in just one place in the body—the heart. **Cardiac muscle tissue is striated, but the smaller cardiac muscle cells have just one nucleus, and they are not under the direct control of the central nervous system.** Adjacent cardiac muscle cells form branching fibers that allow nerve impulses to move from cell to cell.

Smooth Muscle Tissue

The cells of smooth muscle tissue are spindle-shaped, have a single nucleus, and are not striated. Smooth muscle tissue is generally not under the conscious control of the nervous system. Smooth muscle tissue is found in the walls of many internal organs, except the heart. It is responsible for actions not under voluntary control, such as digestion. Although smooth muscle tissue contracts much more slowly than skeletal muscle tissue does, it can maintain its contraction for a much longer period of time.

Muscle Structure

To understand how a muscle works, we can look inside the kind of muscle cell that we understand best—the skeletal muscle cell. Scientists have learned a great deal about skeletal muscle, partly because the regular structure of these cells has made them easy to study.

Under the electron microscope, we can see that the striations in these cells are actually formed by an alternating pattern of thick and thin filaments. The thick filaments are made of a protein called **myosin.** Thin filaments contain another protein, called **actin.** These thick and thin filaments overlap in a regular pattern, producing the striations that appear under the light microscope.

These tiny actin and myosin filaments are the force-producing engines that cause a muscle to contract. One end of the myosin molecule sticks out just enough from the thick filament to form a cross-bridge that makes firm contact with the thin filament. Using the energy supplied by the splitting of ATP, the cross-bridge changes shape, pulling the thin filament along. The cross-bridge then releases the thin filament, snaps back to its original position, and "grabs" the thin filament again to start another cycle. The cross-bridges repeatedly bend, release, and reattach farther along the thin filament.

When hundreds of thousands of actin-myosin cross-bridges go through their cycle in a fraction of a second, the muscle cell contracts with considerable force. This process is known as the **sliding filament theory** of muscle contraction because the thick and thin filaments slide past each other as the muscle shortens. One molecule of ATP supplies the energy for each cycle.

Checkpoint   What is myosin? Actin?

Muscle Contraction

To make well-coordinated movements, muscle contractions must be carefully controlled. In most skeletal muscles, this is the job of motor neurons.

A single motor neuron may form synapses to one or several muscle cells. An impulse in the motor neuron causes the release of a neurotransmitter, **acetylcholine** (as-ih-tihl-KOH-leen), which causes a new action potential. This, in turn, causes the release of calcium ions into the cytoplasm of muscle cells. When calcium flows into the cytoplasm, cross-bridges form, and the muscle contracts.

The contraction stops when enzymes destroy the neurotransmitter. Calcium is then removed from the cytoplasm, and the contraction stops.

Muscles and Movement

Muscles produce force by contracting. Attached to bones by tendons, a muscle can pull two bones together, using the joint between them as a lever. When you lift a heavy object or pull something close to you, it's easy to see how muscle contraction produces the movement.

An individual muscle can pull by contracting, but it cannot push. If that is true, then how can you push a door open or do a pushup in gym class? The answer is that most skeletal muscles are arranged in pairs. These pairs oppose each other and produce forceful movements in either direction. Your upper arm, for example, contains one muscle—the biceps—that flexes, or bends, the arm. On the other side of the upper arm is another muscle—the triceps—that extends the arm. When you do a pushup, the triceps contracts, forcing the arm to extend and push down on the gym floor.

MINI LAB ·········· Comparing ·······

Whose Side Are You On?

PROBLEM   *How do the actions of the muscles of your left hand **compare** with those of your right hand?*

PROCEDURE

1. Count the number of times you can fully open a spring clothes pin with your right thumb and right index finger for 2 minutes. Have your partner time you. Record the results.

2. Rest for 1 minute and repeat step 1. Record the results.

3. Repeat steps 1 and 2 with your left hand. Record the results.

ANALYZE AND CONCLUDE

1. Compare the two performances of your right-hand muscles.

2. How did the performance of your right hand compare with that of your left hand?

3. What conclusions can you draw from these results?

Section Review 3-3

1. **Compare** the three types of muscle tissue.
2. **Describe** the process of muscle contraction.
3. **Critical Thinking—Relating Concepts**   Why are skeletal muscles arranged in pairs?
4. **MINI LAB**   How do the actions of the muscles of your left hand **compare** with those of your right hand?

GUIDE FOR READING

- **List** the two main types of muscle fibers in skeletal muscles.

- **Compare** aerobic exercises and resistance exercises.

AN ATHLETE MAY DEVOTE *hours every day to developing and conditioning the muscular system. To a runner, a swimmer, or a weight lifter, the strength, flexibility, and endurance of the muscular system is the difference between winning and losing. But a well-conditioned muscular system is important even to those of us who are not competitive athletes. We depend on our skeletal muscles— whether walking, running, working, or playing—and we can make many of life's everyday challenges easier by keeping our muscles in good condition.*

Specialized Skeletal Muscle Fibers

If you look at any large office that performs many different jobs, you will find specialists. One person might sell the product, another might handle the bookkeeping, and another the scheduling. What's the advantage of an arrangement like this? By allowing a few people to specialize at different tasks, the jobs get done more quickly and efficiently.

Even though the job description for a muscle is simple—contract on command—a large skeletal muscle contains specialists of its own. **Skeletal muscles contain two main types of muscle fibers—red and white— whose properties make them specialists at different kinds of exercise.**

Red muscle fibers contain large amounts of the reddish oxygen-storing protein **myoglobin.** Red fibers also have rich blood supplies and plenty of mitochondria to produce ATP through aerobic

Figure 3–12
Different types of exercise affect different types of skeletal muscle fibers. (a) *Aerobic exercises, such as bicycling, affect red muscle fibers, whereas* (b) *resistance exercises, such as weight lifting, affect white muscle fibers.* (c) *When planning an exercise program, both aerobic and resistance-type exercises should be included.*

(oxygen-dependent) respiration. Red fibers are also called slow-twitch muscle fibers because they contract slowly after being stimulated by a motor neuron.

Red muscle fibers are usually able to meet their ATP needs from their own mitochondria. Red muscle fibers enable muscles to contract again and again, against slight resistance, without fatigue.

White muscle fibers contain little or no myoglobin, giving them a pale color. They have few mitochondria, but they store large reserves of **glycogen.** Glycogen is a compound that stores excess glucose in the body. When white muscle fibers need extra ATP, that glycogen is broken down to glucose, which is then used anaerobically (without oxygen) to generate ATP by fermentation.

White fibers are also called fast-twitch muscle fibers and can generate powerful contractions. Having few mitochondria, these fibers contain greater densities of contractile proteins than red fibers do. These powerful fibers fatigue easily, however, which means that they can produce maximum contractions for only a few seconds at a time.

Exercise and Muscle Cells

As you probably know, exercising a muscle causes it to get stronger. There are different kinds of exercise, of course, and each kind has different effects on each kind of skeletal muscle cell.

Aerobic exercises—such as running, swimming, and bicycling—cause your body systems to become more efficient. For example, your circulatory system benefits because the number of capillaries in the muscle increases, which increases its blood supply. More myoglobin is synthesized, especially in red fibers. Aerobic exercises also benefit the heart and lungs, helping to increase their capacity. All these effects increase physical endurance—the ability to perform an activity without fatigue. However, aerobic exercises do not result in large increases in muscle size.

Resistance exercises, such as weight lifting, increase muscle size. This effect is most pronounced in the white fibers, which grow in size and add more contractile proteins after such exercises.

Resistance exercises have little effect on red fibers, which means that they do not improve endurance. However, they do have a dramatic effect on maximum muscle strength. Because most skeletal muscles function in opposing pairs, weight training should include exercises that develop both muscles in each pair. This helps an individual to maintain coordination and flexibility.

Different forms of exercise develop different types of muscle fibers. This means that the best exercise programs should blend resistance and aerobic training, helping to develop muscles, heart, and lungs.

Section Review 3-4

1. **List** the two main types of muscle fibers found in skeletal muscles.
2. **Compare** aerobic exercises and resistance exercises.
3. **BRANCHING OUT ACTIVITY** Use a health book as a guide and **design** and **write** an exercise program for yourself that includes both aerobic and resistance exercises. Do not perform your exercise program unless it has been checked and approved by your doctor.

Laboratory Investigation

Mapping Your Sweat Glands

A solution of iodine reacts with starch by turning a blue-black color. When dried iodine comes in contact with the water given off by sweat glands, it becomes a solution again and will react with the starch in a piece of blotting paper, causing it to turn a blue-black color. In this investigation, you will take advantage of these changes to locate sweat glands in your skin.

Problem

Which areas of your skin have the most sweat glands? **Make a prediction** to answer this question.

Materials (per group)

4 squares of blotting paper, 1 cm × 1 cm
medical adhesive tape
iodine solution
cotton swabs

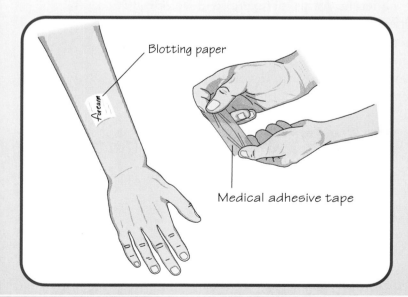
Blotting paper
Forearm
Medical adhesive tape

Procedure

1. **Wash and dry your hands and forearms thoroughly. Roll your sleeves up to above the elbow. Carefully dip the cotton swab into the iodine solution. CAUTION:** *Be careful when using iodine because it stains clothing.*

2. **Find an area in the center of the palm of one of your hands that is free of creases. Using the iodine-soaked cotton swab, paint a 2-cm square on your palm and let it dry.**

3. **Repeat step 2 on the inside of one of your forearms.**

4. **Using a pencil, label one of the blotting-paper squares "Palm" and the other one "Forearm." Have your partner tape the blotting paper square labeled "Palm" over the iodine on your palm and the square labeled "Forearm" over the iodine on your forearm. Allow the blotting paper to remain in place for 20 minutes.**

5. While you are waiting, write a prediction about whether the palm of your hand or your forearm has more sweat glands. Also predict whether all members of the class will have the same results.

6. After 20 minutes, have your lab partner remove the two paper squares. Count the number of blue-black dots on each one. Each dot indicates the presence of an active sweat gland.

7. Construct a data table similar to the one shown. Record the number of dots on the paper square for your palm. In the space marked "Distribution of Sweat Glands," draw or write a description of the pattern of dots.

Observations

1. What difference did you observe in the number of sweat glands per square centimeter on your palm and forearm?

2. What differences were there in the patterns of sweat glands?

DATA TABLE

Location of Sweat Glands	Number of Active Sweat Glands	Distribution of Sweat Glands
Middle surface of palm		
Inside of forearm		

Analysis and Conclusions

1. Which area tested—palm or forearm—had the greatest density of active sweat glands?

2. Were your predictions correct? Explain your answer.

3. How did the information in your data table compare with the information your classmates compiled?

4. What conclusion can you draw about the distribution of sweat glands on the skin?

5. Do all sweat glands produce the same amount of sweat? What evidence did you observe to support your answer?

More to Explore

Using the same materials, design an experiment to find out whether exercise affects the number of sweat glands that are active at any one time.

Study Guide

Summarizing Key Concepts

The key concepts in each section of this chapter are listed below to help you review the chapter content. Make sure you understand each concept and its relationship to other concepts and to the theme of this chapter.

3–1 The Integumentary System

• The integumentary system includes your skin, hair, nails, and a number of important glands in the skin.

3–2 The Skeletal System

• An internal skeleton provides support for the body, attachment sites for muscles, and protection for internal organs.

• There are three kinds of joints in the body. Fixed joints allow little or no movement between bones. Slightly movable joints allow a small amount of movement. Freely movable joints allow a wide range of movement.

3–3 The Muscular System

• Skeletal muscle tissue is generally attached to the bones of the skeleton and is usually under voluntary control. Cardiac muscle tissue is striated, but the smaller cardiac muscle cells have one nucleus and are not under the direct control of the central nervous system. Smooth muscle tissue is generally not under the conscious control of the nervous system.

• When hundreds of thousands of actin-myosin cross-bridges go through their cycle in a fraction of a second, the muscle cell contracts with considerable force.

3–4 The Biology of Exercise

• Skeletal muscles contain two main types of muscle fibers—red and white—whose properties make them specialists at different kinds of exercise.

• Aerobic exercises—such as running, swimming, and bicycling—cause your body systems to become more efficient. Resistance exercises, such as weight lifting, produce an increase in muscle size.

Reviewing Key Terms

Review the following vocabulary terms and their meaning. Then use each term in a complete sentence.

3–1 The Integumentary System

skin	keratin
epidermis	melanin
dermis	hair follicle

3–2 The Skeletal System

periosteum	fixed joint
compact bone	slightly movable joint
Haversian canal	freely movable joint
spongy bone	ligament
osteocyte	tendon
bone marrow	synovial fluid

3–3 The Muscular System

skeletal muscle tissue
cardiac muscle tissue
smooth muscle tissue
myosin
actin
sliding filament theory
acetylcholine

3–4 The Biology of Exercise

myoglobin
glycogen

Recalling Main Ideas

Choose the letter of the answer that best completes the statement or answers the question.

1. The cells that form keratin are found in the
   a. ligaments.
   b. myoglobin.
   c. bone marrow.
   d. epidermis.

2. The dermis helps to regulate body temperature by responses in the
   a. oil glands.
   b. blood vessels.
   c. sweat glands and blood vessels.
   d. sweat glands.

3. The pigment that gives skin its color is called
   a. melanocyte.
   b. keratin.
   c. melanin.
   d. osteocyte.

4. Cartilage is part of the
   a. nervous system.
   b. integumentary system.
   c. muscular system.
   d. skeletal system.

5. Haversian canals contain
   a. bone cells.
   b. nerves and blood vessels.
   c. periosteum.
   d. calcium phosphate crystals.

6. Fixed joints are most flexible
   a. at birth.
   b. in adolescence.
   c. in childhood.
   d. in adulthood.

7. In freely movable joints, the ends of bones are covered with
   a. spongy bone.
   b. cartilage.
   c. bone marrow.
   d. blood vessels.

8. Which contains the greatest amount of skeletal muscle tissue?
   a. cerebrum
   b. kidney
   c. small intestine
   d. foot

9. The tissues that connect muscles to bones are called
   a. ligaments.
   b. tendons.
   c. sliding filaments.
   d. cartilage.

10. Which of the following is true of resistance exercises?
   a. increase the capacity of the heart
   b. increase the number of capillaries
   c. increase muscle size
   d. increase endurance

Putting It All Together

Using the information on pages xii to xiii, complete the following concept map.

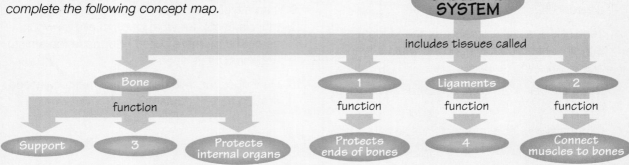

Reviewing What You Learned

Answer each of the following in a complete sentence.

1. What is the integumentary system?

2. Which structures does keratin form in humans and other animals?

3. Which glands are found in the dermis?

4. How are the formation of hair and nails related?

5. What kinds of tissue make up an internal skeletal system?

6. How does compact bone differ from spongy bone?

7. What is the function of osteocytes?

8. List three examples of freely movable joints.

9. Explain the purpose of synovial fluid.

10. How do the tissues that make up the skeleton change during human development?

11. What are the three types of muscles and where are they found?

12. What is acetylcholine?

13. How can muscles, which only contract, enable the skeleton to push as well as pull?

14. What is myoglobin?

15. Explain the benefits of aerobic exercises on the body.

Expanding the Concepts

Discuss each of the following in a brief paragraph.

1. What is meant when a biologist says that "we are alive because our surface is dead"?

2. How does the dermis differ from the epidermis?

3. Name three main classes of joints and their differences.

4. Tendinitis is an inflammation of the tendon. Explain what probably happens when a tennis player develops tendinitis.

5. Using a labeled diagram, describe the structure of a joint.

6. **Compare** the three types of muscle tissue by their function and cellular structure.

7. Describe the sliding filament theory of muscle contraction.

8. Describe the role of calcium in the skeletal system.

9. If an athlete has a greater number of red muscle fibers, for what kinds of events would he or she be more suited? Suppose the athlete had more white fibers?

10. How does the skin help to maintain a balanced environment in humans?

Extending Your Thinking

Use the skills you have developed in this chapter to answer the following.

1. **Classifying** Two athletes have had their muscle tissue analyzed. One athlete's leg muscles contained between 80 and 90 percent red muscle fibers, while the other athlete's leg muscles had almost 70 percent white muscle fiber. Which athlete would you classify as a sprinter, and which one as a marathon runner?

2. **Using the writing process** At birth, the joints in an infant are flexible and not yet fixed. As the child develops, the bones become more rigid and grow together. Use reference materials to find out why the skull bones are flexible in a newborn, yet rigid as an adult. Then write a brief summary of your findings.

3. **Drawing conclusions** Although exercising can increase your strength and endurance, overexercising can have some adverse effects on the body. What are some adverse effects?

Applying Your Skills

Up Close

Biologists use a microscope to better understand the workings of the human body on a cellular level. In this activity, you'll use a microscope to differentiate among the following muscle tissue: smooth, skeletal, and cardiac.

1. Working with a partner, set up a compound microscope and obtain three "mystery slides," labeled A, B, and C, from your teacher.

2. Construct a data table to record the letter of each slide, the identity of the tissue, and characteristics that support your identification.

3. Place slide A on the stage of the microscope and examine it closely.

4. Discuss with your partner the identity of the cells or tissues. You may have to examine all

4. **Constructing a model** Using cardboard for bones and string for muscles, construct a working model of the biceps and triceps muscles of the upper arm. Be sure to show the relationship of these muscles to the humerus, ulna, and radius bones.

5. **Interpreting data** The line graph below plots the force of contraction of three different skeletal muscles. Using the data, describe the differences among the three muscles.

the slides and identify some by a process of elimination.

5. Complete the data table for slide A and repeat the procedure using slides B and C.

• GOING FURTHER •

6. In your journal, think about the ease or difficulty of this activity. Which tissue was the easiest to identify? Which was the most difficult? Explain your answers.

Circulatory and Respiratory Systems

FOCUSING THE CHAPTER
THEME: Systems and Interactions

4–1 The Circulatory System
- **Describe** the structure and function of the circulatory system.
- **Describe** the components of blood.

4–2 The Respiratory System
- **Describe** the structure and function of the respiratory system.

BRANCHING OUT *In Depth*
4–3 The Hazards of Smoking
- **Describe** the effects smoking has on the body.

LABORATORY INVESTIGATION
- **Measure** the products of burning tobacco.

Biology and Your World
BIO JOURNAL

This swimmer knows how important exercise is for his circulatory and respiratory systems. In your journal, make a list of things you do that affect your circulatory and respiratory systems. After completing your list, place a check mark next to those that are harmful. Pick one harmful habit and write a paragraph explaining how you will change or eliminate that habit.

A swimmer taking a deep breath

The Circulatory System

GUIDE FOR READING

- **List** the structures of the circulatory system.
- **Identify** the three types of blood vessels.
- **Compare** the functions of red blood cells, white blood cells, and platelets.

MINI LAB

- **Relate** your pulse rate to your activity level.

ONE OF THE SIGNS OF LIFE *itself is your heartbeat. Even when you drift off to sleep, your heart beats out a steady rhythm. Why is this process so important that it must be kept going even while you sleep? Does it meet some great need of the trillions of cells that live inside you? It certainly does.*

Each breath you take brings air into your body. Oxygen in that air is needed by every one of your cells. Not surprisingly, that oxygen needs to be delivered, and that's where the heart comes in. Its beating produces the force to move oxygen-carrying blood through the circulatory system to every part of your body. The circulatory system supplies cells throughout your body with substances they need to stay alive.

Functions of the Circulatory System

If an organism is composed of a small number of cells, it doesn't really need a circulatory system. Most cells in such organisms are in direct contact with the environment so that oxygen, nutrients, and wastes can easily diffuse across cell membranes from the outside.

Larger organisms, however, don't have this advantage. They need a circulatory system. Most of their cells are not in direct contact with the environment, and the substances made in one part of the organism may be needed in another part. In a way, this is the same problem faced by people who live in a large city. What is needed, of course, is a transportation system that moves people, goods, and waste materials from one place to another. The transportation

Figure 4–1
The circulatory system consists of the heart, the blood vessels, and the blood.
(a) A measure of the pressure produced by the contractions of the heart and the muscles surrounding the heart is known as blood pressure. (b) The heart, which is made up almost entirely of cardiac muscle tissue, contracts at regular intervals, forcing blood through the circulatory system. (c) The instrument that measures blood pressure is called a sphygmomanometer.

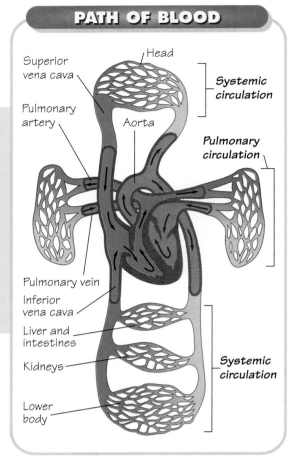

PATH OF BLOOD

Superior vena cava
Head
Systemic circulation
Pulmonary artery
Aorta
Pulmonary circulation
Pulmonary vein
Inferior vena cava
Liver and intestines
Kidneys
Systemic circulation
Lower body

Figure 4–2
In this diagram, the arrows show the path of blood through the body. The path of oxygen-poor blood is shown in blue. The path of oxygen-rich blood is shown in red.

system of a city is its streets, highways, and rail lines. The transportation system of a living organism is its circulatory system.

Humans and other vertebrates have closed circulatory systems. This means that a circulating fluid—called **blood**—is pumped through a system of vessels. **The human circulatory system consists of the heart, a series of blood vessels, and the blood itself.**

The Heart

The heart is a hollow organ near the center of the chest composed almost entirely of muscle. The human heart is really like two separate pumps sitting side by side. Each side has two chambers: an **atrium** (AY-tree-uhm; plural: atria), the upper chamber that receives blood, and a **ventricle,** the lower chamber that pumps blood out of the heart. This

means that the heart has a total of four chambers—two chambers on each side.

Each side of the heart pumps blood to a different part of the circulatory system. The right side of the heart pumps blood from the heart to the lungs. This pathway is called **pulmonary circulation.** Oxygen-poor blood is pumped by the right side of the heart through the lungs, where it gives off carbon dioxide and picks up oxygen. This oxygen-rich blood is then returned to the left side of the heart by the pulmonary veins.

The left side of the heart pumps blood to the rest of the body. This pathway is called **systemic circulation.** Oxygen-rich blood leaves the heart and supplies the body with oxygen-rich blood. By the time that blood returns from systemic circulation, cells throughout the body have picked up much of its oxygen and loaded it with carbon dioxide. In short, it is ready for another trip to the lungs. *Figure 4–2* shows the path of blood through the body.

✓ *Checkpoint*   What is pulmonary circulation? Systemic circulation?

Blood Flow Through the Heart

Blood enters the heart through the right and left atria. As the heart contracts, blood is forced first into the ventricles, then out from the ventricles into circulation. When it contracts, why doesn't some blood flow backward from the ventricles into the atria? Special flaps of tissue called **valves** reach across the passageways between the atria and the ventricles. Blood moving from the atria easily forces these valves open. But when the ventricles contract, the valves slam shut, preventing any backflow. There are four valves in the heart. Each valve ensures that blood moves through the heart in a one-way direction and increases the pumping efficiency of the heart.

Visualizing the Heart

The heart is a powerful muscle that continuously pumps blood throughout the body. It is about the size of a fist and is located near the center of the chest. It beats an average of 70 times per minute at rest.

1 Aorta

The **aorta** is the largest artery in the body. It brings oxygen-rich blood from the left ventricle to the rest of the body.

11 Superior Vena Cava

The superior vena cava is a large vein that brings oxygen-poor blood from the upper part of the body to the right atrium.

2 Pulmonary Artery

The pulmonary artery branches into two arteries after it leaves the right ventricle. Each branch brings oxygen-poor blood to one lung.

10 Pulmonary Veins

The two pulmonary veins bring oxygen-rich blood from each of the lungs to the left atrium.

3 Aortic Valve

The aortic valve prevents blood from flowing back into the left ventricle after it has entered the aorta.

9 Pulmonary Valve

The pulmonary valve prevents blood from flowing back into the right ventricle after it has entered the pulmonary artery.

Left atrium

Right atrium

Left ventricle

Right ventricle

4 Bicuspid Valve

The bicuspid valve prevents blood from flowing back into the left atrium after it has entered the left ventricle.

8 Tricuspid Valve

The tricuspid valve prevents blood from flowing back into the right atrium after it has entered the right ventricle.

5 Pericardium, Myocardium, and Endocardium

There are three layers that make up the walls of the heart. The pericardium and endocardium cover and protect the heart tissues. The middle layer, or myocardium, is responsible for pumping the blood.

7 Inferior Vena Cava

The inferior vena cava is a vein that brings oxygen-poor blood from the lower part of the body to the right atrium.

6 Septum

The septum is a thick muscular wall that divides the heart into two halves and prevents the mixing of oxygen-rich and oxygen-poor blood.

Feel the Beat

PROBLEM *How does your pulse rate* **relate** *to your activity level?*

PROCEDURE

CAUTION: *If you have any respiratory or circulatory conditions, do not perform this activity.*

1. Using the first two fingers of one hand, locate the pulse point on the inside of your wrist. It is next to the tendon near your thumb.

2. Lightly place the same two fingers against the same side of your neck near the corner of your jawbone.

3. At each location, count and record the number of pulses in 1 minute.

4. Repeat steps 1 to 3 after exercising in place for 1 minute.

ANALYZE AND CONCLUDE

1. How did your resting pulse rate compare in the wrist and the neck?

2. What effect did activity have on your pulse rate?

The Heartbeat

Although the heart is a single muscle, all of its cells do not all contract at the same time. Instead, cells of the atria contract first, and a wave of contraction spreads from the right atrium over the rest of the heart. This pattern of contraction makes the heart a more efficient pump, squeezing blood from one chamber to the next. How does this wavelike contraction happen?

Each contraction begins in a small group of cells in the right atrium. Because these cells "set the pace" for the heart as a whole, they are called the **pacemaker.** ● From the pacemaker, the contraction impulse is spread from cell to cell, producing a wave of contractions that reach all four chambers.

Blood Vessels

Blood leaving through the heart travels through a series of blood vessels that will carry it on its round trip through the body and back to the heart. **The three types of blood vessels that blood**

INTEGRATING TECHNOLOGY AND SOCIETY

Some people need an artificial pacemaker to help maintain a steady heart rate. Use reference materials to find out how an artificial pacemaker works.

Figure 4–3
The rhythmic beating of the heart is maintained by the sinoatrial node—the pacemaker— located in the right atrium. The signal to contract spreads from the pacemaker through the cardiac muscle cells, causing the atria to contract. Then the impulse is picked up by the atrioventricular node, which is a bundle of fibers that carry the impulse to the ventricles, causing them to contract.

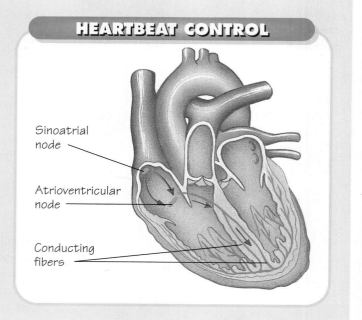

HEARTBEAT CONTROL

Sinoatrial node

Atrioventricular node

Conducting fibers

moves through are the arteries, capillaries, and veins.

Arteries—the superhighways of the circulatory system—are blood vessels that carry blood from the heart to the body. Except for the pulmonary arteries, all arteries carry oxygen-rich blood. Arteries have thick elastic walls that help them withstand the powerful spurts of blood produced when the heart contracts. The lining of an artery is surrounded by layers of elastic tissue and smooth muscle cells that allow an artery to expand under pressure.

Capillaries, the smallest of the blood vessels, are the side streets and alleys of the circulatory system. The exchange of nutrients and wastes takes place in the capillaries. Their walls are only one cell thick and may be so narrow that blood cells must pass through in single file.

Veins collect blood after it has passed through the capillary system. Like arteries, the walls of veins are lined with elastic tissue and smooth muscle. Veins, however, have thin walls and are less elastic than arteries. The largest veins contain one-way valves that keep blood flowing toward the heart. Many veins are located near skeletal muscles, and the contractions of those muscles help to push blood along to the heart. This is one reason why it is important to exercise regularly. Exercise helps to keep blood from accumulating in the limbs and from stretching the veins out of shape.

Blood Pressure

Any pump produces pressure, and the heart is no exception. When the heart contracts, it produces a wave of fluid

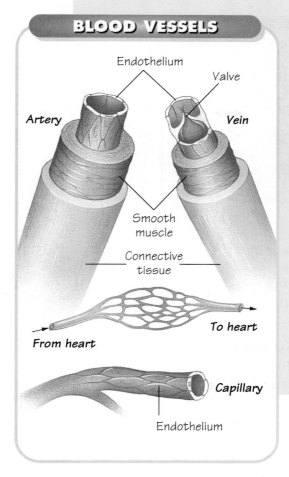

BLOOD VESSELS

Figure 4–4
The layer of smooth muscle in arteries is much thicker than that of veins because the arteries have to withstand the high pressure of blood as it is pumped from the heart. Capillaries, on the other hand, contain only epithelial tissue and are only one cell thick.

pressure in the arteries. Although the force of blood on the walls of the arteries, known as **blood pressure,** falls when the heart relaxes, the system still remains under pressure. This is good, too, because without that pressure, blood would not flow through the arteries and into the capillaries.

The body regulates blood pressure in two different ways. Sensory neurons at several places in the body detect the level of blood pressure and send impulses to the brainstem. When blood pressure is too high, the autonomic nervous system releases neurotransmitters that cause the smooth muscles around blood vessels to relax, lowering blood pressure. When blood pressure is too low, neurotransmitters are released that elevate blood pressure by causing these muscles to contract.

The kidneys also help to regulate blood pressure. Hormones produced by the heart and other organs cause the kidneys to remove more water from the

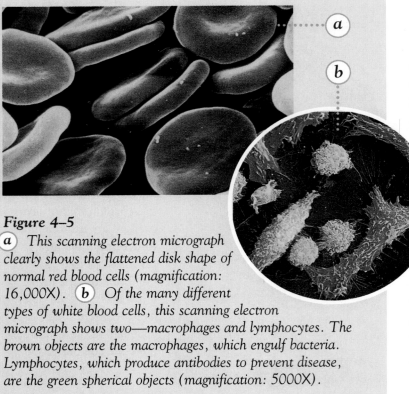

Figure 4–5

(a) *This scanning electron micrograph clearly shows the flattened disk shape of normal red blood cells (magnification: 16,000X).* (b) *Of the many different types of white blood cells, this scanning electron micrograph shows two—macrophages and lymphocytes. The brown objects are the macrophages, which engulf bacteria. Lymphocytes, which produce antibodies to prevent disease, are the green spherical objects (magnification: 5000X).*

blood when blood pressure is high. This reduces blood volume and lowers blood pressure.

Medical problems may result if blood pressure is either too high or too low. High blood pressure forces the heart to work harder, which may weaken or damage the heart muscle. People with high blood pressure are more likely to develop heart disease and to suffer from other diseases of the circulatory system.

The causes of high blood pressure are complex, but one of them is well understood—obesity. Although scientists have developed a number of drugs that can lower blood pressure, high blood pressure is easier to prevent than to cure. Exercise, weight control, and a sensible diet seem to be the keys to avoiding high blood pressure.

Blood

Roughly 8 percent of the mass of the human body is blood. For most of us, that means we contain anywhere from 4

to 6 liters of blood. About 45 percent of the volume of blood consists of living cells—**red blood cells, white blood cells,** and **platelets.** The remaining 55 percent is a fluid called **plasma.**

Plasma itself is 90 percent water. The remaining 10 percent consists of salts, sugars, and three groups of plasma proteins. The first, called serum albumin, helps to regulate osmotic pressure. Other plasma proteins, called globulins, are produced by the immune system and help to protect against infection. And the last of the plasma proteins is fibrinogen, which regulates blood clotting.

Red Blood Cells

Red blood cells are the most numerous cells in the blood—1 milliliter of blood contains nearly 5 million of them. Their scientific name—erythrocyte, means "red cell" and comes from the bright-red **hemoglobin** inside them. Hemoglobin is an iron-containing protein that dramatically increases the ability of blood to carry oxygen. **Red blood cells are oxygen carriers.** As red blood cells pass through the lungs, the hemoglobin within them quickly absorbs dissolved oxygen. When the same cells pass through capillaries in oxygen-poor regions of the body, oxygen is released into the surrounding tissues.

Red blood cells are produced in the bone marrow. As red blood cells develop, they lose their nuclei and their ability to divide. A typical red blood cell has a life span of roughly 120 days, which means that nearly 1 percent of your red blood cells must be replaced each day.

☑ *Checkpoint* What is hemoglobin?

White Blood Cells

White blood cells are blood cells that do not contain hemoglobin. White blood cells are also called leukocytes, which means "white cells." They are much less common than red cells, which outnumber them almost 500 to 1. Like red blood cells, white blood cells are produced in the bone marrow and are released into the blood as cells with nuclei. Unlike red blood cells, white blood cells may live for many months and possibly even for years.

More than 20 different types of white blood cells are known. **White blood cells guard against infection, fight parasites, and attack bacteria.** Some actually engulf and digest these foreign cells. Others attack invading organisms in the tissues of the body. Still others produce chemical signals that activate the body's immune system to help fight infection.

Like an army with units in reserve, the body is able to increase the number of white blood cells dramatically when a "battle" is underway. In fact, a sudden increase in the number of white cells is one way in which physicians can tell that the body is fighting a serious infection.

Platelets and Blood Clotting

Try as we might to protect ourselves against injury, sooner or later just about everyone receives a cut or a scrape. Most of these injuries aren't serious. A minor cut or scrape may bleed for a few minutes, then stop. Have you ever wondered why bleeding stops so quickly?

The answer is that blood has the ability to form a clot, a tangle of microscopic fibers that block the flow of blood. **Blood clotting is made possible by cell fragments, called platelets, and a number of plasma proteins.**

When platelets come into contact with the broken edges of a blood vessel, their surfaces become sticky, and a cluster of platelets develops around the wound. These platelets then release a

Figure 4–6

(a) *In response to an injury to a blood vessel, proteins called fibrin form in the blood. Fibrin produces a netlike web that traps the red blood cells, thus forming a clot that constricts the wound and promotes healing.* (b) *Platelets, which are responsible for blood clotting, are actually fragments of larger cells. This color-enhanced scanning electron micrograph shows some inactive platelets (magnification: 9200X).*

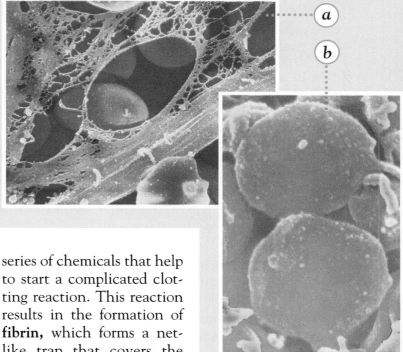

series of chemicals that help to start a complicated clotting reaction. This reaction results in the formation of **fibrin,** which forms a netlike trap that covers the wound and traps the red blood cells. If the wound is small, a network of platelets and fibrin seals the leak within a few minutes, and bleeding stops.

☑ *Checkpoint*   What is fibrin?

Diseases of the Circulatory System

Unfortunately, diseases of the circulatory system are common. ● Many of them stem from a condition known as **atherosclerosis** (ath-er-oh-skluh-ROH-sihs), in which fatty deposits build up on the inner surfaces of arteries. If these deposits get too large, they obstruct the flow of blood.

Atherosclerosis is particularly dangerous in the coronary arteries, a set of small

INTEGRATING CAREERS

Use reference materials to find out the special training needed by a cardiologist, a doctor who treats heart disease.

Figure 4–7
The lymphatic system is made up of lymphatic vessels and lymph nodes. The lymphatic vessels collect lymph—fluid that leaves the circulatory system—and returns it to veins in the neck. The lymph nodes act as filters that prevent harmful materials from entering body cells.

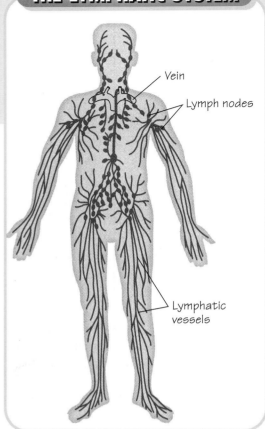

Vein

Lymph nodes

Lymphatic vessels

arteries that bring oxygen and nutrients to the heart muscle itself. If one of these becomes blocked, part of the heart muscle may begin to die from a lack of oxygen, a condition called a heart attack. The symptoms of a heart attack include nausea, shortness of breath, radiating pain down the left arm, and severe, crushing chest pain. People who show symptoms of a heart attack should be given medical attention immediately.

When one of the blood vessels leading to part of the brain is blocked, a stroke results. Brain cells served by that blood vessel gradually die from a lack of oxygen, and brain function in that region may be lost. Depending on the part of the brain that is affected, a stroke may cause paralysis, loss of the ability to speak, and even death.

The Lymphatic System

Fluid from the bloodstream is constantly leaking from the capillaries into the surrounding tissues. The leaking fluid helps to bring salts and nutrients into tissues where they are needed. More than 3 liters of fluid leak from the circulatory system into surrounding tissues every day.

What happens to all this fluid? A network of vessels called the **lymphatic** (lihm-FAT-ihk) **system** collects the fluid—**lymph** (LIHMF)—and returns it to the circulatory system. As *Figure 4–7* shows, these vessels empty the lymph back into general circulation through a vein under the left shoulder. Lymph vessels contain one-way valves, like veins, to keep lymph flowing in one direction.

Section Review 4–1

1. **List** the structures of the circulatory system.
2. **Identify** the three types of blood vessels.
3. **Compare** the functions of red blood cells, white blood cells, and platelets.
4. **Critical Thinking—Applying Concepts**   Hemophilia is a genetic disorder in which the gene for normal blood clotting is missing. How would injections of normal clotting proteins help a hemophiliac?
5. **MINI LAB**   How does your pulse rate **relate** to your activity level?

The Respiratory System

GUIDE FOR READING

- **Describe** the function of the respiratory system.

MINI LAB

- **Measure** your lung capacity.

WHEN PARAMEDICS RUSH TO the aid of an injured person, one of the first things they usually do is to check to see whether the victim is breathing. If the person is not breathing, paramedics will ignore other injuries—even broken bones and serious wounds—to get the person breathing again. There's no time to lose! If breathing stops for more than a few minutes, the person may die!

A well-trained paramedic understands how important the respiratory system is to life. This system provides nearly every cell in the body with oxygen—the same oxygen that is carried throughout the body by the circulatory system.

What Is Respiration?

In biology, the word respiration is used in two slightly different ways. At the cellular level, respiration is defined as the release of energy from the breakdown of food molecules in the presence of oxygen. Without oxygen, cells lose much of their ability to produce ATP, and that means that they cannot synthesize new molecules, pump ions, carry nerve impulses, or even move.

Because trillions of cells have a pressing need for oxygen, the human body must find a way to get that oxygen to them. It must also dispose of the carbon dioxide produced when food molecules are broken down. At the level of the organism, respiration is the exchange of gases—oxygen and carbon dioxide—between the organism and its environment.

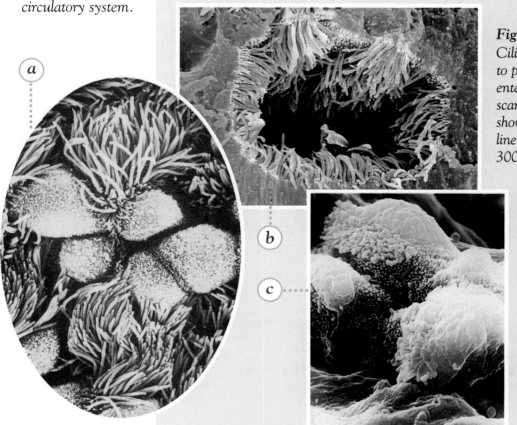

Figure 4–8
Cilia and goblet cells work together to prevent foreign particles from entering the lungs. **(a)** *This scanning electron micrograph shows a close-up of the cilia that line the trachea (magnification: 3000X).* **(b)** *In this cross section of the trachea, the cilia have been colored green (magnification: 3570X). The yellow structures at the base of the cilia are goblet cells, which produce mucus.* **(c)** *Once the incoming air has been cleaned and filtered, it enters the alveoli of the lungs, where actual gas exchange takes place. (magnification: 5100X).*

Visualizing Human Respiration

The human respiratory system is responsible for bringing oxygen to the blood so that it can be distributed to the body cells. In addition, it removes carbon dioxide from the body.

1 Nose and Mouth
Air enters the body through the nose and mouth, where it is filtered, warmed, and moistened.

2 Pharynx
After the air has been filtered, warmed, and moistened, it enters the pharynx, which is also a passageway for food.

3 Larynx
From the pharynx, air enters the larynx. The larynx also contains the vocal cords.

4 Trachea (Windpipe)
After the larynx, air enters the trachea—the main airway to the lungs. The trachea divides into two bronchi.

5 Bronchi
The bronchi (singular: bronchus) are the tubes that bring air to the lungs from the trachea. Each bronchus leads to one lung.

6 Bronchioles
Once inside the lungs, the bronchi branch into smaller and smaller air passageways called bronchioles. The bronchioles continue to divide until they finally end in clusters of tiny air sacs.

7 Alveoli
The alveoli (singular: alveolus) are tiny air sacs that appear in grape-like clusters. Surrounding each alveolus is a network of capillaries, where gas exchange takes place.

8 Intercostal Muscles
These muscles cause the chest cavity to expand when air is inhaled and get smaller when air is exhaled.

9 Diaphragm
A dome-shaped muscle called the diaphragm separates the chest cavity from the abdominal cavity. Breathing is directed by contracting and relaxing the diaphragm.

10 Pleural Membranes
Each lung is enclosed by two membrane layers called the pleural membranes. The pleural membranes form an airtight seal between the lungs and the chest wall.

11 Epiglottis
The epiglottis is a flap of tissue that prevents food from entering the trachea.

Ribs

The Human Respiratory System

The function of the respiratory system is to bring about the exchange of oxygen and carbon dioxide. With each breath, air enters the body through the air passageways and fills the lungs, where gas exchange takes place.

As air moves through the respiratory system, it is warmed, moistened, and filtered. Many of the cells lining the respiratory system produce a thin layer of protective mucus. This layer also traps inhaled particles of dust or smoke. Cilia lining the passageways then sweep such materials away from the lungs, keeping them clean and open for the important work of gas exchange. The human respiratory system is illustrated on page 74.

☑ **Checkpoint** What do cilia do?

Gas Exchange and Hemoglobin

There are nearly 300 million alveoli in a healthy lung, providing an enormous surface for gas exchange. Oxygen dissolves in the moisture on the inner surface of the alveoli and then diffuses across the thin capillary walls into the blood. Carbon dioxide in the bloodstream diffuses in the opposite direction—across the wall of the alveolus and into the air within it.

The process of gas exchange in the lungs is very efficient. The air that you

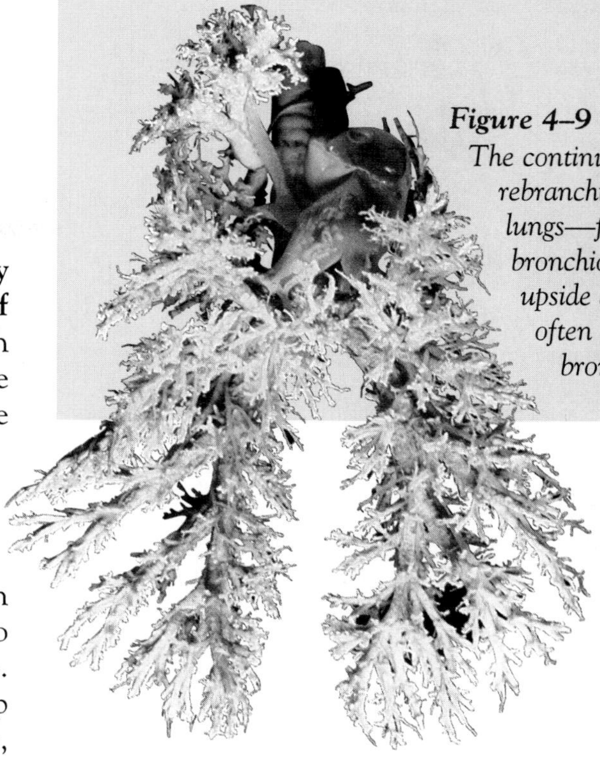

Figure 4–9
The continuous branching and rebranching of tubes in the lungs—from bronchi to bronchioles—resembles an upside down tree, so it is often given the name the bronchial tree.

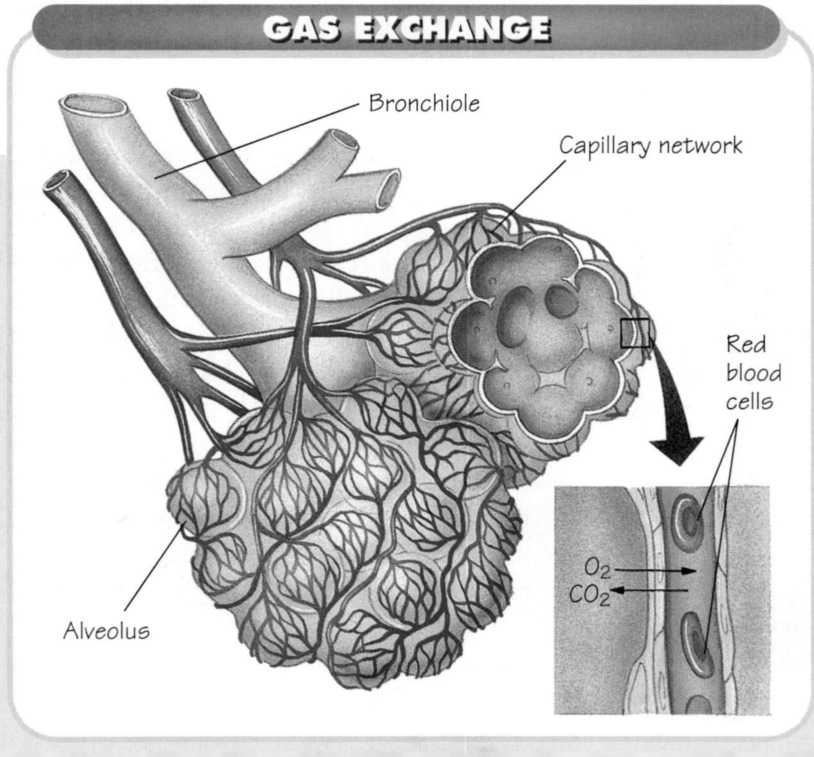

GAS EXCHANGE

Bronchiole

Capillary network

Red blood cells

O_2
CO_2

Alveolus

Figure 4–10
Gas exchange takes place in the alveoli of the lungs. Oxygen enters the blood by diffusing through the alveolus into the capillaries. Carbon dioxide, on the other hand, diffuses from the blood into the alveoli, where it will be exhaled out of the body.

MINI LAB .... *Measuring* ......

A Ballooning Effect

PROBLEM *How can you **measure** your lung capacity?*

PROCEDURE

CAUTION: *If you have any respiratory or circulatory conditions, do not perform this activity.*

1. Take two normal breaths. On the next breath, inhale as much air as you can. Then exhale into an empty round balloon, trying to empty your lungs as much as possible.

2. Hold the balloon closed while your partner uses a string to measure the circumference of the balloon at its widest part. Record the measurement.

3. Repeat steps 1 and 2.

4. Properly dispose of the balloons when you are finished.

ANALYZE AND CONCLUDE

1. How did your measurements compare? Compare them with those of other members of your class.

2. How did the measurements of males and females compare?

3. Do you think people who exercise regularly would have a larger lung capacity? Explain why or why not.

Figure 4–11
CAREER TRACK
Emergency Medical Technicians are trained to evaluate injuries and provide appropriate first-aid care. Certification in cardiopulmonary resuscitation (CPR) and advanced first aid is required for EMT certification.

inhale contains 21 percent oxygen and 0.04 percent carbon dioxide. Exhaled air is usually less than 15 percent oxygen and 4 percent carbon dioxide. This means that the lungs remove about one third of the oxygen in the air that you inhale and increase the carbon dioxide content of that air by a factor of 100!

As you may recall, oxygen dissolves easily. You may therefore wonder why hemoglobin is needed at all. The reason is efficiency. Hemoglobin binds with so much oxygen that it increases the oxygen-carrying capacity of the blood more than 60 times.

Breathing

Breathing is the movement of air into and out of the lungs. Surprisingly, there are no muscles connected to the lungs. The force that drives air into the lungs comes from ordinary air pressure. The lungs are sealed in two sacs, called the pleural membranes, inside the chest cavity. At the bottom of the cavity is the diaphragm. When you inhale, or breathe in, the diaphragm contracts and expands the volume of the chest cavity. Because the chest cavity is tightly sealed, this creates a partial vacuum inside the cavity. Atmospheric pressure does the rest, filling the lungs as air rushes through the breathing passages.

Most of the time, exhaling is a passive event. When the diaphragm muscle relaxes, elastic tissues surrounding the chest cavity return to their original positions, placing pressure on the lungs. As a result of that pressure, air rushes back out of the lungs. As you know, sometimes you exhale with much greater force, as when you blow out a candle. Muscles surrounding the chest cavity provide that extra force, contracting vigorously just as the diaphragm relaxes.

☑ *Checkpoint* What is breathing?

The Price of an Organ Donation

Heart and lung diseases strike millions of people each year. Those people whose organs cannot perform at a level that can keep them alive are candidates for heart or lung transplants. In order to receive a heart or lung transplant, these people must meet strict guidelines. After qualifying for a transplant, their names are placed on national waiting lists that match them with organs as they become available.

The Problems of Organ Donations

The problem with waiting for a heart or a lung is that there are not enough donors to keep up with the demand. In fact, twice as many people are on waiting lists as there are healthy organs available.

Unfortunately, organs of this type are donated only when other people die. That is, if they have given written permission or if their families give permission upon their death. Some states have a check-off box on driver's licenses that authorize organ donation in the event of death.

Although most people say they would be willing to donate their organs, few actually fill out a donor card. As a result, there are not enough available organs to meet the needs.

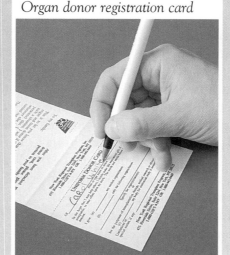
Organ donor registration card

The Debate

Recently, someone suggested that families should be paid for the organs. This plan would require that a 1984 federal law making it illegal to receive payment for organs be changed. Some people believe that donating organs is a moral duty and that payment would merely encourage people to do the right thing.

Others believe that it is unethical to pay for organs. They fear that families might be too eager to receive payment and go against the wishes of the potential donor.

Critics also say that the idea of paying for organs would increase the costs of organ transplants. At present, the cost of obtaining an organ for transplant is nearly $50,000.

Making the Connection

There is also concern over who would be able to pay for the organs. Would only those patients who could afford them get organs because they could pay the price? Or would insurance companies be responsible for payment? What other reasons for or against this plan are there? Would you support this plan? Explain why or why not.

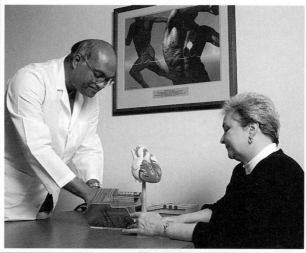
Heart specialist explaining procedure to a patient

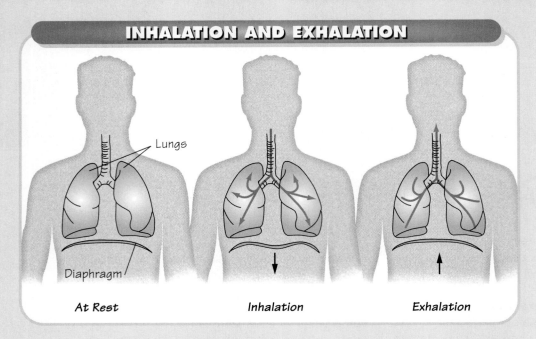

INHALATION AND EXHALATION

Lungs

Diaphragm

At Rest

Inhalation

Exhalation

Figure 4–12
At rest, the pressure inside the lungs is equal to the atmospheric pressure, or pressure outside the lungs. During inhalation, the diaphragm contracts, increasing the size of the chest cavity. This action causes the pressure inside the lungs to decrease and air to enter. As the diaphragm relaxes, the chest cavity gets smaller, which increases the pressure in the lungs. To equalize the pressure again, air is exhaled.

How Breathing Is Controlled

As you know, you can control your breathing almost anytime you want—whether it's to blow up a balloon or to play a musical instrument. But this does not mean that breathing is purely voluntary. If you hold your breath for a minute or so, you'll see what we mean. Your chest begins to feel tight, your throat begins to burn, the muscles in your mouth and throat struggle to keep from breathing, and eventually your body takes over. It "forces" you to breathe!

Breathing is such an important function that your nervous system simply will not let you have complete control over it. The brain controls this process in a breathing center located in the medulla oblongata—part of the brain just above the spinal cord. Autonomic nerves from the medulla oblongata to the diaphragm and chest muscles produce the cycles of contraction that bring air into the lungs.

How does the medulla know when it's time to breathe? Cells in the breathing center monitor the amount of carbon dioxide in the blood. As the carbon dioxide level rises, nerve impulses from the center cause the diaphragm to contract, bringing air into the lungs. The higher the carbon dioxide level, the stronger these impulses. If the carbon dioxide level reaches a critical point, the impulses become so powerful that you cannot stop your breathing.

The breathing center responds to high carbon dioxide levels, and not to a lack of oxygen. As a result, when the air is thin, people sometimes do not sense a problem, and must be told to begin breathing pressurized air.

Section Review 4-2

1. **Describe** the function of the respiratory system.
2. **Critical Thinking—Inferring**   As you have read, the breathing center in the brain responds to the level of carbon dioxide in the blood and not to the oxygen level. What consequences could this have on people at high altitudes?
3. **MINI LAB**   How can you **measure** your lung capacity?

GUIDE FOR READING

- **List** the substances in cigarette smoke.

- **Describe** some health problems caused by smoking tobacco.

WHEN IT IS FUNCTIONING *well, the respiratory system is simple and efficient. First, air enters through the breathing passages. Next, that air inflates the millions of alveoli in the lungs. And finally, oxygen from the air diffuses across thin membranes to enter the bloodstream, where it is quickly absorbed by hemoglobin. The circulatory system does the rest, taking this oxygen-rich blood to the rest of the body.*

When people smoke, things can go wrong. The passageways can be blocked, the lungs themselves can be damaged, and other gases can interfere with hemoglobin. Understanding the biology behind the dangers of smoking is one of the best ways to avoid them.

Tobacco Use

Tobacco is a plant that was cultivated and smoked by Native Americans long before Europeans emigrated to the North American continent. The dried leaves of the plant are chewed or smoked in pipes, cigars, and cigarettes.

Tobacco contains many different chemical compounds. When it burns, many harmful compounds are produced. **Three of the most dangerous substances in tobacco are tar, carbon monoxide, and nicotine.** Tar is a brown sticky mixture of chemicals, nicotine is a stimulant drug, and carbon monoxide is a poisonous gas. When tobacco smoke is inhaled, these compounds quickly enter the airways and blood, affecting the body.

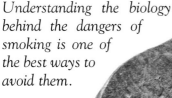

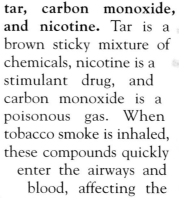

Figure 4–13
Smoking causes many different disorders. Notice how (a) *the lung of a nonsmoker differs from* (b) *that of a smoker. The holes in the smoker's lung are caused by ruptured alveoli.* (c) *Parts of this tobacco plant are used to make cigarettes, cigars, pipe tobacco, and chewing tobacco. Smoking any of these products has the greatest impact on the lungs.*

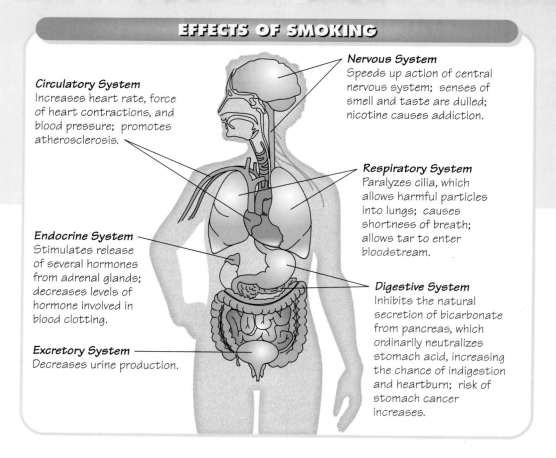

Figure 4–14
This illustration shows the effects of smoking on different systems of the body.

Circulatory System
Increases heart rate, force of heart contractions, and blood pressure; promotes atherosclerosis.

Nervous System
Speeds up action of central nervous system; senses of smell and taste are dulled; nicotine causes addiction.

Endocrine System
Stimulates release of several hormones from adrenal glands; decreases levels of hormone involved in blood clotting.

Respiratory System
Paralyzes cilia, which allows harmful particles into lungs; causes shortness of breath; allows tar to enter bloodstream.

Excretory System
Decreases urine production.

Digestive System
Inhibits the natural secretion of bicarbonate from pancreas, which ordinarily neutralizes stomach acid, increasing the chance of indigestion and heartburn; risk of stomach cancer increases.

INTEGRATING CAREERS

A respiratory therapist works with people who have respiratory problems. What are some responsibilities of a respiratory therapist?

Effects on the Respiratory System

As you have read earlier, the upper part of the respiratory system is generally able to filter out dust and foreign particles that might otherwise damage the lungs. ● Incredibly, millions of people engage in a habit—smoking tobacco—that damages and eventually destroys this protective system.

The respiratory system helps to protect the body from impurities and disease. Cilia and mucus keep dust and other foreign particles away from the lungs. Nicotine and carbon monoxide paralyze the cilia. With the cilia out of action, the inhaled particles stick to the walls of the respiratory tract or enter the lungs. The paralyzing effects of just one cigarette can last up to an hour!

In response to the irritation of cigarette smoke, the respiratory system increases mucus production. Without cilia to sweep it along, mucus builds up and obstructs the airways. This explains why smokers often cough—they have to clear their airways. Smoking also results in the swelling of the lining of the respiratory tract, which results in less air flow to the alveoli.

The tar in cigarettes affects the respiratory system, too. The tar accumulates in the lungs, where it can pass directly into the bloodstream. And a number of compounds in tar can cause cancer.

☑ **Checkpoint** What happens to the cilia as a result of carbon monoxide and nicotine?

Respiratory Disorders Caused by Smoking

Smoking can cause such respiratory diseases as bronchitis, emphysema, and lung cancer. In **bronchitis,** the bronchi become swollen and clogged with mucus. Even smoking a moderate number of cigarettes can produce bronchitis. People with bronchitis often find simple activities, such as climbing stairs, difficult.

Long-term smoking can also cause **emphysema.** Emphysema is a loss of elasticity in the tissue of the lungs. This makes breathing difficult. People with emphysema cannot get enough oxygen to the body tissues or rid the body of carbon dioxide.

The most serious consequence of smoking is **lung cancer.** Nearly 180,000 people in the United States develop lung cancer each year, and very few survive it. Lung cancer is particularly deadly because it spreads easily—small groups of cancer cells from the lungs break off and spread to other places in the body. This is called metastasis. By the time the cancer is detected, it usually has spread to dozens of other places in the body, causing a painful death. Lung cancer claims 87 percent of its victims in the first five years after it is detected.

✓ *Checkpoint* What is bronchitis?

Effects on the Circulatory System

Smoking affects the circulatory system, too. Every part of the circulatory system—the heart, the blood vessels, and the blood—is affected by smoking. **People who smoke have twice the rate of heart disease of nonsmokers. Besides an increased chance of a heart attack or stroke, smokers often have high blood pressure.** The circulatory system is most affected by the nicotine and carbon monoxide found in the smoke of tobacco products.

Carbon monoxide is an invisible, odorless, and highly poisonous gas. This gas can attach to the oxygen-binding site of hemoglobin. In fact, carbon monoxide binds more tightly than oxygen itself! Recall that hemoglobin is the oxygen-carrying agent in the blood. As more carbon monoxide combines with it, it has less room for oxygen. This continues until the oxygen-carrying ability of the blood is almost gone. As a result, the heart must work harder in order to deliver oxygen to the cells of the body.

The nicotine in cigarette smoke causes blood vessels to constrict, thus inhibiting blood flow. It also causes a rise in resting heart rate—an added burden for the heart. Nicotine also causes blood pressure to rise.

In addition, smoking tends to increase the buildup of fatty materials on the walls of blood vessels. This buildup leads to the development of atherosclerosis.

Effects on Other Body Systems

As you can see in *Figure 4–14,* smoking affects other body systems as well. Because nicotine is a stimulant drug, it has effects similar to those of other stimulant drugs, especially on the nervous system. In addition, smoking affects the digestive system, the endocrine system, and the excretory system.

INTEGRATING CHEMISTRY

What are some other sources of carbon monoxide?

Section Review 4–3

1. **List** the main components of cigarette smoke.
2. **Describe** some health problems caused by smoking tobacco.
3. **BRANCHING OUT ACTIVITY** **Design** and **construct** a poster for a middle school classroom that discourages students from smoking. Have your teacher approve your poster before it is displayed.

Laboratory Investigation

Burning Tobacco

Scientists have identified many harmful substances that are produced when tobacco is burned in a cigarette, pipe, or cigar. Of these, the most dangerous are nicotine, tar, and carbon monoxide. In this investigation, you will see how much tar is produced when different tobacco products are burned.

Problem

How can you **measure** the products of burning tobacco?

Materials (per group)

triple-beam balance
filter paper
tobacco from a cigarette, pipe, and cigar
cotton
test tube
test-tube holder
test-tube rack
Bunsen burner
matches

Procedure

1. Place a piece of filter paper on a triple-beam balance. Using the balance, measure 2 g of cigarette tobacco. Place the tobacco in a test tube.

2. Copy the data table shown on a separate sheet of paper. Record your measurements in your data table.

3. Find the mass of a wad of cotton large enough to fill the opening of the test tube. Record its mass.

4. Put the cotton wad into the open end of the test tube.

5. Using a test-tube holder, heat the bottom of the test tube over a Bunsen burner flame. **CAUTION:** *Be careful with open flames. Keep the cotton pointed away from the flame, and keep the opening of the test tube away from others.*

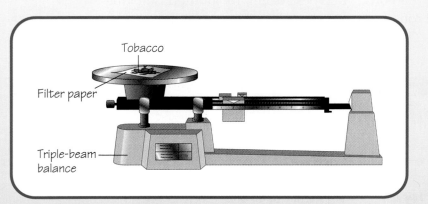

Tobacco

Filter paper

Triple-beam balance

DATA TABLE

Type of Tobacco	Mass of Cotton Before Heating	Mass of Cotton After Heating	Difference in Mass

6. **After heating the tobacco for 3 minutes, turn off the Bunsen burner and place the test tube in a rack to cool.**

7. **Remove the cotton wad and measure and record its mass.**

8. **Follow the same procedure—steps 1 to 6— with the pipe tobacco and cigar tobacco.**

Observations

1. What did you observe on the inside of the test tube while the tobacco was burning?

2. Did the appearance of the cotton change after it was heated?

3. Describe the appearance of tar.

Analysis and Conclusions

1. Based on its appearance, what effect would tar have on the respiratory system?

2. Which of the three types of tobacco produced the most tar? How do you know?

3. Which type produced the least tar?

4. What could be done to make these measurements more precise?

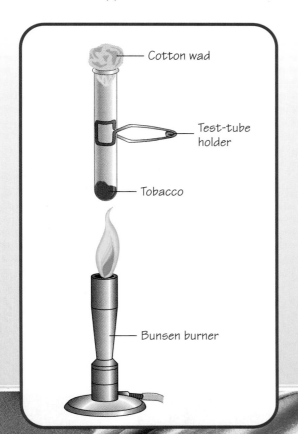

Cotton wad

Test-tube holder

Tobacco

Bunsen burner

More to Explore

Design an experiment to find out whether different cigarettes produce different amounts of tar.

Study Guide

Summarizing Key Concepts

The key concepts in each section of this chapter are listed below to help you review the chapter content. Make sure you understand each concept and its relationship to other concepts and to the theme of this chapter.

4–1 The Circulatory System

- The human circulatory system consists of the heart, a series of blood vessels, and the blood.

- The three kinds of blood vessels are arteries, capillaries, and veins.

- Red blood cells are oxygen carriers. White blood cells guard against infection, fight parasites, and attack bacteria. Platelets are responsible for blood clotting.

4–2 The Respiratory System

- The function of the respiratory system is to bring about the exchange of oxygen and carbon dioxide.

4–3 The Hazards of Smoking

- Three of the most dangerous substances in tobacco are tar, carbon monoxide, and nicotine.

- Smoking can cause such respiratory diseases as bronchitis, emphysema, and lung cancer.

- People who smoke have twice the rate of heart disease than nonsmokers. Besides an increased chance of a heart attack or stroke, smokers often have high blood pressure.

Reviewing Key Terms

Review the following vocabulary terms and their meaning. Then use each term in a complete sentence.

4–1 The Circulatory System

blood
atrium
ventricle
pulmonary circulation
systemic circulation
valve
aorta
pacemaker
artery
capillary
vein

blood pressure
red blood cell
white blood cell
platelet
plasma
hemoglobin
fibrin
atherosclerosis
lymphatic system
lymph

4–2 The Respiratory System

pharynx
larynx
trachea
bronchus
alveolus
diaphragm
epiglottis

4–3 The Hazards of Smoking

bronchitis
emphysema
lung cancer

Recalling Main Ideas

Choose the letter of the answer that best completes the statement or answers the question.

1. The upper chambers of the heart are called the
   - **a.** atria.
   - **b.** myocardium.
   - **c.** ventricles.
   - **d.** septum.

2. Oxygen-rich blood returns from the lungs to the heart's
   - **a.** left atrium.
   - **b.** right atrium.
   - **c.** left ventricle.
   - **d.** right ventricle.

3. Oxygen-poor blood enters the lungs from the
   - **a.** left atrium.
   - **b.** left ventricle.
   - **c.** right atrium.
   - **d.** right ventricle.

4. The largest vessel that transports oxygen-rich blood away from the heart is the
   - **a.** pulmonary artery.
   - **b.** pulmonary vein.
   - **c.** vena cava.
   - **d.** aorta.

5. Red blood cells contain an oxygen-absorbing protein called
   - **a.** fibrinogen.
   - **b.** serum albumin.
   - **c.** hemoglobin.
   - **d.** plasma.

6. Oxygen and carbon dioxide are exchanged with the circulatory system at the
   - **a.** pharynx.
   - **b.** bronchi.
   - **c.** alveoli.
   - **d.** bronchioles.

7. The medulla oblongata regulates breathing by monitoring the blood's level of
   - **a.** carbon dioxide.
   - **b.** oxygen.
   - **c.** hemoglobin.
   - **d.** carbon monoxide.

8. The condition that results from a loss of elasticity in the lungs is
   - **a.** bronchitis.
   - **b.** lung cancer.
   - **c.** emphysema.
   - **d.** stroke.

9. Which stimulant drug is found in cigarette smoke?
   - **a.** globulin
   - **b.** nicotine
   - **c.** tar
   - **d.** carbon dioxide

Putting It All Together

Using the information on pages xii to xiii, complete the following concept map.

return oxygen-poor blood to → **THE HEART** → pumps oxygen-rich blood through

Veins

1

exchange of oxygen and carbon dioxide takes place in

2

ssessment

Reviewing What You Learned

Answer each of the following in a complete sentence.

1. Explain the function of the circulatory system.

2. What is the difference between pulmonary circulation and systemic circulation?

3. What are the functions of the valves located in the heart and veins?

4. Explain the function of the pacemaker.

5. List the parts of the blood.

6. What is the name and function of the substance in red blood cells that gives them their red color?

7. How do platelets aid in blood clotting?

8. What is a function of the lymphatic system?

9. List, in order, the organs through which air passes on its way to the lungs.

10. Trace the path of oxygen as it moves from an alveolus to the capillaries.

11. Describe what happens when the diaphragm muscle relaxes.

12. What are three components of cigarette smoke?

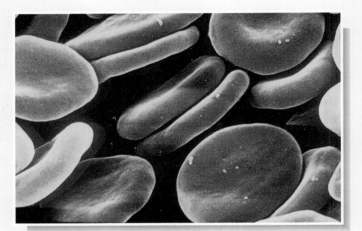

Expanding the Concepts

Discuss each of the following in a brief paragraph.

1. What is the difference between a closed circulatory system and an open circulatory system?

2. Draw a labeled diagram to trace the flow of blood from your "big" toe to your fingers.

3. Compare red blood cells and white blood cells.

4. How would you **relate** an elevated white blood cell count to the presence of an infection?

5. What is atherosclerosis? How does it affect blood pressure?

6. How are a stroke and a heart attack similar? How are they different?

7. How does respiration at the cellular level compare with respiration at the level of the organism?

8. If your body didn't contain hemoglobin, how might it look and work?

9. Children born at high altitudes develop more alveoli and more blood vessels in their lungs than children born at low altitudes. Is this an advantage or a disadvantage? Explain your answer.

10. Explain how smoking affects the circulatory system.

Extending Your Thinking

Use the skills you have developed in this chapter to answer the following.

1. **Applying concepts** Even if you don't smoke, you may be exposed to secondhand smoke. This "passive smoking" exposes you to carbon monoxide. What effect does passive smoking have on your ability to perform in sports?

2. **Giving examples** *Pneumo-* or *pneum-* are prefixes taken from Greek words meaning "related to air." For example, pneumonia is an inflammation of the lungs. Find other examples of words that have these prefixes and write their definitions.

3. **Designing an experiment** Design an experiment to find out how breathing rate varies in different age groups after short-term exercise. Exercise is considered short term if it is minimal and a person recovers in a brief amount of time.

4. **Using the writing process** Studies have shown that smoking tobacco harms the circulatory and respiratory systems of the body. As a result, many people believe that tobacco should be classified as an illegal drug. However, in some parts of the country, farmers depend upon their tobacco crops for their income and would face financial problems if tobacco use decreased. Choose one side of this issue and write a persuasive argument supporting your stand.

5. **Measuring** People who smoke often do not have the physical stamina that nonsmokers have. How could you measure the lung capacity of a smoker? Would you expect to find the same capacity as in a nonsmoker?

Applying Your Skills

Have a Heart

Place your right hand on your chest as if you were going to salute the flag. Can you feel the beating of your heart? Your heart is responsible for pumping blood to all parts of your body. Does your heart rate change if you are sitting, standing, or lying down? Try this activity to find out.

1. Sit down for 2 minutes. After 2 minutes, take your pulse for 1 minute. Record your pulse in your journal.

2. Stand for 2 minutes. Then take your pulse for 1 minute and record it in your journal.

3. Now lie down on the floor for 2 minutes. Then take your pulse for 1 minute and record it in your journal.

• **GOING FURTHER** •

4. Compare your standing, sitting, and lying-down pulse rates.

5. Did you observe any difference in the rates per minute? In your journal, explain your reasons for any differences.

Digestive and Excretory Systems

FOCUSING THE CHAPTER
THEME: Systems and Interactions

5–1 Nutrition
- **Identify** the role played by food in the body.
- **Discuss** the function of the major nutrients in the body.

5–2 The Digestive System
- **Discuss** the function of the digestive system.
- **Outline** the steps in the process of digestion.

5–3 The Excretory System
- **Describe** how the excretory system functions.

BRANCHING OUT *In Action*

5–4 A Cure for Ulcers?
- **Explain** how ulcers are caused and how they can be treated.

LABORATORY INVESTIGATION
- **Design an experiment** to determine the effect of air exposure on the vitamin C content of foods.

Biology and Your World

BIO JOURNAL

Perhaps you know someone who undergoes regular dialysis treatments or who has a transplanted kidney. Find out why renal patients require these treatments and how the lives of these individuals change as a result of having to undergo the treatments. Describe your findings in your journal.

False-color X-ray image of the abdomen showing the large intestine

Nutrition

GUIDE FOR READING

- **Explain** the function of food in the body.

- **List** the various classes of nutrients in the body.

MINI LAB

- **Observe** the presence of iron in cereal.

HOW IMPORTANT IS FOOD IN your life? Before you answer, think of some of the most important holidays or occasions you celebrate. What pictures come to mind? No matter where you live, chances are that a meal was the centerpiece of that special day. To most of us food is more than just nourishment—it is an important part of our culture. Human societies around the globe organize meetings and family gatherings around certain kinds of food.

The need to eat is one of your body's first priorities. In this section, you will see why your body needs food and what kinds of food are required to keep it healthy and strong.

Energy and Materials

Why do you need food? The most obvious answer is energy—the ability to do work. You need energy to climb stairs, lift books, run, and even to think. Like a car that needs gasoline, your body needs fuel for all that work, and food is your fuel.

But there is another reason that you need food. There's an old saying that "you are what you eat." And, like many sayings, it teaches us a valuable lesson. **The foods that we eat not only provide us with the energy to perform various types of actions, they also contain the materials from which our body cells and tissues are made.**

The energy available in food can be measured in a surprisingly simple way—by burning it! The amount of heat given off is measured and expressed in terms of calories. ● A calorie is the amount of heat energy needed to raise the temperature of 1 gram of water by 1 degree Celsius. On packaged foods, nutrition labels use the unit **Calorie,** which

INTEGRATING PHYSICS

What is energy? Work? How are they related? Measured?

Figure 5–1
People of all cultures devote a great deal of time and effort to the (a) *preparation and presentation of food. By doing so, eating, which is necessary to maintain life, is made more enjoyable. Food provides* (b) *this gymnast with the muscular strength he needs to support himself on the parallel bars and* (c) *these soccer players with the energy they need to run and kick.*

MINI LAB .... Observing ....

Magnetism in Your Cereal?

PROBLEM   *How can you **observe** the iron in your cereal?*

PROCEDURE

1. In a sealable plastic bag, crush 50 grams of a dry breakfast cereal that contains 100 percent of the U.S. Required Daily Allowance for iron.

2. Shake all the crushed cereal to one corner of the bag. Pass the magnet under the cereal and observe what happens. Use the magnet to drag any particles that are attracted to it to the empty part of the bag.

3. Remove the magnetized cereal and find its mass.

ANALYZE AND CONCLUDE

1. What percentage of the cereal was attracted by the magnet?

2. What evidence do you have that iron was in the cereal?

3. Describe a procedure you could use to compare the amount of iron in the cereal at the top of a cereal box and at the bottom.

Figure 5–2
CAREER TRACK
One of the jobs of a dietician is to help people choose a diet that will best meet that person's bodily needs.

represents 1000 calories, or 1 kilocalorie. Thus, a teaspoon of sugar contains 16 Calories, or 16,000 calories.

The basic energy needs of an average-sized teenager are between 1800 and 2800 kcal per day. If you engage in vigorous physical activity, however, your energy needs may be higher. What kinds of foods can meet those energy needs? Just about any kind. Chemical pathways in the body's cells can extract energy from almost any type of food.

✓ *Checkpoint*   What is the function of food in the body?

Nutrients

Although the body is able to manufacture many of the molecules it needs, it must still obtain the materials for this from the food it takes in. **The classes of nutrients that are part of any healthy diet are water, carbohydrates, fats, proteins, vitamins, and minerals.**

Water

Water is the most important of all nutrients. Water is needed by every cell in our body, and it makes up the bulk of blood, lymph, and other body fluids. Water dissolves food taken into the digestive system. Water in the form of sweat cools the body. Water is lost from the body as vapor in every breath we exhale and as the primary component of urine.

If enough water—at least a liter a day—is not taken in to replace what is lost, dehydration can result. This leads to problems with the circulatory, respiratory, and nervous systems. Drinking plenty of pure water is one of the best things you can do to help keep your body healthy.

Carbohydrates

Carbohydrates are major sources of food energy. Sugars—found in fruits, honey, sugar cane and sugar beets—are examples of simple carbohydrates.

It's All in the Analysis

You and a friend have just read an article in a sports magazine that says that diets high in fats increase an individual's chances of getting heart disease and certain cancers when the individual gets older. The article also points out that sufficient fiber—found in fruits, vegetables, beans, and whole grain breads—helps to lower the chance of getting these diseases.

Your friend wonders whether his diet is helping to prevent disease or causing it. He has decided to find out just how his diet compares with a balanced diet recommended by nutritionists. Using the list of all the foods he ate the day before, answer the questions that follow.

Breakfast
2 scrambled eggs
2 slices white bread
1 teaspoon butter
orange juice ($\frac{3}{4}$ cup)

Lunch
fast-food cheeseburger
   (bun, one-quarter pound
   beef, 1 slice cheese,
   mayonnaise, lettuce)
French-fried potatoes (1 cup)
milkshake (12 oz)

Dinner
fried chicken (6 oz)
roasted potatoes (1 cup)
asparagus ($\frac{1}{2}$ cup)
1 slice white bread
1 glass soda

Snacks
potato chips
   (one small bag)
pretzels (1 cup)

Serving size   One serving from the bread group is equal to 1 slice of bread or $\frac{1}{2}$ cup cooked cereal, rice, or pasta. One serving from the vegetable group is equal to $\frac{1}{2}$ cup cooked or raw vegetables, 1 cup leafy raw vegetables, or $\frac{1}{2}$ cup cooked beans. A serving of fruit is the size of a medium apple or banana, $\frac{1}{2}$ cup diced or cooked fruit, or $\frac{3}{4}$ cup juice. One cup of milk or yogurt or $1\frac{1}{2}$ ounces of cheese are equal to one serving from the milk group. One egg or 3 ounces of meat make up a serving from the meat group.

• T H I N K   A B O U T   I T •

1. Using the Food Guide Pyramid on page 94, classify the foods your friend ate by food group.

2. Determine how many servings of each food group your friend consumed.

3. Did your friend meet the minimum number of servings recommended in the guide? Explain your answer.

4. Based on the guide, what would you recommend to your friend regarding his diet?

VITAMINS

VITAMIN	FOOD SOURCES	FUNCTION	RESULTS OF VITAMIN DEFICIENCY
Water-Soluble Vitamins			
B_1 (thiamine)	Yeast, liver, grains, legumes	Coenzyme for carboxylase	Beriberi, general sluggishness, heart damage
B_2 (riboflavin)	Milk products, eggs, vegetables	Coenzyme in electron transport (FAD)	Sores in mouth, sluggishness
Niacin	Red meat, poultry, liver	Coenzyme in electron transport (NAD)	Pellagra, skin and intestinal disorders, mental disorders
B_6 (pyridoxine)	Dairy products, liver, whole grains	Amino acid metabolism	Anemia, stunted growth, muscle twitches and spasms
Pantothenic acid	Liver, meats, eggs, whole grains, and other foods	Forms part of coenzyme A, needed in Krebs cycle	Reproductive problems, hormone insufficiencies
Folic acid	Whole grains and legumes, eggs, liver	Coenzyme in biosynthetic pathways	Anemia, stunted growth, inhibition of white cell formation
B_{12}	Meats, milk products, eggs	Required for enzymes in red cell formation	Pernicious anemia, nervous disorders
Biotin	Liver and yeast, vegetables, provided in small amounts by intestinal bacteria	Coenzyme in a variety of pathways	Skin and hair disorders, nervous problems, muscle pains
C (ascorbic acid)	Citrus fruits, tomatoes, potatoes, leafy vegetables	Required for collagen synthesis	Scurvy: lesions in skin and mouth, hemorrhaging near skin
Choline	Beans, grains, liver, egg yolks	Required for phospholipids and neurotransmitters	Not reported in humans
Fat-Soluble Vitamins			
A (retinol)	Fruits and vegetables, milk products, liver	Needed to produce visual pigment	Poor eyesight and night blindness
D (calciferol)	Dairy products, fish oils, eggs (also sunlight on skin)	Required for cellular absorption of calcium	Rickets: bone malformations
E (tocopherol)	Meats, leafy vegetables, seeds	Prevents oxidation of lipids in cell membranes	Slight anemia
K (phylloquinone)	Intestinal bacteria, leafy vegetables	Required for synthesis of blood-clotting factors	Problems with blood clotting, internal hemorrhaging

Figure 5–3
The table lists the food sources and the functions of the fourteen essential vitamins. Notice that the vitamins are categorized as water soluble or fat soluble. Because fat-soluble vitamins can be stored in the fatty tissues of the body, these vitamins should not be taken in excess of daily required amounts or they can become toxic.

Starches—found in grains, potatoes, and vegetables—are examples of complex carbohydrates. Starches are easily broken down by the digestive system into simple sugars and passed into the bloodstream, where they can provide energy to cells throughout the body.

Many carbohydrate-rich foods also contain cellulose, commonly referred to as "fiber." Unlike starch, the sugars in cellulose are linked together in such a way that humans and many other animals cannot break them apart. Even though we cannot digest cellulose, it is still important in the diet. Cellulose, or fiber, adds bulk to the material moving through the digestive system. This bulk helps the muscles of the digestive system to process foods more effectively. Foods such as lettuce, whole grain breads, and bran are rich in fiber.

MINERALS

MINERAL	FOOD SOURCES	FUNCTION	RESULTS OF MINERAL DEFICIENCY
Calcium	Milk, cheese, legumes, dark-green vegetables	Bone formation, blood-clotting reactions, nerve and muscle function	Stunted growth, weakened bones, muscle spasms
Phosphorus	Milk products, eggs, meats	Bones and teeth, ATP and related nucleotides	Loss of bone minerals
Potassium	Most foods	Acid-base balance, nerve and muscle function	Muscular weakness, heart problems, death
Chlorine	Salt	Acid-base balance, nerve and muscle function, water balance	Intestinal problems, vomiting
Sodium	Salt	Acid-base balance, nerve and muscle function, water balance	Weakness, diarrhea, muscle spasms
Magnesium	Green vegetables	Enzyme cofactors, protein synthesis	Muscle spasms, stunted growth, irregular heartbeat
Iron	Eggs, leafy vegetables, meats, whole grains	Hemoglobin, electron-transport enzymes	Anemia, skin lesions
Fluorine	Drinking water, seafood	Structural maintenance of bones and teeth	Tooth decay, bone weakness
Iodine	Seafood, milk products, iodized salt	Thyroid hormone	Goiter (enlarged thyroid)

Fats

Fats, or lipids, may have a bad reputation in today's society, but in proper amounts they are still an important part of a healthy diet. Your body needs certain essential fatty acids to manufacture the lipids in cell membranes and to produce certain hormones. Fats that can meet these requirements are found in most foods. In fact, only 60 grams of vegetable oil—about 2 tablespoons—meet the daily fatty acid needs of an average person.

Despite the fact that little fat is actually required in the diet, about 40 percent of the Calories in the diet of a typical American come from fat! Most nutritionists believe that this is far too much fat and may lead to serious health consequences, such as high blood pressure, heart disease, obesity, and diabetes.
☑ *Checkpoint*   What are fats?

Proteins

Proteins are important nutrients because of the amino acids they contain. The body uses the amino acids in proteins to build new cells and tissues. Rapidly growing tissues, including those

Figure 5–4
Nine of the body's important minerals are listed in this table, which also identifies some of the foods in which the mineral is found and the function the mineral has in the body.

in the skin and the lining of the digestive system, must constantly replace dead and dying cells with new ones. Of the 22 most common amino acids, your body is able to make 14—the other 8 must be obtained from food. Diets that are deficient in protein interfere with cell growth and can cause serious health problems.
☑ *Checkpoint*   What is the function of proteins in the body?

Vitamins and Minerals

If you think of proteins, fats, and carbohydrates as the building blocks of the body, you might think of vitamins as the tools that help to put them together. Vitamins are organic molecules that the body needs to help perform important chemical reactions.

Although vitamins are needed in very small amounts, vitamin deficiencies can have serious, even fatal, consequences.

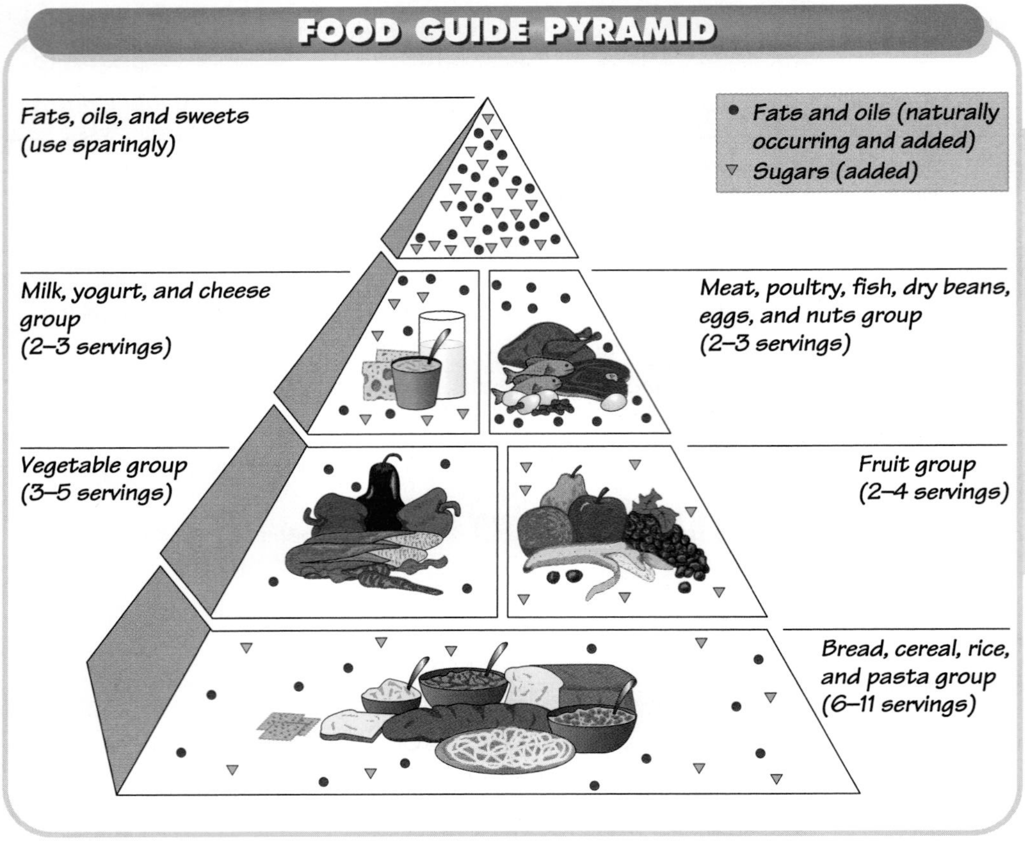

FOOD GUIDE PYRAMID

Fats, oils, and sweets
(use sparingly)

- Fats and oils (naturally occurring and added)
▽ Sugars (added)

Milk, yogurt, and cheese group
(2–3 servings)

Meat, poultry, fish, dry beans, eggs, and nuts group
(2–3 servings)

Vegetable group
(3–5 servings)

Fruit group
(2–4 servings)

Bread, cereal, rice, and pasta group
(6–11 servings)

Figure 5–5
The food guide pyramid illustrates the main characteristics of a balanced diet. Carbohydrate-rich foods should make up the major portion of the diet, while foods containing fats and sugars should be eaten sparingly.

Fourteen vitamins, listed in **Figure 5–3** on page 92, are generally recognized as essential to human health—and there may be more. Eating a diet containing a variety of foods will supply the daily vitamin needs of nearly everyone.

As you know, food stores and pharmacies sell vitamin supplements containing the minimum daily requirement of each important vitamin. Unfortunately, taking extra-large doses of vitamins does not benefit the body and in some cases may cause it harm.

Minerals are inorganic substances that are needed in small amounts by the body. **Figure 5–4** on page 93 lists nine of the most important minerals. Calcium, for example, is required to produce the calcium phosphate that goes into bones and teeth. Iron is needed to make hemoglobin, the oxygen-carrying protein in red blood cells. And thyroxine, a hormone required for normal growth and development, cannot be synthesized without iodine.

☑ **Checkpoint** What roles do vitamins and minerals play in the body?

Balancing the Diet

It's no easy matter to figure out the best balance of nutrients for the human diet, but nutritional scientists have done their best to do exactly that. The result is the food pyramid shown in **Figure 5–5.** The basic idea behind the pyramid is sound and simple—you should eat a variety of fresh foods each day, and you should limit your intake of fatty foods.

Section Review 5-1

1. **Explain** the function of food in the body.
2. **List** the various classes of nutrients in the body.
3. **Critical Thinking—Evaluating** Why should you eat a balanced diet?
4. **MINI LAB** How can you **observe** the presence of iron in cereal?

GUIDE FOR READING

- **Explain** the function of the digestive system in the body.
- **Describe** the action of insulin and glucagon.

FOOD PRESENTS EVERY ANIMAL *with at least two challenges. The first, of course, is how to obtain it. Then, when an animal has caught, gathered, or engulfed its food, it faces a new challenge—how to break that food down into small molecules that can be passed to the cells that need them. In this section, we will focus our attention on this challenge.*

To meet this challenge, the body is equipped with a remarkable organ system that begins to process food as soon as it is placed in the mouth. As the food passes through these organs, it gets disassembled, contributing its value to the body along the way.

The Digestive Tract

The human digestive system, like those of other vertebrates, is built around an alimentary canal—a one-way tube that passes through the body. **The function of the digestive system is to convert foods into simple molecules that can be absorbed and used by the cells of the body.**

The Mouth

Food enters the **mouth,** where the work of the digestive system begins. Chewing, which takes place in the mouth, seems simple enough—teeth tear and crush the moistened food to a fine paste until it is ready to be swallowed. But there is a great deal more to it than that.

Teeth are anchored in the bones of the jaw and are connected to the jaw by a network of blood vessels and nerves that enter through the roots of the teeth. The surfaces of the teeth, which are much tougher than ordinary bone, are protected by a coating of mineralized enamel. Teeth do much of the mechanical work

Figure 5–6
The foods we eat—such as (a) *pizza,* (b) *meats and vegetables, and* (c) *strawberries—must be broken down into molecules that are further broken down to release the energy and provide the nutrients they contain. The process by which foods are broken down is known as digestion.*

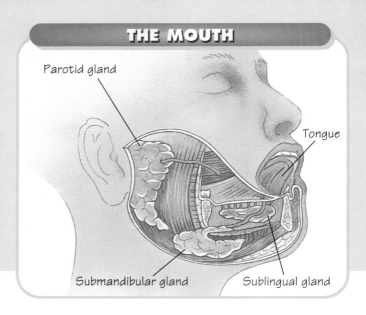

Figure 5–7
Digestion begins in the mouth, where teeth cut, grind, and crush food into a paste with the aid of saliva. Saliva, a fluid that is produced by salivary glands, not only moistens the food for easy swallowing, it also contains enzymes that begin to break large, complex starch molecules into simple glucose molecules.

Parotid gland

Tongue

Submandibular gland

Sublingual gland

of digestion by cutting, tearing, and crushing food into small fragments.

Human teeth include incisors, which are sharp enough to cut directly through meat; cuspids and bicuspids, which grasp and tear food; and molars, which have large, flat surfaces ideal for grinding food. Human tooth structure is intermediate between that of a plant-eating herbivore, in which molars are most common, and a carnivore, in which incisors are prominent. Our tooth structure reflects a mixed diet of meats and plants.

In the mouth, saliva, a fluid produced by the mouth's three pairs of **salivary glands,** helps to moisten the food and make it easier to chew. The release of saliva is under the control of the nervous system, and it can be triggered by the scent of food—especially when you are hungry!

Saliva not only helps to moisten food, it also helps to ease its passage through the digestive tract. Saliva also contains an enzyme called **amylase,** which breaks the chemical bonds in starches, releasing sugars. If you chew on starchy foods like crackers long enough, they will begin to taste sweet—a taste that comes from the chemical action of amylase on starch. Saliva also contains **lysozyme,** an enzyme that fights infection by digesting the cell walls of many bacteria.

Food is passed from the mouth into the rest of the digestive system by swallowing. Pushed by the tongue and muscles of the throat, the chewed clump of food, called a bolus, is forced down the throat. Just as this happens, a flap of tissue, known as the epiglottis (ehp-uh-GLAHT-ihs), is forced over the opening to the air passageways. This prevents food from clogging the air passageways—most of the time, anyway!

☑ *Checkpoint* What is amylase?

The Esophagus

After the bolus is swallowed, it passes through the **esophagus,** or food tube, into the stomach. Did you know that food can travel through the esophagus whether you're sitting up, lying down, or standing on your head? Even in astronauts, food passes through the esophagus in the weightlessness of space. The reason is that food is moved along by contractions of smooth muscle surrounding the esophagus. Known as **peristalsis** (per-uh-STAL-sihs), these contractions, which occur throughout the alimentary canal, squeeze the food through the 25 centimeters of the esophagus.

The Stomach

Food from the esophagus empties into a large muscular sac called the **stomach.** A thick ring of muscle, known as the cardiac sphincter, closes the esophagus after food has passed into the stomach,

Figure 5–8

Once food is swallowed, it is forced through the alimentary canal—esophagus, stomach, small intestine, and large intestine—by the action of peristalsis, a series of periodic muscular contractions. Just below the entry to the large intestine is a small pouch known as the appendix. In humans the appendix is of little importance except when it becomes infected. This condition, which is known as appendicitis, usually requires the surgical removal of the appendix.

ESOPHAGUS, STOMACH, AND SMALL INTESTINE

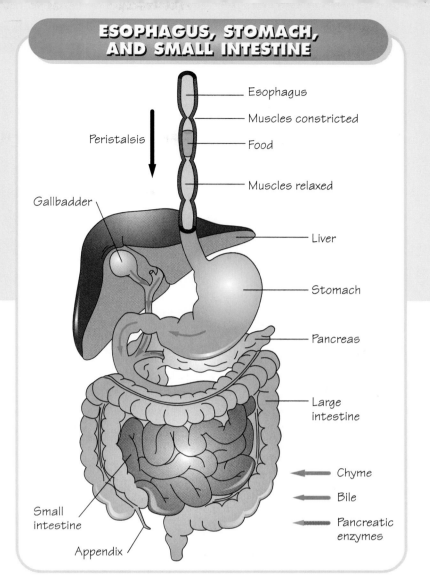

preventing the contents of the stomach from moving back into the esophagus. The size of the stomach enables you to eat a few large meals a day, rather than having to nibble all the time. Its walls produce a powerful combination of enzymes and strong acids, and contractions of its smooth muscles thoroughly mix the food you swallow.

The lining of the stomach contains millions of microscopic **gastric glands** that release a number of substances into the stomach. Some of these glands produce mucus, a fluid that lubricates and protects the stomach wall. Other glands produce hydrochloric acid, and still others produce **pepsin.** 🌀 Pepsin, an enzyme that digests proteins, works best at low pH. Remember that low pH corresponds to high acidity. ● The combination of pepsin and hydrochloric acid in the stomach unfolds large proteins in foods and breaks them into smaller polypeptide fragments.

As digestion proceeds, stomach muscles contract to churn and mix stomach fluids and food, gradually producing a mixture known as chyme (KIGHM). After a few hours in the stomach, the pyloric valve—located at the junction of the stomach and small intestine—opens, and chyme is forced into the duodenum.

☑ *Checkpoint*   What is chyme?

The Small Intestine

The duodenum is the first of three parts of the **small intestine,** and it is the place where most of the chemical work of digestion takes place. As chyme enters from the stomach, it is mixed with enzymes and digestive fluids from the other accessory digestive organs and even from the lining of the duodenum itself.

Located just below the stomach is a gland called the **pancreas,** which serves two important functions. One function is to produce hormones that regulate blood sugar, which we will examine later. Within the digestive system, the pancreas plays the role of master chemist, producing enzymes that break down carbohydrates, proteins, lipids, and nucleic acids. The pancreas also produces sodium

INTEGRATING CHEMISTRY

What is pH? How does pH characterize acids? Bases?

Labels in top diagram: Intestinal folds, Villus, Capillaries, Microvilli, Small intestine, Villi, Intestinal gland, Lymph vessel, Arteriole, Venule

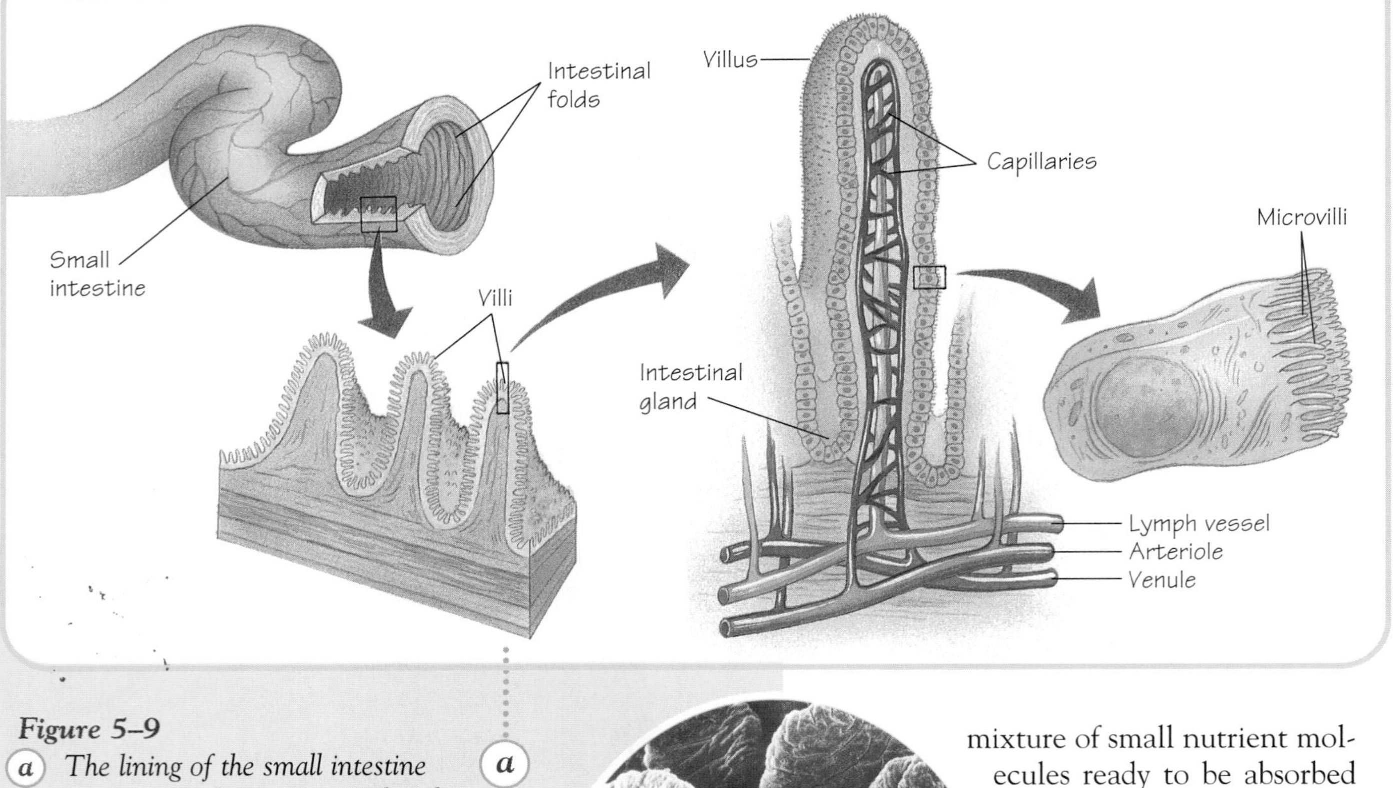

Figure 5–9

(a) The lining of the small intestine consists of folds that are covered with tiny projections called villi. Within each villus there is a network of blood capillaries and lymph vessels that absorb and carry away nutrients.

(b) This electron micrograph of villi shows how they greatly increase the surface area of the small intestine (magnification: 300X).

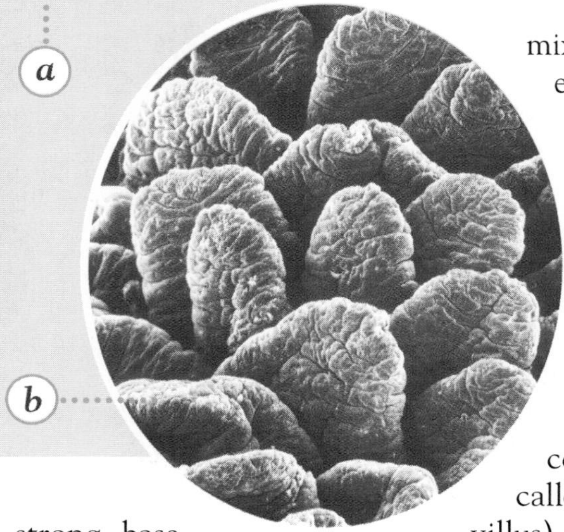

bicarbonate, a strong base that neutralizes stomach acid so that these enzymes can go to work.

To aid in this process, the **liver,** a large gland just above the stomach, produces **bile,** a fluid loaded with lipids and salts. Bile acts almost like a detergent, dissolving and dispersing the droplets of fat found in fatty foods. This makes it possible for enzymes to reach these fat molecules and break them down.

By the time chyme enters the remaining parts of the small intestine, nearly all the chemical work of digestion has been completed. The chyme is now a rich mixture of small nutrient molecules ready to be absorbed by the body. The remaining parts of the small intestine—the jejunum and the ileum—are specially adapted to absorb these nutrients. Nearly 7 meters in length, the folded surfaces of the jejunum and the ileum are covered with projections called **villi** (VIHL-igh; singular: villus). The surfaces of the cells of the villi are themselves covered with thousands of fingerlike projections known as microvilli. Slow, wavelike contractions of smooth muscles move the chyme along this absorptive surface.

Nutrient molecules are rapidly absorbed into the cells lining the small intestine. Sugars, amino acids, and other nutrients are then passed directly into the bloodstream. Fats take a different route. They are transported into tiny lymph vessels before being delivered to the bloodstream.

As you might expect, blood leaving the capillaries of the small intestine is nutrient-rich after a meal. Does this mean that levels of sugars and other nutrients in the blood rise and fall dramatically during the day? Not at all. All the blood leaving the small intestine passes through the liver before it flows to the rest of the body. This unusual arrangement places the liver in a position to monitor the blood before it enters the general circulation.

Not long after you eat something sweet, blood from the small intestine is loaded with energy-producing sugar. The liver efficiently removes most of the extra sugar from the blood and stores it in the form of glycogen, a polysaccharide. Liver cells keep this nutrient in reserve, and when blood sugar levels begin to fall, they release the stored sugars.

☑ *Checkpoint* What are villi?

The Large Intestine

Nearly all the available nutrients have been removed from the chyme that enters the **large intestine,** or colon. The primary job of the colon is to remove water from the undigested material that is left, producing a concentrated waste material known as feces. This material passes through the rectum and is eliminated from the body.

Water is moved quickly across the colon wall while rich colonies of bacteria grow on the undigested material. These intestinal bacteria are helpful to the digestive process—some even produce compounds that the body is able to use, including vitamin K.

Regulating Nutrient Levels

Regulating the level of blood sugar is one of the body's most important jobs. If the blood has too little sugar, organs—including the brain—that depend upon it as a source of energy will begin to suffer. Two hormones produced by the pancreas help to regulate blood sugar. Inside the pancreas there are tiny "islands" of cells known as the **islets of Langerhans.** Some of these cells produce **insulin,** a polypeptide hormone.

When the blood sugar level rises, as it might after a meal, the islets of Langerhans in the pancreas detect this and release insulin into the bloodstream. **Insulin stimulates cells in the liver, muscles, and fatty tissues to remove sugar from the bloodstream and store it in the form of glycogen and fat.**

When blood sugar levels fall, as they might after several hours without eating, another hormone, called **glucagon,** is released by the islets of Langerhans. **Glucagon stimulates the liver, muscles, and fatty tissues to break down glycogen and fats and to release sugars into the blood.** This raises blood sugar back to a safe level.

When the body cannot produce enough insulin, blood sugar cannot be regulated and a disorder known as diabetes mellitus results. Most forms of juvenile-onset diabetes, a type of diabetes mellitus, can be treated with a carefully controlled diet and daily injections of insulin.

Section Review 5-2

1. **Explain** the function of the digestive system in your body.
2. **Describe** the action of insulin and glucagon in your body.
3. **Critical Thinking—Relating** What functions do the enzymes amylase and pepsin serve in digestion?

The Excretory System

GUIDE FOR READING

- **Explain** the function the kidneys perform in the body.
- **Describe** the processes of filtration and reabsorption.

MINI LAB

- **Relate** the structure of a kidney to its function.

INTEGRATING CHEMISTRY

How does protein metabolism produce urea?

THE CHEMISTRY OF THE *human body is a marvelous thing. An intricate system of checks and balances controls everything from your blood pressure to your body temperature. Nutrients are absorbed, stored, and carefully released just as they are needed. But every living system, including the human body, produces chemical wastes—byproducts of chemical reactions that are no longer useful. Some are even* toxic. Therefore, the body occasionally needs to throw things away. The body relies on a group of organs that work together to remove the unwanted, and often toxic, wastes.

Chemical Wastes

The elimination of chemical wastes from the body is known as excretion. The lungs, for example, excrete carbon dioxide, a chemical waste produced when energy is captured from food compounds. The skin excretes excess water and salt in sweat. This makes the lungs and the skin part of the excretory system, a system of organs that remove chemical wastes from the body. In this section, however, we will focus our attention on a pair of organs whose main function is excretion—the **kidneys.**

Why does the body need organs specialized for excretion? Part of the answer has to do with the chemistry of proteins. When the body uses the amino acids from proteins for food, it sometimes must remove their amino ($-NH_2$) groups.

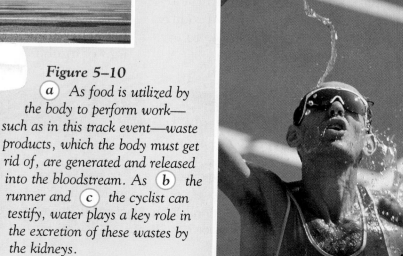

Figure 5–10
(a) As food is utilized by the body to perform work—such as in this track event—waste products, which the body must get rid of, are generated and released into the bloodstream. As (b) the runner and (c) the cyclist can testify, water plays a key role in the excretion of these wastes by the kidneys.

Figure 5–11

(a) The breakdown of an amino acid such as alanine yields pyruvic acid and ammonia. The pyruvic acid is used for energy, while the ammonia is converted to urea by a complex series of reactions.

(b) The kidneys function in the removal of urea as well as the regulation of water in the bloodstream.

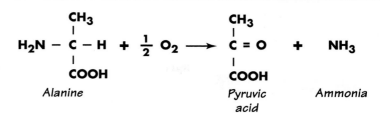

PROTEIN METABOLISM

$$H_2N - \overset{\overset{\displaystyle CH_3}{|}}{\underset{\underset{\displaystyle COOH}{|}}{C}} - H \;+\; \tfrac{1}{2}\,O_2 \;\longrightarrow\; \overset{\overset{\displaystyle CH_3}{|}}{\underset{\underset{\displaystyle COOH}{|}}{C}} = O \;+\; NH_3$$

Alanine   Pyruvic acid   Ammonia

$$2NH_3 \;+\; CO_2 \;\longrightarrow\; H_2N - \overset{\overset{\displaystyle }{}}{\underset{\underset{\displaystyle O}{||}}{C}} - NH_2 \;+\; H_2O$$

Ammonia   Carbon dioxide   Urea   Water

THE EXCRETORY SYSTEM

Vena cava

Aorta

Renal artery

Kidney

Renal vein

Ureter

Urinary bladder

Urethra

This produces ammonia, NH_3, a poisonous compound that the body quickly converts to urea. ● Urea is less toxic than ammonia and is very soluble in water, but it still must be removed from the bloodstream. **The removal of urea— a substance that is the result of the metabolism of proteins in body cells— along with the regulation of water in the bloodstream, is the principal job of the kidneys.**

☑ *Checkpoint* What is the function of the kidneys?

The Kidneys

The kidneys, each about the size of a fist, are located on either side of the spinal column in the lower back. Blood flows into each kidney through a **renal artery** and leaves through a **renal vein.** A third vessel, called the **ureter,** leaves each kidney, carrying fluid to the **urinary bladder.**

Within each kidney is a complex filtration system that removes urea, excess water, and other wastes from the blood. As purified blood is returned to the body, these wastes are collected to form a fluid known as urine. Urine is stored in the bladder and then is eliminated from the body.

The Nephrons

Each kidney contains about a million tiny functional units known as **nephrons.** Refer to the illustration on page 103 as you read about the workings of a nephron. Blood enters each nephron through a single arteriole (small artery) and leaves through a venule (small vein). Each nephron also contains a collecting duct, which leads to the renal pelvis. Wastes and excess water are

MINI LAB ···········Relating··········

Examining a Kidney

PROBLEM   *How does the structure of a kidney **relate** to its function?*

PROCEDURE

1. Obtain a mammal kidney and five different-colored pushpins.

2. Using reference materials, place a pin in or next to the renal artery, renal vein, and ureter. Slice the kidney lengthwise and identify as many structures as you can.

3. Use colored pencils and a file card to make a key to identify each part.

ANALYZE AND CONCLUDE

1. How does the size of the kidney you labeled compare with the size of a human kidney?

2. What structures and functions of the kidney are easier to understand when a real organ is examined?

removed from the bloodstream and gathered in the collecting duct. When blood enters the nephron, it flows into a spherical meshwork of thin-walled capillaries called a **glomerulus**—the filtering unit of the nephron. The blood is under such pressure in these small vessels that much of the blood plasma seeps out, almost like water from a leaky garden hose.

Filtration and Reabsorption

Blood cells, platelets, and plasma proteins are too large to leave the blood as it passes through the glomerulus. **In the glomerulus, blood plasma—containing water, salts, sugars, and nutrients— filters out of the bloodstream and is collected in Bowman's capsule.** This plasma, called the primary filtrate, is then passed from **Bowman's capsule** to the proximal tubule. It looks as though most

of this plasma is about to be thrown away, but appearances can be deceiving.

More than 180 liters of blood plasma pass into the tubules of the kidneys each day. Needless to say, if you excreted this much fluid, life would be very difficult! Fortunately, this is not what happens. **As fluid moves through the proximal tubule, nearly all the material first removed from the blood is put back into the blood.** This process is called **reabsorption.**

Why should the nephron first throw nearly everything away, only to reabsorb most of the water and dissolved materials? This is a bit like cleaning a room by first carrying everything out into the hallway, then bringing back only the things you want to keep. The likely answer is that this is exactly what makes the kidney such an excellent filter.

By first removing nearly everything from the bloodstream, the kidneys ensure that drugs, poisons, and other dangerous compounds will be taken out of the bloodstream. As they then reabsorb most of what they have filtered out, these toxic compounds are left in the proximal tubule, where they will be eliminated in the urine.

Concentration and Water Balance

As the kidneys reabsorb material into the bloodstream, they draw back nearly 99 percent of the water that had first been filtered out. Urine, which now moves through the nephron toward the ureter, is further concentrated in a region of the nephron known as the **loop of Henle.** Depending on the demands of the body, the nephron can produce urine that is very concentrated, which conserves water, or very dilute, which eliminates water.

☑ *Checkpoint*   How do kidneys filter and reabsorb plasma?

Visualizing Kidney Structure and Function

The most important organs of the excretory system are the kidneys, which consist of numerous tiny fluid-filtering structures called nephrons.

1 Renal Artery and Renal Vein

The renal artery brings blood to the kidney, while the renal vein carries the filtered blood away.

2 Renal Cortex and Renal Medulla

The human kidney consists of an outer renal cortex and an inner renal medulla, in which nephrons perform the task of filtration.

4 Bowman's Capsule

Water, nutrients, and wastes are filtered from the blood that enters the glomerulus. This filtrate is collected in Bowman's capsule.

5 Proximal Tubule

Most of the water and nutrients are reabsorbed into the blood as the filtrate passes through the proximal tubule of the nephron.

6 Distal Tubule

Wastes that still remain in the blood are secreted into the distal tubule of the nephron and become part of the urine.

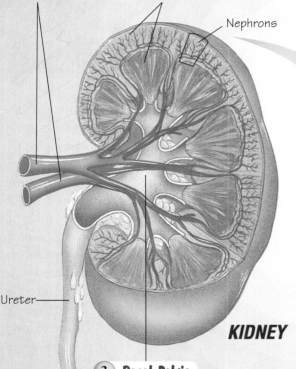

Nephrons

Ureter

KIDNEY

3 Renal Pelvis

The collecting ducts at the ends of nephrons merge and empty urine into the inner region of the kidney, called the renal pelvis, from which the urine is carried to the urinary bladder by way of the ureter.

Scanning electron micrograph of a glomerulus (magnification: 400X)

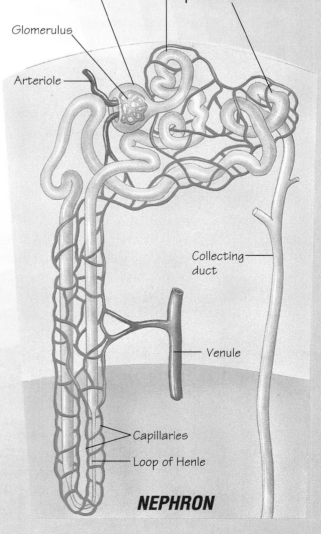

Glomerulus

Arteriole

Collecting duct

Venule

Capillaries

Loop of Henle

NEPHRON

Figure 5–12

When disease or injury reduces kidney function, a kidney dialysis machine is used to filter the blood—much like the kidney itself. These young patients are undergoing kidney dialysis on a beach, using portable kidney dialysis machines. As their blood flows through porous tubes inside the machine, it is bathed in a solution whose composition is close to that of blood plasma. Waste products diffuse into this solution, returning purified blood to the patient. Kidney dialysis makes it possible for people to lead relatively normal lives while waiting for the transplant of a healthy kidney, which will set them free from dialysis machines.

Control of Water Balance

When you drink a glass of water, it is quickly absorbed by the digestive system and passed into the bloodstream. If that's all that happened, every time you took in fluids your blood would become more dilute. Osmosis would cause water to flow into the tissues of the body, and many of the tissues would swell. Needless to say, this doesn't usually happen. The reason, of course, is that the kidneys remove that excess water.

The kidneys don't accomplish this by removing any more water in filtration—they do it by putting less water back into the bloodstream during reabsorption. The kidneys, however, don't make this "decision" on their own—they have help from the brain.

The hypothalamus region of the brain closely monitors the water content of the blood. When it is about right, the hypothalamus signals the pituitary gland to release an **antidiuretic hormone** (ADH). ADH causes its target cells, in the tubules of the kidneys, to reabsorb more water. This action returns more water to the bloodstream and produces a concentrated urine that conserves water. If the water content of the blood rises, ADH is not released, and the tubules reabsorb much less water. A dilute urine is produced, and the body quickly eliminates the excess water.

Section Review 5-3

1. **Explain** the function the kidneys perform in your body.
2. **Describe** the processes of filtration and reabsorption.
3. **Critical Thinking—Comparing** How does the process that takes place within the glomerular capillaries differ from the one that occurs in the capillaries surrounding the collecting tubule?
4. **MINI LAB** How does the structure of a kidney **relate** to its function?

BRANCHING OUT **In Action**

A Cure for Ulcers?

SECTION **5–4**

GUIDE FOR READING

- **Explain** how ulcers are caused and **describe** how they can be treated.

FOR MANY YEARS, DR. JOHN Warren, a pathologist at Royal Perth Hospital in Western Australia, had examined tissue taken from ulcer patients. In nearly all of them, he found a curious corkscrew-shaped bacterium. In 1982, he brought these bacteria to the attention of Barry Marshall, a 30-year-old physician at the hospital.

Marshall then examined his own ulcer patients and discovered that nearly all of them had this bacterium in their stomach linings. Could this bacterium be the cause of ulcers? And if so, what would be the implications of this discovery? Before we discuss the answer to these important questions, you need to learn what ulcers are and how they are treated today.

Peptic Ulcers

As you have read earlier, powerful acids and enzymes are released into the stomach during the process of digestion. They are capable of breaking down just about anything you eat—animal or vegetable. If that's the case, you might wonder why the stomach doesn't digest itself! Why don't these acids eat holes right through the lining of the stomach itself? The answer is that sometimes they do.

Normally, the lining of the stomach is protected by a thick layer of mucus. In addition, the cells lining the stomach are tightly connected to each other, which prevents acid from leaking between them. Finally, millions of damaged cells in the lining are discarded every day and replaced by new ones. Most of the time, these three mechanisms keep the lining strong and healthy.

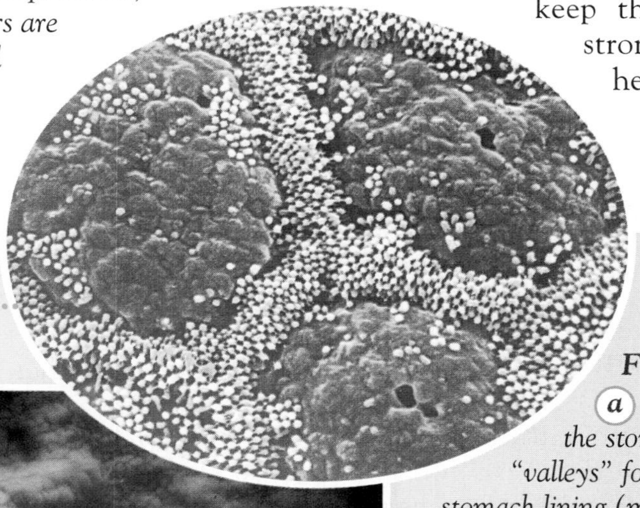

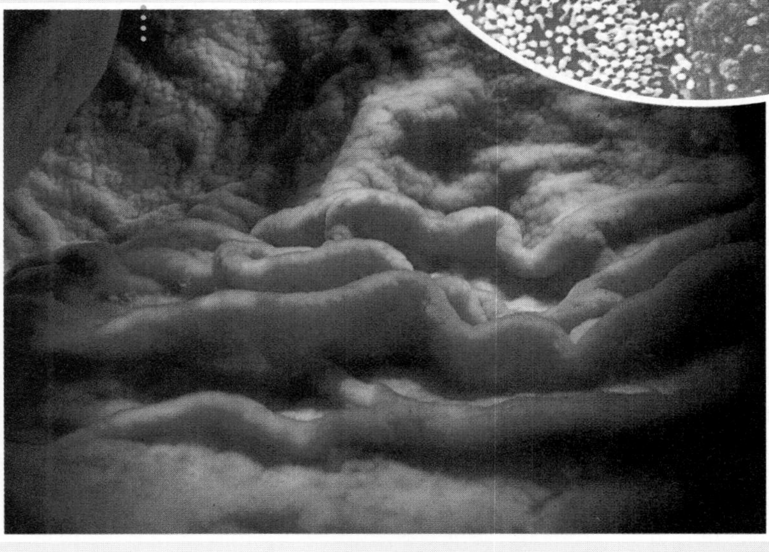

Figure 5–13
(a) A view of the inner surface of the stomach shows the "hills" and "valleys" formed due to folds in the stomach lining (magnification: 15X). (b) A scanning electron micrograph of a portion of the stomach lining shows epithelial cells surrounded by droplets of mucus (magnification: 3550X). The layer of mucus, which is viscous and alkaline, helps protect the lining of the stomach from the damaging effects of acidic secretions.

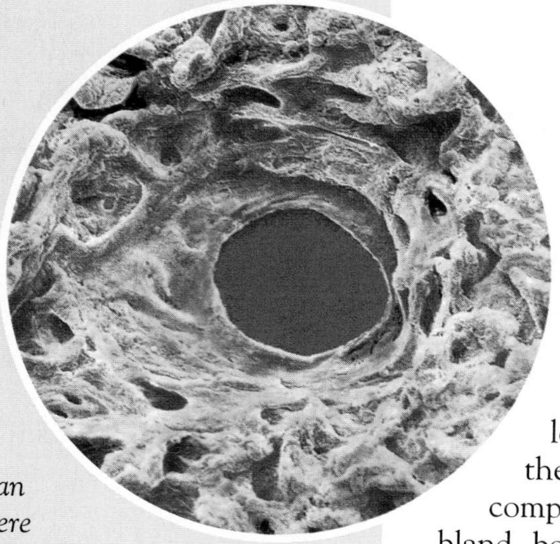

Figure 5-14

Because acid can damage the lining of the stomach, physicians assumed that a peptic ulcer, such as one shown in this scanning electron micrograph, was caused by the production of too much stomach acid. And because stress, overeating, and spicy foods stimulate acid production, each of these was assumed to play a role in causing an ulcer. As a result, ulcer victims were often told to relax, avoid certain foods, and take medication that suppressed the release of stomach acid.

Sometimes, however, stomach acids make direct contact with the cells of the stomach lining. This damages these cells in the same way that a strong acid would burn the skin of your hand. The pain and inflammation that results is known as **gastritis**—inflammation of the stomach.

If acid continues to attack these cells, it may literally eat its way through the stomach lining to produce a deep crater or even a hole in the stomach wall. This kind of damage is known as a **peptic ulcer.** Because the ulcer is actually an open wound, each release of acid into the stomach causes intense pain.

Peptic ulcers present serious medical problems for people around the world. As much as 10 percent of the adult population of the United States suffers from ulcers at some point in their lives. In some countries, the numbers are greater.

Because the release of stomach acid causes further damage to the ulcer, physicians have tried to prevent the release of stomach acid as a way of treating ulcers. A number of drugs can block the release of stomach acids, and physicians have prescribed these drugs to help ulcers heal themselves. Unfortunately, the success rate for this kind of treatment has been very low. Even when doctors were able to heal ulcers using such drugs, the ulcers usually reappeared when the drugs were stopped.

What was the result? There were millions of people taking expensive, ineffective drugs. To make matters worse, by blocking acid release, these drugs interfere with the normal digestive process. To compensate, ulcer patients must eat bland, boring foods that do not require stomach acid for their digestion.

☑ *Checkpoint* What is a peptic ulcer?

What Causes Ulcers?

With so many treatments that didn't work and so much guesswork as to what caused ulcers, could it be that the real cause of this problem was something else? Something hidden in the bodies of ulcer patients? In the early 1980s, two young Australian medical scientists, Dr. John Warren and Dr. Barry Marshall, began to wonder. Could the bacterium—now known as *Helicobacter pylori*—that they both found in their ulcer patients be the cause of ulcers? After months of unsuccessful attempts, Marshall finally found the right conditions to grow this bacterium in the laboratory.

Before long, Marshall had found compounds that killed *H. pylori* in the test tube. He then used these drugs in combination with some antibiotics on his ulcer patients. Seven out of ten patients were completely cured of ulcers. He was sure that he had found the answer to this terrible affliction.

A Daring Experiment

You might think that the scientific community would have jumped at Marshall's exciting results. But his initial reports were met with skepticism. Most scientists believed that acid and stress caused ulcers, and they pointed out that

Marshall had never proved that this bacterium could actually cause an ulcer.

In June 1984, Marshall decided to try the ultimate experiment. He walked into his lab, mixed up a strong dose of *H. pylori* bacteria in a test tube, and swallowed it. Three days later, Marshall awoke with the excruciating pain of gastritis—the first sign that acid has attacked the wall of the stomach and an ulcer is developing. Vomiting and stomach pain kept on for days. He had proven—at least to his own satisfaction—that this bacterium was the cause of gastritis and ulcers.

Rigorous Testing

Marshall then conducted a full-scale experiment, with 100 ulcer patients, to test his ideas. He divided his patients into four groups. One of the groups received no medication, one received just antibiotics, one received the exact mixture of *H. pylori*-killing drugs and antibiotics that Marshall now thought best, and one just the *H. pylori*-killing drugs. After a year, the results were very clear.

Ulcers persisted in three of the groups. But in one group—the one receiving Marshall's combination of *H. pylori*-killing drugs and antibiotics—the *H. pylori* bacteria and the ulcers were gone in 70 percent of the patients. **Dr. Marshall had successfully shown that the *H. pylori* bacteria could cause ulcers and that ulcers could be cured by destroying the bacteria.** In the last few years, one medical panel after another has endorsed Marshall's work, and other scientists have duplicated his findings. By using newer, more powerful antibiotics, cure rates as high as 90 percent have now been reported. Doctors around the world are now getting used to a new bit of knowledge: Ulcers can be cured!

Barry Marshall's work is a perfect example of the scientific method in action. Part luck, part intuition, and part Marshall's hard work had produced the kind of overwhelming evidence that was needed to overcome the doubts of other scientists—and, ultimately, to save thousands of human lives.

Figure 5–15
Today, peptic ulcers are thought to be caused by a bacterium called Helicobacter pylori, *which means "screw-shaped bacterium from the stomach" (magnification: 5100X). Approximately 50 percent of Americans over the age of 50 are infected with* H. pylori. *In some developing countries, nearly all adults are infected with* H. pylori. *Infections by this bacterium seem to run in the family, which suggests that it is spread from person-to-person by contaminated drinking water, eating utensils, and food. Public health officials around the world are now devising ways to deal with this bacterium.*

Section Review 5–4

1. **Explain** how ulcers are caused and describe how they can be treated.
2. **BRANCHING OUT ACTIVITY** Many drugs originally marketed as anti-ulcer medications because they suppress acid release are now sold over the counter for antacid relief and the prevention of heartburn. **Formulate a hypothesis** to explain why this has happened.

Laboratory Investigation

DESIGNING AN EXPERIMENT

Vitamin C in Fruit Juice

Although many vertebrate animals can synthesize their own vitamin C, humans cannot. For this reason, you need to consume foods that will supply you with adequate amounts of this essential nutrient. Vitamin C is found in many vegetables, such as potatoes and broccoli, but orange juice is probably the best source for vitamin C. In this investigation, you will design an experiment to determine the effect exposure to air has on the vitamin C content of selected foods.

Problem

How does exposure to air affect the vitamin C content of certain foods? **Design an experiment** to answer the question.

Suggested Materials

small beakers
100 percent orange juice, refrigerated
water
burette
indophenol solution
other kinds of fruit drinks
glass stirring rod
funnel

Suggested Procedure

1. Set up your equipment as shown in the diagram.

2. While carefully standing on a chair, pour orange juice into the funnel at the top of the burette. Record the initial level of the juice in milliliters.

3. Pour 10 mL of indophenol indicator solution into a beaker. **CAUTION:** *Be careful using indophenol because it stains. Do not drink any of the substances used in the lab. Wash your hands thoroughly after cleaning up.*

4. Place the beaker below the burette and turn the stop valve to the open position so that only one drop of orange juice falls into the indophenol.

5. As each drop of juice falls into the indophenol, stir the mixture and note the color.

6. Keep adding drops until the blue indicator color becomes colorless when you stir. Turn the burette valve off.

7. **Read the level of the juice in the burette. Record this measurement.**

8. **Using the same technique as in steps 1 to 7, design an experiment to determine the effect that exposure to air has on the vitamin C content in orange juice. You may also wish to do a similar experiment with powdered drinks that are fortified with vitamin C.**

9. **Propose a hypothesis and write up your procedure. Make sure the procedure has only one variable and includes a control.**

10. **Obtain the approval of your teacher before carrying out your experiment.**

⊙bservations

1. How many milliliters of the orange juice were needed to change the color of the indophenol?

2. Construct a bar graph to compare the number of milliliters of juice required in each trial of your experiment.

3. How did your data compare with that of other groups?

Ⓐnalysis and Conclusions

1. What is the relationship between the volume of juice required to reach the end point of the titration and the vitamin C content of the juice?

2. Under what conditions did the orange juice have the highest vitamin C content? The lowest? Did your results support your hypothesis?

3. Do the results of your experiment suggest how to handle foods with vitamin C? Explain your answer.

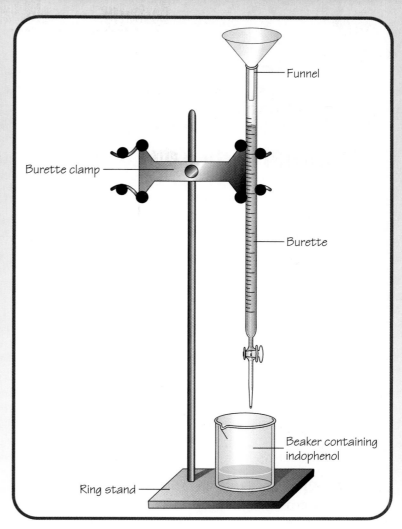

Funnel

Burette clamp

Burette

Beaker containing indophenol

Ring stand

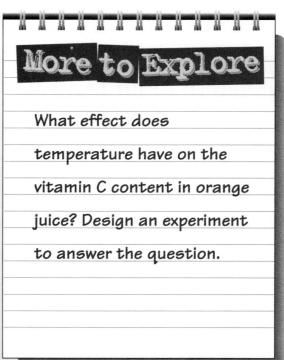

More to Explore

What effect does temperature have on the vitamin C content in orange juice? Design an experiment to answer the question.

Study Guide

Summarizing Key Concepts

The key concepts in each section of this chapter are listed below to help you review the chapter content. Make sure you understand each concept and its relationship to other concepts and to the theme of this chapter.

5–1 Nutrition

- Foods provide energy to perform work and raw materials to build body tissues.
- Food energy is measured in units of the Calorie, which is equivalent to 1000 calories.
- A human body needs water, carbohydrates, fats, proteins, vitamins, and minerals.
- Carbohydrates, fats, and proteins provide energy and the material to build body tissues. Vitamins and minerals are needed in small amounts for the proper functioning of the body.

5–2 The Digestive System

- The digestive system converts food into simple molecules that the body can use.
- The process of digestion begins in the mouth by the action of enzymes such as amylase and pepsin. Food is digested in the stomach and is absorbed by the cells of the villi, which make up the lining of the small intestine.
- Insulin and glucagon help in regulating nutrient levels in the blood.

5–3 The Excretory System

- The kidneys remove wastes, such as urea, and regulate the water in the bloodstream.
- The kidneys, consisting of nephrons, carry out the filtration of blood plasma.
- The urine produced passes through the ureter to the bladder.

5–4 A Cure for Ulcers?

- Recent experiments indicate that the *H. pylori* bacterium can cause ulcers—craters in the stomach wall—by reducing the stomach's layer of protective mucus.

Reviewing Key Terms

Review the following vocabulary terms and their meaning. Then use each term in a complete sentence.

5–1 Nutrition

Calorie

5–2 The Digestive System

mouth	small intestine
salivary gland	pancreas
amylase	liver
lysozyme	bile
esophagus	villus
peristalsis	large intestine
stomach	islet of Langerhans
gastric gland	insulin
pepsin	glucagon

5–3 The Excretory System

kidney	glomerulus
renal artery	Bowman's capsule
renal vein	reabsorption
ureter	loop of Henle
urinary bladder	antidiuretic hormone
nephron	

5–4 A Cure for Ulcers?

gastritis	peptic ulcer

Recalling Main Ideas

Choose the letter of the answer that best completes the statement or answers the question.

1. The amount of heat energy given off by food is measured in

   a. ATP.
   b. calories.
   c. glucose molecules.
   d. carbohydrates.

2. Examples of carbohydrates include

   a. vegetable oils.
   b. amino acids.
   c. sugars and starches.
   d. lipids.

3. The foods at the top of the Food Guide Pyramid should be eaten

   a. only sparingly.
   b. at every meal.
   c. four to six servings a day.
   d. six to eleven servings a day.

4. The enzyme amylase breaks down the chemical bonds in

   a. fats.
   b. proteins.
   c. sugars.
   d. starches.

5. Food moves through the alimentary canal by

   a. the cardiac sphincter.
   b. gravity.
   c. air pressure.
   d. peristalsis.

6. Insulin is produced by the

   a. stomach.
   b. duodenum.
   c. pancreas.
   d. liver.

7. Where in the nephron is the blood plasma filtered out of the bloodstream?

   a. glomerulus
   b. Bowman's capsule
   c. collecting tubule
   d. loop of Henle

8. Which hormone returns more water to the bloodstream?

   a. insulin
   b. glucagon
   c. ADH
   d. pepsin

9. A peptic ulcer is an inflammation of the

   a. gums.
   b. stomach wall.
   c. colon.
   d. kidneys.

10. Dr. Barry Marshall's research showed that peptic ulcers are caused by

    a. acid-blocking drugs.
    b. stress and anxiety.
    c. a virus.
    d. a bacterium.

Putting It All Together

Using the information on pages xii to xiii, complete the following concept map.

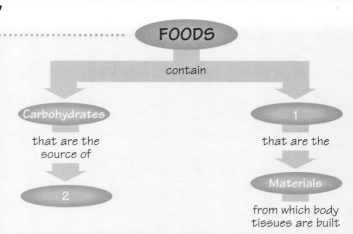

FOODS

contain

Carbohydrates

that are the source of

2

1

that are the

Materials

from which body tissues are built

Reviewing What You Learned

Answer each of the following in a complete sentence.

1. Why must humans consume nutrients?
2. How much energy does a calorie represent?
3. What are six categories of essential nutrients?
4. Why is cellulose an important part of the diet?
5. How are vitamins and minerals similar? How are they different?
6. What are some food sources of vitamin K? What is the function of this vitamin in the body?
7. What is the Food Guide Pyramid? Explain the significance of this shape.
8. Why is it important to chew food thoroughly before swallowing?
9. Explain the function of peristalsis.
10. List the organs that make up the excretory system.
11. What essential nutrients are the primary sources of wastes that the kidneys excrete?
12. What is urine?
13. Explain the function of a kidney dialysis machine.
14. What is gastritis?

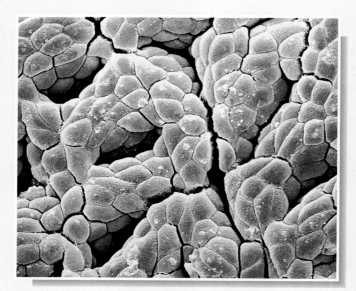

Expanding the Concepts

Discuss each of the following in a brief paragraph.

1. Plants are autotrophs and humans are heterotrophs. Explain what makes them different.
2. How might sipping water with a meal aid in digestion?
3. How does the liver contribute to digestion before and after absorption?
4. In what order do the fats, carbohydrates, and proteins in a mouthful of food begin chemical digestion? Explain your answer.
5. What enzymes and hormones does the pancreas produce? Explain their functions.
6. Explain how kidneys remove wastes. Relate the structure of a kidney to its function.
7. How does insulin affect the liver, muscles, and fatty tissues?
8. How might the kidneys respond to dehydration?
9. Describe the "feedback" mechanism that helps the kidneys maintain the body's water balance.
10. How could washing your hands before preparing a meal reduce the incidence of stomach ulcers?

Extending Your Thinking

Use the skills you have developed in this chapter to answer the following.

1. **Observing**   Obtain a pocket-sized mirror. Hold it about 3 cm from your mouth and exhale onto it. What substance do you observe on the mirror? Explain how your observation illustrates a function of the excretory system.

2. **Relating**   Create a poster describing a "Specials of the Day" menu. Include selections for a breakfast, lunch, and dinner that will appeal to your classmates and that also follow the dietary guidelines in the Food Guide Pyramid.

3. **Predicting**   If you had your gallbladder removed, would you have to change your diet? Explain your answer.

4. **Applying concepts**   Explain how the work of the Australian physicians John Warren and Barry Marshall on *Helicobacter pylori* involved each of the following parts of the scientific method:

- Developing a question
- Stating a problem
- Gathering and interpreting data
- Formulating a hypothesis
- Experimenting

5. **Hypothesizing**   Some scientists predict that more minerals than the ones already known will be discovered to be essential nutrients. For example, garlic may contain minerals that help fight infection. Formulate a hypothesis to explain how this may happen.

Applying Your Skills

A Recipe for Tenderness

The molecules in protein-rich foods—such as meats, eggs, and cheese—are often complex and enormous in size. Each protein molecule is coiled and folded so that the bonds between its atoms must be broken down bit by bit to reach its center. The stomach has seven different protein-digesting enzymes. In this activity, you will observe the effects of several enzymes.

1. Obtain four test tubes containing solidified gelatin.

2. Add 1 mL of each of the following three solutions to the top of the gelatin: fresh pineapple, canned pineapple, meat tenderizer, and water. Why is water a part of this investigation? Why is gelatin used?

3. Put the test tubes in a refrigerator for 24 hours. After 24 hours, measure the amount of gelatin that has dissolved in each of the test tubes. Record your results in a bar graph.

4. Was there any difference between the actions of the fresh and the canned pineapple? How can you explain your results?

5. Carefully clean out the test tubes using hot water and properly discard the contents.

• GOING FURTHER •

6. Design an experiment to compare the effects of two brands of meat tenderizers containing different enzymes.

Reproductive System

6–1 The Human Reproductive System

- **Identify** the organs of the male reproductive system and **describe** their functions.

- **Identify** the organs of the female reproductive system and **describe** their functions.

6–2 Fertilization and Development

- **Sequence** the events from the fertilization of an egg through childbirth.

BRANCHING OUT *In Depth*

6–3 Sexually Transmitted Diseases

- **Describe** some of the most common sexually transmitted diseases.

LABORATORY INVESTIGATION

- **Observe** the microscopic structures of reproductive organs and gametes.

Biology and Your World

BIO JOURNAL

The infants in this photograph may look contented and easy to care for; however, raising a child is harder than you may think. Have you ever baby-sat for a younger sibling or another person's child? Was this easier or harder than you expected? In your journal, describe your experience. If you have never cared for a younger child, describe what you think the experience would be.

A group of babies

The Human Reproductive System

GUIDE FOR READING

- **Describe** the functions of the male and female reproductive systems.

- **List** the four phases of the menstrual cycle.

WHAT IS THE SINGLE MOST important day in your life? If you said "my birthday," you are not alone. Not only is your birthday important to you, it's also important to those closest to you. Think about how many things depend on your birthday. Your birthday determines when you are allowed to go to school, when you qualify for a driver's license, and when you may vote.

To the rest of society, your birthday may indeed be the day your life began. To a biologist, however, birth is as much the end of a process—the process of reproduction—as it is a beginning. The trillions of cells in a newborn baby all come from the fusion of two reproductive cells. Human reproduction is the story of how these cells are produced and come together to form a single cell, from which a new life develops.

Human Sexual Development

For the first six weeks of development, male and female human embryos are nearly identical. Then, in the seventh week, the primary reproductive organs, which will eventually produce reproductive cells, or **gametes** (GAM-eets), begin to develop into either **ovaries** in females or **testes** (TEHS-teez; singular: testis) in males.

The ovaries and testes are endocrine glands. The ovaries produce estrogens—a group of steroid hormones that cause development of the female reproductive organs. And the testes produce androgens—steroid hormones that cause the male reproductive organs to develop. Although the male and female reproductive organs develop from the same tissues in the embryo, these hormones determine whether they will develop in the male or female pattern.

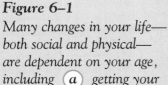

Figure 6–1

Many changes in your life— both social and physical— are dependent on your age, including **a** *getting your driver's license,* **b** *graduating from high school, and* **c** *shaving.*

During childhood, the reproductive glands, or gonads, continue to produce small amounts of estrogen and androgen, which help to shape development. However, the gonads are not capable of producing reproductive cells until puberty, a period of rapid sexual development that usually occurs in the early teenage years. During puberty, the gonads complete their development and the reproductive system becomes fully functional. Puberty may occur at any time between 9 and 15 years of age, and on average occurs about a year earlier in females than in males.

Puberty begins when hormone levels begin to increase. The hypothalamus releases substances that signal the pituitary gland to begin producing two hormones—**follicle-stimulating hormone** (FSH) and **luteinizing hormone** (LH).

In males, LH causes certain cells in the testes to produce **testosterone** (tehs-TAHS-ter-ohn), the principal androgen, or male hormone. FSH and testosterone are necessary for other cells in the testes to develop into **sperm,** the male gametes. These diploid (2n) cells undergo meiosis, which results in 4 haploid (n) cells, each of which contains 23 chromosomes. After the completion of meiosis, these cells develop into mature sperm cells with long flagella.

In addition to sperm development, testosterone is responsible for the development of a male's secondary sex characteristics. In puberty, the male's voice deepens, he begins to grow body hair, and he finds it easier to develop large muscles. ●

In females, FSH and LH stimulate the ovaries to produce the female sex hormones, **progesterone** and **estrogen,** responsible for the development of female secondary sex characteristics, such as breast development and widening of the hips. In addition, these hormones work with FSH and LH to produce female gametes called **ova** (singular: ovum), or eggs.

INTEGRATING HEALTH

Testosterone is a natural anabolic steroid. What are some of the risks involved in taking a synthetic anabolic steroid?

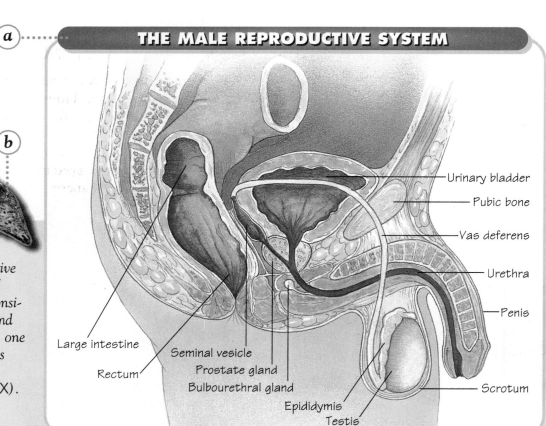

THE MALE REPRODUCTIVE SYSTEM

a

b

Urinary bladder

Pubic bone

Vas deferens

Urethra

Penis

Scrotum

Testis

Epididymis

Bulbourethral gland

Prostate gland

Seminal vesicle

Rectum

Large intestine

Figure 6–2

ⓐ *The male reproductive system is a collection of organs and glands responsible for the production and delivery of* ⓑ *sperm, one of which is shown in this electron micrograph (magnification: 87,413X).*

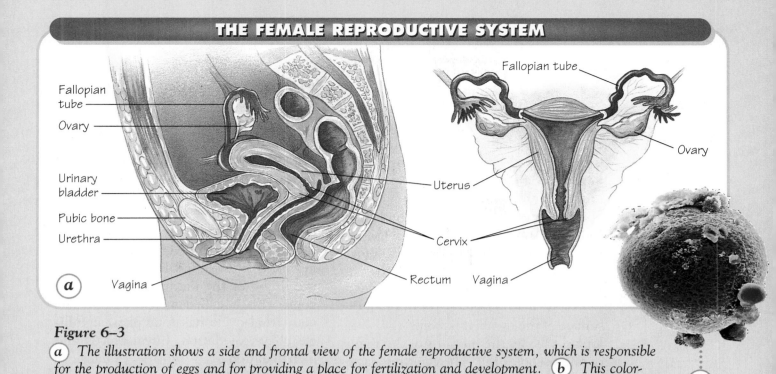

Fallopian tube

Ovary

Urinary bladder

Pubic bone

Urethra

a

Vagina

Fallopian tube

Uterus

Cervix

Ovary

Rectum

Vagina

b

Figure 6–3

a *The illustration shows a side and frontal view of the female reproductive system, which is responsible for the production of eggs and for providing a place for fertilization and development.* **b** *This color-enhanced electron micrograph of a single human egg shows its protective covering (colored red) as well as the remnants from the follicle (colored yellow) in which the egg developed (magnification: 470X).*

The Male Reproductive System

The male reproductive system has the task of producing and delivering sperm. Sperm are produced in the testes, which descend from the abdominal cavity just before birth into a sac called the **scrotum,** located outside the body cavity. This location keeps the temperature of the testes about 2°C cooler than the rest of the body, for sperm development.

The testes are made up of tightly coiled tubules called **seminiferous** (sehm-uh-NIHF-er-uhs) **tubules.** More than 100 million sperm cells are produced in the seminiferous tubules every day. When mature, the sperm travel into the **epididymis** (ehp-uh-DIHD-ih-mihs), where they are stored. After a brief period, they are released into the **vas deferens** (VAS DEHF-uh-rehnz). The vas deferens extends upward from the scrotum into the abdominal cavity.

Glands lining the reproductive tract—including the seminal vesicle, the prostate, and the bulbourethral gland—release a nutrient-rich fluid called semen, in which sperm are suspended.

The Female Reproductive System

The female reproductive system produces gametes, too. However, the fact that fertilization and development of a baby both take place inside the female's body places special demands on the female reproductive system. In contrast to the millions of sperm produced each day, the ovaries produce, on average, just one egg every 28 days or so. Each time an egg is released from one of the ovaries, the rest of the reproductive tract must be prepared to nourish and support a developing embryo.

FSH stimulates the development of a **follicle**—a cluster of cells that contains a developing egg. As the follicle gets larger and larger, the egg passes through the early stages of meiosis. When meiosis is complete, a single large haploid (n) egg and three smaller cells called polar bodies are produced. Because the polar bodies have little cytoplasm, they disintegrate.

While the follicle is developing, cells surrounding the egg produce larger and larger amounts of estrogen. When the level of these hormones reaches a critical point, hormones from the pituitary gland cause the follicle to rupture, and the egg is released into one of the two **Fallopian tubes.** The release of an egg is known as **ovulation.**

As the mature egg breaks through the surface of the ovary, it is swept into a Fallopian tube by the motions of thousands of microscopic cilia. The egg then passes into a muscular chamber called the **uterus.** The outer end of the uterus is called the cervix. Beyond the cervix is a canal known as the vagina, which is the passageway that leads to the outside of the body.

The Menstrual Cycle

Ovulation is just one of a series of events that occur in a pattern called the **menstrual cycle.** The menstrual cycle takes, on average, about 28 days. As an egg develops, the lining of the uterus is prepared to receive it. If the egg is fertilized after ovulation, it is implanted in the uterus and embryonic development begins. If it is not fertilized, the egg and the lining of the uterus pass out of the body. This is called menstruation. **The menstrual cycle has four phases: follicle phase, ovulation, luteal phase, and menstruation.**

Follicle Phase

The follicle phase begins when the level of estrogen in the bloodstream is low. The hypothalamus senses the low level of estrogen and causes the pituitary

Figure 6–4

The menstrual cycle, which is controlled by hormones produced by the ovary (progesterone and estrogens) and the pituitary gland (FSH and LH), occurs on average about every 28 days. Notice the changes in hormone levels in the blood, the development of the follicle, and the changes in the uterine lining during the cycle, illustrated in the diagram.

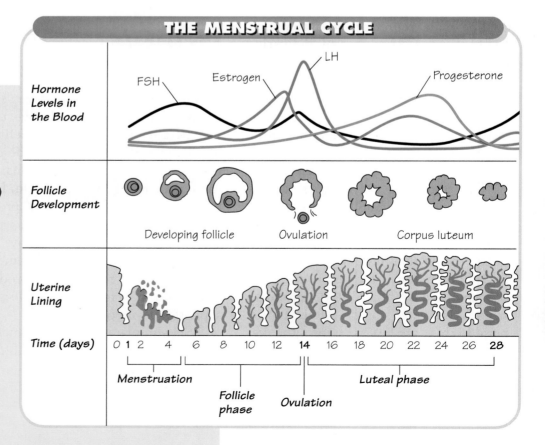

gland to release FSH and LH into the bloodstream. These hormones act on the ovary, stimulating a follicle to develop to maturity. As the egg develops, the cells of the follicle produce more and more estrogen. Estrogen causes the lining of the uterus to thicken in preparation for a fertilized egg.

Ovulation

Ovulation is the shortest phase of the cycle. When the egg is mature, the pituitary gland sends out a burst of LH. LH causes the wall of the follicle to break open and the egg is released into one of the Fallopian tubes.

Luteal Phase

The luteal phase of the cycle begins after the egg is released. As the egg moves through the Fallopian tube, the cells of the ruptured follicle undergo a transformation. The follicle turns yellow and is now known as the **corpus luteum** (KOR-puhs LOOT-ee-uhm), which means "yellow body" in Latin. The corpus luteum continues to produce estrogen, but now produces large amounts of progesterone too. Progesterone stimulates cell and tissue growth in the lining of the uterus, preparing it for pregnancy. Progesterone also inhibits the release of LH and FSH.

The chances of an egg being successfully fertilized are greatest around the time of ovulation. If the egg is not fertilized, the corpus luteum breaks down and estrogen levels decrease.

Menstruation

Menstruation begins when the level of estrogen in the blood becomes so low that the lining of the uterus cannot be maintained. Tissues detach from the uterine wall and are discharged through the vagina along with blood and the unfertilized egg. Menstruation usually lasts 3 to 7 days. When it ends, a new cycle begins.

What starts a new cycle? The drop in estrogen that causes menstruation is sensed by the hypothalamus. It signals the pituitary gland to release FSH, which starts the development of a new follicle—and the cycle begins all over again.

Figure 6–5
When hormone levels reach a certain point, an egg bursts from one of the ovaries into a Fallopian tube. The halo around the egg in this photograph is a protective layer of follicle cells called the corona radiata.

Section Review   6-1

1. **Describe** the functions of the male and female reproductive systems.
2. **List** the four phases of the menstrual cycle.
3. **Critical Thinking—Interpreting Diagrams**   Which hormone is at its highest level during ovulation?

Fertilization and Development

- **Describe** fertilization.
- **Describe** the importance of the placenta.

MINI LAB

- **Construct a model** of early human development.

A SINGLE CELL FORMED BY THE fusion of sperm and egg begins the process of development. To produce this cell, the reproductive system must bring these two gametes together. In humans and most other mammals, the fertilized egg develops within the body of its mother. This means that the human reproductive system must not only produce reproductive cells, it must also protect and nourish the developing embryo from fertilization to birth.

Fertilization

During sexual intercourse, the penis is inserted into the vagina to a point just below the cervix. Involuntary smooth muscle contractions of the penis cause an ejaculation, which is the release of several milliliters of semen into the vagina.

Semen contains as many as 100 million sperm per milliliter. Therefore, it's no exaggeration to say that after they are released, millions of sperm swim through the uterus toward the Fallopian tubes. Of the millions of sperm released, only a relatively small number will reach the upper region of the Fallopian tube. If an egg is present in one of the Fallopian tubes, its chances of being fertilized by one of these sperm are very good.

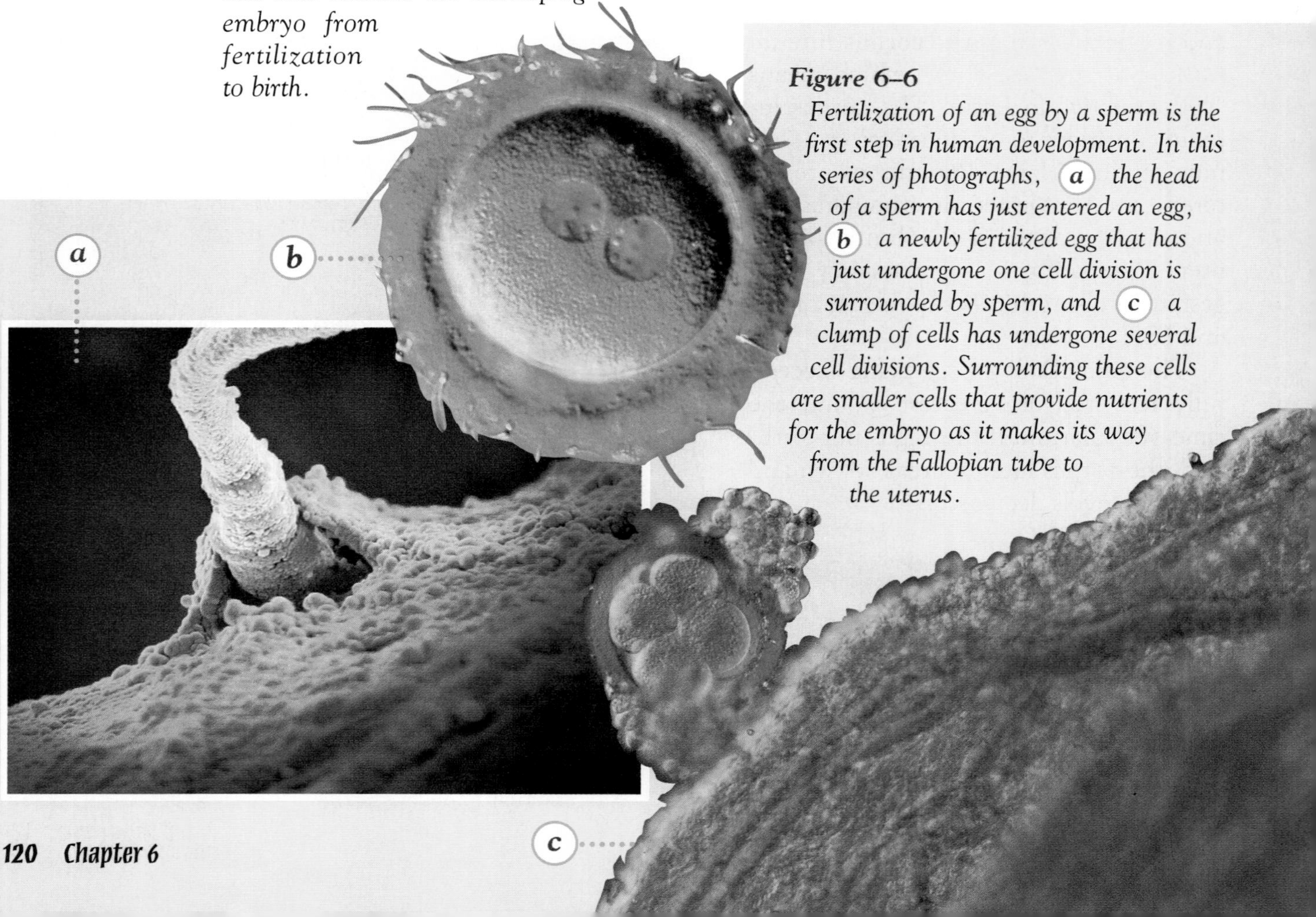

Figure 6–6

Fertilization of an egg by a sperm is the first step in human development. In this series of photographs, **a** *the head of a sperm has just entered an egg,* **b** *a newly fertilized egg that has just undergone one cell division is surrounded by sperm, and* **c** *a clump of cells has undergone several cell divisions. Surrounding these cells are smaller cells that provide nutrients for the embryo as it makes its way from the Fallopian tube to the uterus.*

The Fusion of Egg and Sperm

It might seem impossible for such a tiny sperm to fuse with the much larger egg. The egg is surrounded by a thick, protective layer that also includes cells from the follicle in which the egg developed. However, the outermost protective layer also contains binding sites to which sperm cells can attach. When a sperm attaches to these cells, a sac at the end of the sperm breaks open, releasing powerful enzymes that help to dissolve the protective layers around the egg.

Very often, more than one sperm attaches to the egg, and each begins to work its way through to the egg cell membrane. **As soon as one of the sperm makes direct contact with the egg cell membrane, the two cells fuse, the tail of the sperm breaks away, and the sperm nucleus enters the egg's cytoplasm. This process is known as fertilization.** Then, immediately following **fertilization,** rapid electrical and chemical changes take place in the egg cell membrane that prevent any other sperm cells from entering. A **zygote** (ZIGH-goht), or a fertilized egg, has been formed, and development begins.

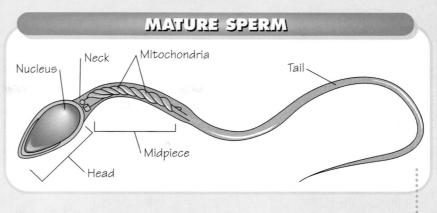

MATURE SPERM

Figure 6–7

(a) *A single human sperm consists of a head, a midpiece, and a tail. The head contains the nucleus, with its genetic material. The midpiece is packed with mitochondria that are needed for energy production. And the tail is used to propel the sperm forward.* (b) *Once inside a female's body, sperm are attracted by chemicals produced by an egg, causing all sperm to swim in the same direction toward the egg.*

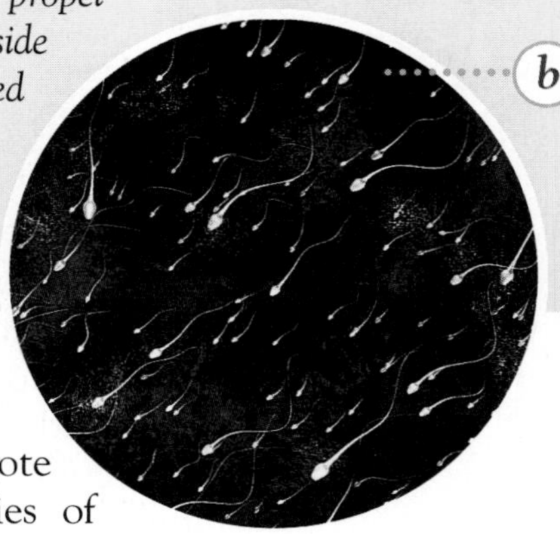

Cell Division

The newly formed zygote goes through a rapid series of cell divisions, gradually forming a solid ball of cells known as a **morula** (MOR-yoo-luh). As cell division in the zygote continues, it gradually develops a hollow cavity and becomes known as a blastocyst. Three to four days after ovulation, the blastocyst attaches itself to the wall of the uterus. The blastocyst may not look like much, but within a few months it will develop into the trillions of cells in a human baby. The precision and intricacy of this process is wonderful to behold—no builder ever executed a plan more exacting, yet the blueprints for this remarkable process are written on the smallest possible scale, the DNA sequence in the nucleus of a single human cell.

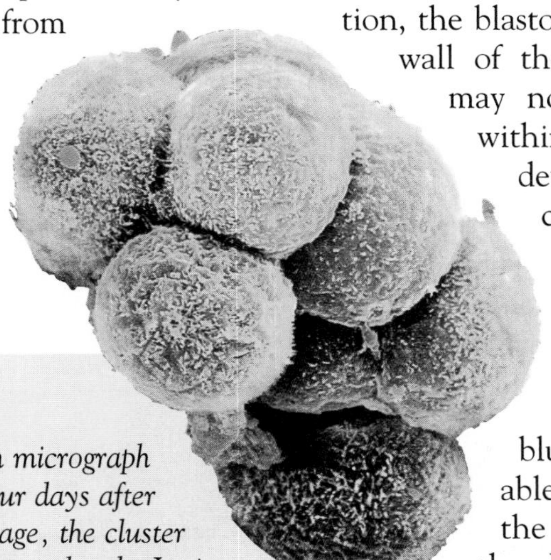

Figure 6–8

This scanning electron micrograph shows an egg about four days after fertilization. At this stage, the cluster of cells is known as a morula, the Latin word for mulberry (magnification: 1350X).

Figure 6–9

Once an egg is released from an ovary, it may become fertilized in a Fallopian tube. If fertilization occurs, the fertilized egg becomes known as a zygote. As the zygote continues its trip toward the uterus, it undergoes many cell divisions, becoming a morula and then a hollow ball of cells called a blastocyst. The blastocyst implants itself in the uterine wall and development begins.

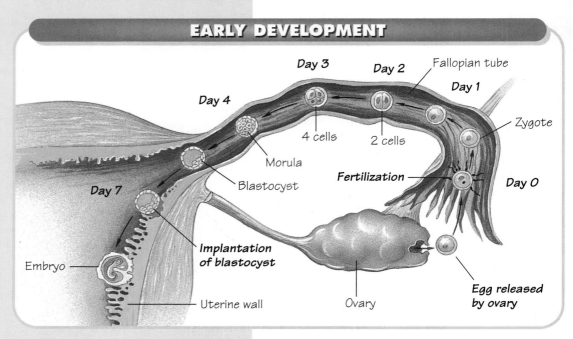

EARLY DEVELOPMENT

Implantation

The cells of the zygote then grow into the uterine wall in a process known as **implantation.** Implantation is critical to the zygote for two reasons. First, the outermost cells of the zygote and the cells in the uterine wall will grow together to form structures that will nourish and support the developing **embryo.** Without that support, the zygote would not have enough stored food to develop on its own. Second, and most importantly, implantation produces chemical signals that preserve the uterine lining.

Here's how those chemical signals work. Recall that the corpus luteum, which produces progesterone, remains active for about two weeks after ovulation. Then it breaks down, progesterone synthesis stops, and the uterine wall is discarded in menstruation. However, as soon as they implant in the uterine wall, the outermost cells of the zygote produce a substance called **human chorionic gonadotropin** (HCG). HCG is a powerful chemical signal that keeps the corpus luteum alive and active. As a result, the uterine lining is preserved and the embryo can continue to develop.

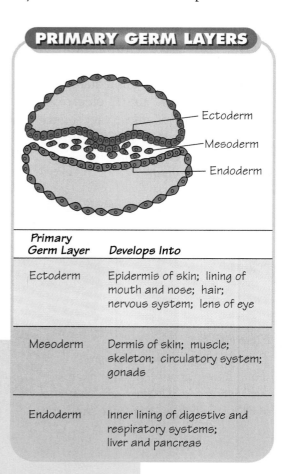

PRIMARY GERM LAYERS

Primary Germ Layer	Develops Into
Ectoderm	Epidermis of skin; lining of mouth and nose; hair; nervous system; lens of eye
Mesoderm	Dermis of skin; muscle; skeleton; circulatory system; gonads
Endoderm	Inner lining of digestive and respiratory systems; liver and pancreas

Figure 6–10

During gastrulation, the three primary germ layers—ectoderm, mesoderm, and endoderm—are formed. All embryonic structures are derived from one of these three layers.

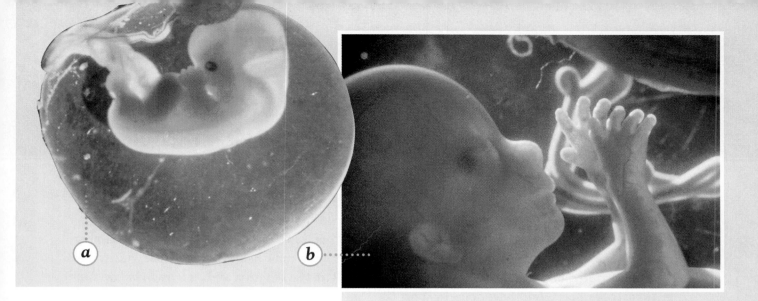

The Developing Embryo

The early events of embryonic development are the same for humans as they are for most other mammals. The outer layer of the blastocyst grows into the uterus, surrounding the tissues of the developing embryo. A mass of cells that forms on one side of the blastocyst will become the embryo itself. In the first two weeks after fertilization, the cells in this mass sort themselves into two distinct layers.

Gastrulation

In a process known as **gastrulation** (gas-troo-LAY-shuhn), cells from the upper layer migrate inward to form a third layer between the first two. These three layers of cells—the ectoderm, mesoderm, and endoderm—are known as the primary germ layers of the embryo. In *Figure 6–10,* you can see that all the other organs and tissues of the embryo will be formed from these three primary germ layers.

The outer layers of the blastocyst form two important membranes that surround the embryo. These extra-embryonic membranes, located outside the embryo, are called the amnion and the chorion. Both of these membranes fill with fluid that helps to cushion the embryo and protect it from injury.

✓ *Checkpoint*   What is gastrulation?

Figure 6–11
Up until the eighth week of development, a developing human is called an embryo. After this time, it is referred to as a fetus. (a) *At six to seven weeks after fertilization, the embryo is 13- to 18-mm long, has the beginnings of eyes, a beating heart, fingers, and a brain, which is nearly as large as the rest of the body.* (b) *By the fourth month, the ears, nose, and mouth have formed. Notice the umbilical cord, which connects the fetus to the placenta.*

Neurulation

Near the end of the third week of development, an especially critical event—neurulation—takes place. At about the seventeenth day after fertilization, the ectoderm begins to thicken into a line pointing to the head of the embryo. Gradually, this thickening produces a groove, and the raised edges of the groove move toward each other, forming a tube. By the end of the twenty-third day, the tube has sealed and then sunk beneath the ectoderm. What is this tube, and why is its formation so important? This neural tube, as it is called, becomes the nervous system. One end of the tube will eventually develop into the brain, and the remainder of the tube will become the spinal cord. The remaining ectoderm will then begin to form the skin of the embryo.

✓ *Checkpoint*   What is neurulation?

Picturing Pregnancy

During a class discussion of human reproduction, one of your classmates says, "I have always wondered how the fetus 'knows' when it is time to be born. And how does it know to stay inside the uterus for nearly nine months?"

Your teacher shows the class an illustration that may help answer these questions. Look at the diagram and line graph below, then answer the questions that follow.

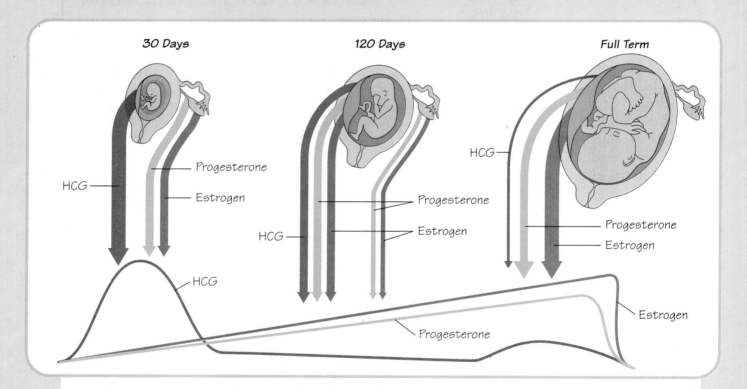

THINK ABOUT IT

1. What organs produce progesterone and estrogen at 30 days and 120 days in the pregnancy? How does this change at full term?

2. Which hormone is most abundant at 30 days? Give evidence to support your answer.

3. Which hormones are increasing at 120 days? Which hormone is decreasing?

4. Describe what happens to the levels of the hormones at the end of the pregnancy.

5. Based on what you know about the roles of these hormones, predict the "birth" day.

124 Chapter 6

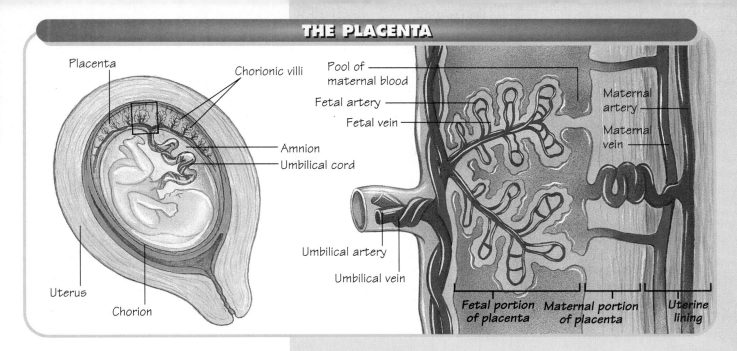

The Placenta

During the first few weeks of development, the cells of the embryo simply absorb nourishment from the surrounding cells of the mother. But within a few days, the embryo is too large for this to continue to meet its needs. Shortly after gastrulation is complete, the embryo forms an organ that will supply its needs for the rest of its development—the **placenta.**

In the fourth week of development, the amniotic sac expands to the point where it completely surrounds the embryo. This expansion squeezes the other extra-embryonic tissue into a thin stalk, connecting the embryo to the uterus. This stalk is the beginning of the **umbilical cord.**

You might think that the best way to bring food and oxygen to the embryo would be to link its blood directly to its mother through the umbilical cord. However, if this were the case, diseases could easily spread from mother to child. Serious problems could also result if the embryo and mother have different blood groups. So it should not be surprising that the blood supplies of mother and embryo do not mix directly.

Figure 6–12
The placenta, formed from the chorion layer of the embryo and the uterine lining of the mother, is the connection between the mother and the developing embryo. Although fetal blood vessels branch extensively into pools of maternal blood, there is no mixing of blood. The placenta provides a large surface area for diffusion of oxygen, carbon dioxide, nutrients, and wastes between fetus and mother.

Instead, they come into very close contact in the placenta. The placenta forms at the base of the umbilical cord, where it meets the uterine wall. Tiny blood vessels from the embryo pass through pools of maternal blood. Although the blood supplies do not mix, food, oxygen, carbon dioxide, and metabolic wastes pass back and forth between mother and embryo. **As the embryo grows, the placenta serves as its main organ of respiration, nourishment, and excretion.** Anything that the mother takes into her body, including drugs, passes through the placenta to the embryo.

✓ *Checkpoint*   What is the placenta?

Fetal Development

In the next few weeks, the skeletal system and the limbs of the embryo take shape. This is a particularly important time for the embryo because a number of

INTEGRATING HEALTH

Use reference materials to find out what happens when an embryo and mother have different Rh factors in their blood.

Modeling

Early Human Development

PROBLEM
*How can you **construct a model** of human development?*

PROCEDURE

1. Use modeling clay and reference materials to create a three-dimensional representation of each of the following stages in early human development: zygote, first cell division, morula, blastocyst, five-week embryo, and eleven-week fetus.

2. Label each model with its name and an estimation of its actual size.

ANALYZE AND CONCLUDE

1. At which stage can you begin to recognize human structures?

2. What changes have occurred at each stage of development?

external factors can disrupt development at this point. Although the placenta does act as a barrier to some disease-causing organisms, others—such as rubella (German measles) and most drugs, including alcohol, tobacco, and medications—can penetrate the placenta and prevent normal development.

By the end of eight weeks, the embryo is called a **fetus.** Its muscular system enables it to move around a bit, and its sexual organs have developed to the point where it is possible to tell a male from a female. Its heartbeat becomes loud enough to be heard through a stethoscope. It now begins to grow rapidly, and by the end of six months, it is nearly 35 centimeters long and has a mass of between 500 and 800 grams.

As the fetus enters its seventh month of growth, reflexes in its nervous system enable it to respond to sudden noises. Its lungs are enlarging rapidly, and its digestive system is almost ready to function. In many respects, after six months of growth, the fetus is almost ready to lead an independent existence.

Pregnancy usually continues for three more months, however, and there is good reason for that. A baby born early in the last three months of development may have serious problems adjusting to life outside. In particular, the respiratory system is not fully matured. Many babies born at this time are unable to regulate their body temperature. For this reason, premature babies are always at risk and must be given special care to increase their chances of survival.

✓ *Checkpoint* At what stage is an embryo called a fetus?

Figure 6–13
CAREER TRACK
A physician assistant performs routine medical care—physical examinations, administering injections and immunizations, administering or ordering certain medical procedures such as X-rays—and generally instructs and counsels patients.

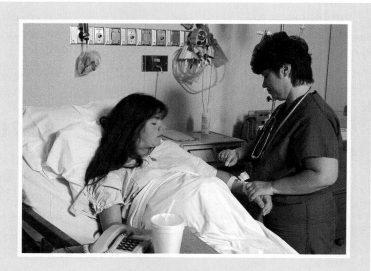

Labor and Birth

Childbirth in humans takes place, on average, about nine months after fertilization. It is not known exactly how the body "decides" when it is time for a child to be born. The immediate signal is a pituitary hormone called **oxytocin.** This hormone stimulates contractions of the smooth muscles surrounding the uterus. Slowly at first, these muscles begin a series of contractions known as labor. As the contractions become more frequent and more powerful, the opening of the cervix expands until it reaches a diameter of nearly 10 centimeters—large enough for the head of the baby to pass through. At some point during this time, the amniotic sac bursts and the fluid in the sac passes out of the mother's body.

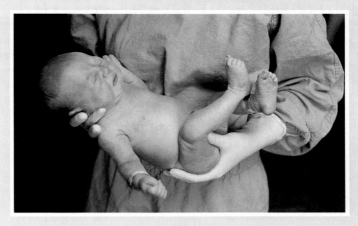

Figure 6–14
About nine months after fertilization, a baby is born. Identification bands, which match those of the mother, are placed around the baby's wrist and ankle.

Childbirth

When the cervix has fully expanded and contractions come at intervals of 2 to 3 minutes, childbirth is about to begin. Contractions of the uterus force the baby, usually head first, out through the cervix, the vagina, and into the world.

As the baby leaves its mother's body, it may cough or cry to open up its fluid-filled lungs and take its first breath. Blood flow to the placenta dries up, and the placenta itself detaches from the wall of the uterus. It will follow the baby out through the birth canal. The umbilical cord is tied and cut, leaving only a small piece attached to the baby. The baby is now ready to begin life on its own.

After Childbirth

Just a few hours after childbirth, a pituitary hormone known as **prolactin** stimulates the production of milk in the breast tissues of the mother. By nursing her child soon after it is born, the mother stimulates the release of more oxytocin, which also helps to stop uterine bleeding. The mother also passes an important secretion to the baby in her first breast milk. This fluid, called colostrum, contains a remarkable mixture of special antibodies produced by the immune system. Colostrum helps to protect the baby from infections for many weeks. Colostrum is gradually replaced by mature milk. The milk that humans and other mammals produce for their offspring is a complete food. It contains all the vitamins, minerals, and other nutrients that the baby needs for the first few months of life.

Section Review 6–2

1. **Describe** fertilization.
2. **Describe** the importance of the placenta.
3. **Critical Thinking—Hypothesizing** What might happen to a fetus if the placenta became detached from the uterine wall?
4. **MINI LAB** How can you **construct a model** of early human development?

GUIDE FOR READING

- **List** three common sexually transmitted diseases caused by bacteria.

- **List** three common sexually transmitted diseases caused by viruses.

MINI LAB

- **Interpret data** from a graph to learn about an STD.

INTEGRATING HEALTH

Use reference materials to find out about STDs caused by protozoans, fungi, and arthropods.

IT IS A BIOLOGICAL FACT THAT human reproduction can take place only when living sperm cells come in contact with an egg. As you have read, these reproductive cells are sheltered from contact with the outside world, surrounded with nutrient-rich fluids to support their activities, and pass directly from the reproductive tract of the male into that of the female. Internal fertilization is an effective method of reproduction. However, it also creates a perfect opportunity for disease-causing organisms to exploit the reproductive system.

STDs—A Growing Problem

Diseases that are spread from one person to another by sexual contact are known as **sexually transmitted diseases,** or STDs. Sexually transmitted diseases are a serious health problem in the United States, infecting millions of people each year and accounting for thousands of deaths. ❀ Both bacteria and viruses can cause STDs. ● Because each sexual contact carries with it the risk of an STD, it is important to know and understand the most serious of these diseases.

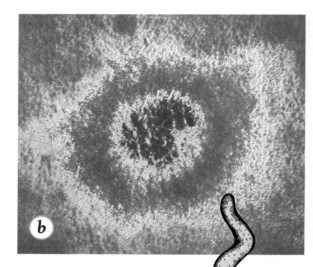

b

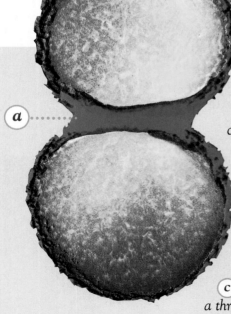

a

c

Figure 6–15

Most sexually transmitted diseases are caused by bacteria and viruses. (a) Gonorrhea is caused by the bacterium called Neisseria gonorrhoeae, which is kidney-shaped and often found in pairs (magnification: 29,000X). (b) There are two forms of herpes virus, called Herpes simplex Type 1 and Type 2. Herpes simplex Type 1 causes sores around the mouth. Herpes simplex Type 2 causes sores on the reproductive organs and is sexually transmitted. Although the two forms are identical in appearance, they are different in their chemical makeup. This electron micrograph shows Herpes simplex Type 1 (magnification: 200,000X). (c) The bacterium that causes syphilis, Treponema pallidum, is a threadlike, spiral-shaped bacterium (magnification: 4000X).

Bacterial Diseases

Although many of the most serious STDs are caused by bacteria, they can usually be treated and cured with antibiotics. Early detection and treatment are necessary to prevent any serious consequences of infection. **Three common STDs caused by bacteria are syphilis, gonorrhea, and chlamydia.**

Syphilis

One of the most serious and dangerous bacterial STDs is **syphilis.** This disease is caused by a corkscrew-shaped bacterium called a spirochete. The syphilis spirochete is a delicate organism that dies quickly when exposed to the air. However, sexual contact provides it with the perfect opportunity to pass from one person to another.

The first sign of this disease appears from 10 to 90 days after infection—a hard sore called a chancre (SHAN-ker) forms at the point where the organism passes through the skin. The sore disappears after a few weeks, but the infection does not. The spirochete spreads throughout the body, gradually infecting the circulatory and nervous systems.

In its early stages, syphilis can be cured with large doses of antibiotics. If left untreated, however, syphilis can cause serious physical damage and may even be fatal.

☑ *Checkpoint*　What is syphilis?

Gonorrhea

Another serious STD is **gonorrhea.** Gonorrhea infects the urinary and reproductive tracts, and it is easily passed from person to person through sexual contact. Males are usually aware of being infected because the bacterium causes pain during urination and may result in the discharge of blood and pus. In females, the symptoms are much milder. Many

females do not even know they are infected. This is particularly dangerous, because gonorrhea can produce pelvic inflammatory disease (PID), which may make it impossible to ever have children.

☑ *Checkpoint*　What is gonorrhea?

Chlamydia

The single most common STD in the United States is one you may never have heard of—**chlamydia.** The bacterium that causes this disease thrives in the moist reproductive tracts of both males and females. It produces only a few symptoms, which may include a mild burning sensation during urination. Because of this, most people with chlamydia are unaware of the infection and continue to spread it to others without being treated. This is a cause for serious concern because long-term infection with this bacterium is now the leading cause of preventable infertility among women in their thirties.

☑ *Checkpoint*　What is chlamydia?

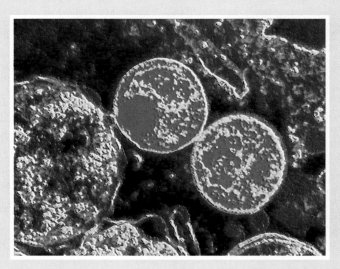

Figure 6–16
Chlamydia trachomatis, *the bacterium that causes chlamydia, is a viruslike bacterium. The two smaller spheres in this color-enhanced electron micrograph show two* Chlamydia *bacteria (magnification: 40,000X).*

MINI LAB .... *Interpreting* ....

Number Sense

PROBLEM   *What can you learn about an STD by* **interpreting data** *on a graph?*

Year	Number of Cases of Syphilis (per 100,000 people)	Year	Number of Cases of Syphilis (per 100,000 people)
1985	11.5	1990	20.0
1986	11.5	1991	17.0
1987	14.5	1992	13.5
1988	17.0	1993	10.0
1989	19.0	1994	7.5

Source: Centers for Disease Control and Prevention, September 1995

PROCEDURE

1. Use the data in the table to construct a line graph.
2. List some generalizations you can make from the graph.

ANALYZE AND CONCLUDE

1. In which year was the number of reported cases of syphilis the highest? The lowest?
2. Based on the line graph you constructed, what can you say about the general trend in the number of cases between 1985 and 1994?
3. From this data, what trends could you predict for the next 10 years?

Viral Diseases

Unlike bacteria-caused STDs, which can usually be treated with antibiotics if discovered early enough, there are currently no drugs that will cure viral STD infections. Therefore, STDs caused by viruses are particularly serious. **Three common STDs caused by viruses are genital herpes, hepatitis B, and AIDS.**

Genital Herpes

One of the most common STDs is **genital herpes.** A virus known as Herpes Type II infects the genital areas of males and females, causing small reddish blisters. Visible evidence of the virus may disappear for weeks or months at a time, but the infection stays in the body. Visible herpes blisters may appear without warning, causing pain and shedding virus particles that may be passed on to sexual partners. There are some drugs available that can help to reduce the severity of genital herpes outbreaks, but none that can permanently cure the infection.

☑ *Checkpoint*   What is genital herpes?

Hepatitis B

Hepatitis B is a virus that infects the liver and kills several thousand people each year. Unlike other STDs, the hepatitis B virus can survive on objects outside the body for a long period of time. Although there is now an effective vaccine, there is no cure for hepatitis B once an individual has been infected. Hepatitis B is particularly common among people with many sexual partners and presents a serious health risk.

☑ *Checkpoint*   How does hepatitis B differ from other STDs?

AIDS

In many respects, the most dangerous STD of all is **AIDS** (acquired immune deficiency syndrome). The virus that causes AIDS attacks the immune system, leaving the person vulnerable to a variety of infections. Virus particles are present in the blood, semen, and vaginal fluids of people infected with AIDS. Therefore, sexual contact is one of the principal ways in which the disease is spread from person to person. Currently, there is no cure for AIDS.

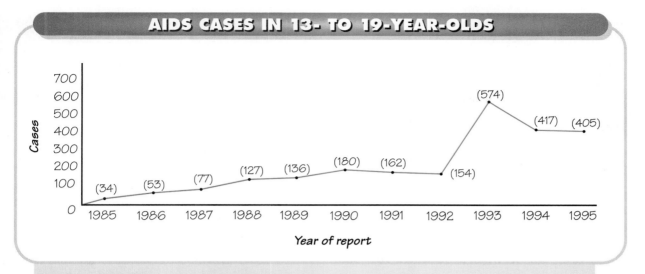

AIDS CASES IN 13- TO 19-YEAR-OLDS

Cases — Year of report

(34) 1985, (53) 1986, (77) 1987, (127) 1988, (136) 1989, (180) 1990, (162) 1991, (154) 1992, (574) 1993, (417) 1994, (405) 1995

Figure 6–17

This graph shows the number of AIDS cases in 13- to 19-year-olds in the United States from 1985 through 1995. Notice the sharp increase in 1993, followed by a gradual decline.

Avoiding STDs

As you have seen, STDs are serious diseases that are spread by sexual contact. Are there any ways to avoid these diseases, which can ruin your health and even threaten your life? Yes, there are. The great irony of STDs is that although many of them cannot be cured, all of them can be prevented by understanding what conditions they require to spread from person to person.

Nearly all STDs infect the reproductive tracts of males and females. This usually means that bacteria or infectious virus particles are present in semen or vaginal fluids of infected individuals. Because these fluids are exchanged during intercourse, infectious particles from one person can easily be transmitted to another.

STDs require intimate contact between people for infections to be transmitted. Therefore, individuals who engage in sexual intercourse risk not only an unintended pregnancy but serious diseases as well. In contrast, abstaining from sexual contact provides complete protection against all STDs and pregnancy as well.

Section Review 6-3

1. **List** three common sexually transmitted bacterial diseases.
2. **List** three common sexually transmitted viral diseases.
3. **MINI LAB** What can you learn about an STD by **interpreting data** from a graph?
4. **BRANCHING OUT ACTIVITY** Choose one of the sexually transmitted diseases discussed in this chapter and research the effects it would have on a pregnant woman or her developing fetus. **Summarize** your findings in a brief report.

Laboratory Investigation

Reproductive Organs and Gametes

The egg and sperm are microscopic structures that can best be observed in slides that have been professionally sectioned, stained, and preserved. In this investigation, you will examine some prepared slides and use the knowledge you have gained from this chapter to interpret what you see.

Problem

What can you **observe** in the microscopic structure of reproductive organs and gametes?

Materials (per group)

compound microscope
prepared slides of the following:
   human testis
   ovary
   sperm

Procedure

1. Obtain a prepared slide of the cross section of a human testis. Using the low-power objective of the microscope, examine the slide and draw what you see. Find an area that has well-defined circular structures. These are the seminiferous tubules.

2. Switch to the high-power objective on the microscope. Select one seminiferous tubule and draw the structures inside it.

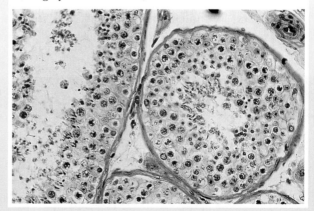

Cross section of a human testis (magnification: 250X)

3. Locate and identify the cells at various stages of development. The cells located just inside the walls of the tubule are the cells in which meiosis begins. The cells closest to the center of the tubule are at later stages of meiosis, and the cells closest to the center of the tubule are the sperm.

4. Obtain a prepared slide of human sperm. Using the low-power objective of the microscope, examine the slide. Locate one sperm and then switch the microscope to high power. Draw what you observe.

5. Obtain a prepared slide of a human ovary and observe it under the low-power objective of the microscope. Locate a large cell that has a distinct nucleus surrounded by a lightly stained area of cytoplasm. This is an egg.

Cross section of a human ovary and egg (magnification: 250X)

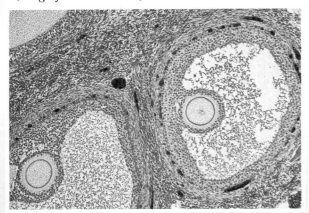

6. Find the largest follicle, a fluid-filled cavity that surrounds an egg. Switch the microscope to high power and draw what you observe. Try to locate the fluid-filled space, the egg itself, the egg's nucleus, and the layers of follicle cells surrounding the egg.

Observations

1. How many enlarged follicles with mature eggs did you observe in the cross section of the ovary?

2. How many mature sperm did you observe in the seminiferous tubule?

Analysis and Conclusions

1. How much of the testis did you see?

2. Explain how a human testis is able to produce millions of sperm each day.

3. How does the volume of cytoplasm in the egg compare with the volume of cytoplasm in the sperm?

4. Which structures were easiest to identify? Which were the hardest?

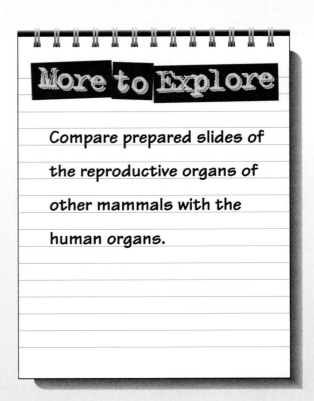

More to Explore

Compare prepared slides of the reproductive organs of other mammals with the human organs.

Study Guide

Summarizing Key Concepts

The key concepts in each section of this chapter are listed below to help you review the chapter content. Make sure you understand each concept and its relationship to other concepts and to the theme of this chapter.

6–1   The Human Reproductive System

- The male reproductive system has the task of producing and delivering sperm. The female reproductive system produces gametes, too. Because fertilization and the development of a baby both take place inside the female's body, this puts special demands on the female reproductive system.

- The menstrual cycle has four phases: follicle phase, ovulation, luteal phase, and menstruation.

6–2   Fertilization and Development

- As soon as one sperm makes direct contact with the egg cell membrane, the two cells

fuse, the tail of the sperm breaks away, and the sperm nucleus enters the egg's cytoplasm. This process is called fertilization.

- As the embryo grows, the placenta serves as its main organ of respiration, nourishment, and excretion.

6–3   Sexually Transmitted Diseases

- Three common STDs caused by bacteria are syphilis, gonorrhea, and chlamydia.

- Three common STDs caused by viruses are genital herpes, hepatitis B, and AIDS.

Reviewing Key Terms

Review the following vocabulary terms and their meaning. Then use each term in a complete sentence.

6–1   The Human Reproductive System

gamete
ovary
testis
follicle-stimulating
   hormone
luteinizing hormone
testosterone
sperm
progesterone
estrogen
ovum

scrotum
seminiferous tubule
epididymis
vas deferens
follicle
Fallopian tube
ovulation
uterus
menstrual cycle
corpus luteum

6–2   Fertilization and Development

fertilization
zygote

morula
implantation

embryo
human chorionic
   gonadotropin
gastrulation
placenta

umbilical cord
fetus
oxytocin
prolactin

6–3   Sexually Transmitted Diseases

sexually transmitted disease
syphilis
gonorrhea
chlamydia
genital herpes
hepatitis B
AIDS

Recalling Main Ideas

Choose the letter of the answer that best completes the statement or answers the question.

1. Among other changes, human gonads begin to produce reproductive cells during
   a. puberty.
   b. the first six weeks of development.
   c. formation of the zygote.
   d. childhood.

2. Testosterone controls the development of
   a. secondary sex characteristics.
   b. secondary sex characteristics and sperm.
   c. sperm.
   d. eggs.

3. Fertilization generally takes place in the
   a. ovary.
   b. uterus.
   c. vagina.
   d. Fallopian tube.

4. During the follicle phase, cell and tissue growth in the uterus is stimulated by
   a. progesterone.
   b. FSH.
   c. estrogen.
   d. LH.

5. In the developing embryo, the neural tube forms from the
   a. ectoderm.
   b. endoderm.
   c. mesoderm.
   d. amnion.

6. As the embryo develops, the placenta supplies it with
   a. metabolic wastes.
   b. blood and oxygen.
   c. food and blood.
   d. food and oxygen.

7. Childbirth is initiated by
   a. the cervix.
   b. prolactin.
   c. oxytocin.
   d. colostrum.

8. Genital herpes is caused by a
   a. bacterium.
   b. virus.
   c. protozoan.
   d. fungus.

Putting It All Together

Using the information on pages xii to xiii, complete the following concept map.

PITUITARY GLAND

releases

in females stimulates — 1 — in males stimulates

Ovaries

2

which release

which control — which release

Testosterone

3 — 4

which controls

which prepares

5

6

Reviewing What You Learned

Answer each of the following in a complete sentence.

1. What are the two human gametes called?

2. What is puberty?

3. Identify two secondary sex characteristics of human males.

4. Where is progesterone produced, and what is its function?

5. Explain ovulation.

6. What change in the blood triggers menstruation?

7. Where does fertilization usually take place? Where does the fertilized egg go next?

8. How does a zygote form?

9. Describe a blastocyst.

10. What is gastrulation?

11. From what tissue does the umbilical cord form?

12. When does an embryo become a fetus?

13. What hormone stimulates contractions of the uterus?

14. What is the first symptom of a syphilis infection?

15. Name three sexually transmitted diseases caused by a virus.

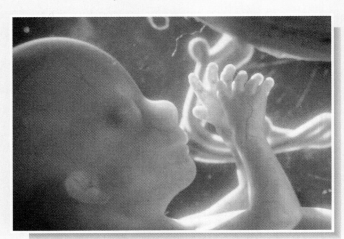

Expanding the Concepts

Discuss each of the following in a brief paragraph.

1. Compare estrogens and androgens. Where are they produced, and what do they control?

2. Trace the path of a sperm as it travels from a testis to the outside of the body.

3. Trace the path of an unfertilized egg as it travels from the ovary to the outside of the body.

4. Compare the number of sperm produced with the number of eggs produced. Suggest reasons for the difference.

5. Describe the four phases of the menstrual cycle.

6. Identify and describe the function of the hormones produced by the pituitary gland that have a role in reproduction.

7. Diagram and label the interactions of the egg and sperm that result in fertilization.

8. Describe the changes a zygote goes through as it travels through a Fallopian tube until it implants itself on the uterine wall.

9. Explain what the presence of HCG in the blood of a female indicates.

10. Describe the process of neurulation.

11. Compare the symptoms of syphilis and genital herpes.

12. Why is AIDS considered to be the most dangerous STD?

Extending Your Thinking

Use the skills you have developed in this chapter to answer the following.

1. **Modeling** Construct a model placenta. Explain how it acts as a lifeline between mother and baby.

2. **Developing hypotheses** The World Health Organization (WHO) states that the percentage of adults in the United States who are reported to have at least one STD is much higher than the percentage in other countries. Develop a hypothesis to account for this difference.

3. **Making judgments** You have learned that drugs can be passed from the mother to the embryo or fetus through the placenta. Drinking alcohol during pregnancy can cause irreversible problems for a baby, including slowed growth, later behavioral problems, and mental retardation. Should drinking alcohol during pregnancy be made illegal? Why or why not?

4. **Interpreting data** Examine the graph showing the reported rates of gonorrhea. In what year was the rate of gonorrhea highest in the United States? Lowest? What changes have taken place between 1970 and 1994? Predict how many people might contract gonorrhea in a city of one million.

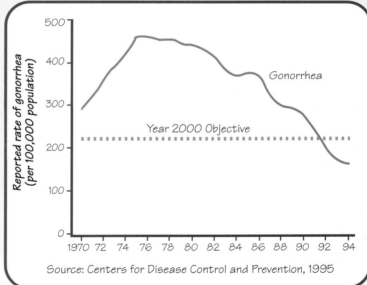

Source: Centers for Disease Control and Prevention, 1995

Applying Your Skills

In Vitro Fertilization

Since the birth of Louise Brown in 1979, in vitro fertilization has enabled some couples with reproductive problems to conceive a child from their own egg and sperm. In this research project, you'll apply the information in this chapter to explain how in vitro *fertilization works.*

1. Obtain reference materials on *in vitro* fertilization from an encyclopedia, library book, magazine articles, or other sources.

2. Describe the reproductive problems that *in vitro* fertilization can overcome.

3. List the steps in the *in vitro* fertilization process.

4. Explain each step, comparing it with the process of fertilization described in this chapter.

• **GOING FURTHER** •

5. In your journal, discuss reasons for and against this means of reproduction.

Immune System

Biology and Your World

BIO JOURNAL

Some bacteria—such as *E. coli*, seen as yellow-green rods in this photograph—are harmless most of the time. Other bacteria, however, can cause serious disease. In the 1920s and 1930s, antibiotics that could help treat bacterial infections were discovered. Imagine that you lived before the discovery of antibiotics. How might your life be different from the way it is today?

Macrophages attacking Escherichia coli bacteria (magnification: 5400X)

GUIDE FOR READING

- **Define** disease.
- **State** the germ theory of disease.
- **List** Koch's postulates.

MINI LAB

- **Predict** the growth of bacteria by using a model.

"IF YOU'VE GOT YOUR HEALTH, you've got everything." There's a lot of truth to this old saying. Good health makes it possible for you to work, study, and play. Unfortunately, most of us take our health for granted—until we catch a cold or develop a disease, something that interferes with the body's normal activities. When that happens, the value of good health becomes all too obvious. Why do we get sick? What is the best way to avoid disease? In this section, we will try to answer these questions.

Defining Disease

A disease is any change that disrupts the normal functions of the body. Some diseases, such as Huntington disease or cystic fibrosis, are genetic. Others, such as brown lung, a disease of coal miners, are produced by materials in the environment. But many diseases are produced by other organisms, including bacteria, fungi, protozoans, and viruses. A disease-causing organism is called a **pathogen**—literally, a "sickness-maker." The diseases caused by pathogens are generally known as **infectious diseases** because the organisms that cause them usually enter, or infect, the body of the person they make ill.

☑ *Checkpoint* What is an infectious disease?

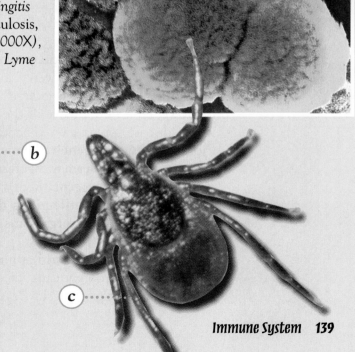

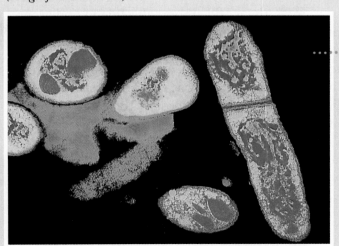

Figure 7–1

Diseases are caused by a variety of pathogens, including (a) Neisseria meningitis, *the bacterium that causes meningitis (magnification: 20,580X),* (b) Mycobacterium tuberculosis, *the bacterium that causes tuberculosis (magnification: 30,000X), and* (c) Borrelia burgdorferi, *the bacterium that causes Lyme disease, which is carried by the deer tick shown here (magnification: 12X).*

MINI LAB — Predicting

Another Generation

PROBLEM *How can you use a model to **predict** the growth of bacteria?*

PROCEDURE

1. Place a kidney bean (or other small object), representing a bacterium, on the table. Wait 30 seconds—which represents the actual 30 minutes that it takes a bacterium to divide—and then put another kidney bean down next to the first.

2. After another 30 seconds, add one kidney bean for each kidney bean that is already on the table.

3. Repeat step 2 until there are 128 kidney beans on the table. Construct a data table to record each generation and the number of bacteria produced.

ANALYZE AND CONCLUDE

1. How much time does it take to produce 128 bacteria?

2. Predict how many bacteria would be produced in 24 hours.

3. What can you infer from this activity about why it is necessary to treat wounds quickly?

The Germ Theory of Disease

At one time, many people believed that infectious diseases were caused by evil spirits. In the mid-nineteenth century, however, a new theory of the way in which disease spread gained acceptance. **Pioneered by the French chemist Louis Pasteur and the German bacteriologist Robert Koch, the germ theory of disease suggested that infectious diseases were caused by microorganisms, which many people call "germs."**

As you know, the world around us is filled with microorganisms of various shapes and descriptions. How can we be sure which of these scores of possible organisms actually causes a particular disease? Koch provided the answer in a series of rules, called **Koch's postulates,** that are used to identify the microorganism that causes a specific disease. **Koch's postulates include the following:**

- **The pathogen should always be found in the body of a sick organism (the host) and should not be found in a healthy organism.**

- **The pathogen must be isolated and grown in a pure culture.**

- **When purified pathogens are injected into a new host, they cause the disease.**

- **The same pathogen should be re-isolated from the second host and grown in a pure culture. The pathogen should still be the same as the original pathogen.**

By focusing attention on the biological causes of disease, Pasteur, Koch, and many other scientists produced a revolution in human thinking. For the first time, disease did not seem to be an unavoidable consequence of being alive. And, if a particular pathogen could be identified, there was hope that the disease it caused could be prevented or cured.

Pathogens

Many of the microorganisms that fill the world around also live in and around the human body. The large intestine, for example, harbors dense colonies of bacteria. Bacteria and yeast are found in the mouth, throat, and excretory system. Fortunately, most of these organisms are harmless, and a few of them are actually beneficial.

This being the case, why are some organisms considered pathogens? In some cases, the pathogens actually destroy cells as they grow. Many pathogens, including viruses and many bacteria, grow directly inside cells of the human body, eating their food and ultimately destroying the cell. Other pathogens, including many bacteria, produce **toxins,** or poisons that disrupt bodily functions and produce illness. Finally, many pathogens, especially parasitic worms, produce sickness when they block the flow of blood, remove nutrients from the digestive system, and disrupt other bodily functions. *Figure 7–2* lists some of the most common pathogens, including viruses and bacteria, and the diseases they cause.

Viruses are tiny particles that invade and replicate within living cells. Viruses attach to the surface of a cell, insert their genetic material in the form of RNA or DNA, and take over many of the functions of the host cell. Nearly all living organisms—including plants, insects, mammals, and even bacteria—can be infected by viruses.

Although bacteria are often helpful, certain bacteria cause some of the most serious diseases of all. Bacteria are one of the main reasons why it is important to handle food carefully. Bacteria grow quickly in warm, partially-cooked food

Figure 7–2
This chart lists some of the viruses, bacteria, protozoans, worms, and fungi that cause disease. Notice how each disease is spread.

PATHOGENS AND DISEASE

TYPE OF PATHOGEN	DISEASE	ORGANISM THAT CAUSES THE DISEASE	METHODS OF SPREADING THE DISEASE
Viruses	Smallpox	Variola	Airborne; personal contact
	Common cold	Rhinovirus	Airborne; direct contact with infected person
	Influenza	Two types (A, B), plus many subtypes	Airborne; droplet infection; direct contact with infected person
	Measles	Measles	Droplets in air; direct contact with secretions of infected person
	AIDS	HIV	Sexual contact; contaminated blood products or hypodermic needles
	Chickenpox	Varicella	Airborne; direct contact with infected person
Bacteria	Tuberculosis	Mycobacterium tuberculosis	Droplets in air; contaminated milk and dairy products
	Meningitis	Neisseria meningitis	Direct exposure to organism
	Diphtheria	Corynebacterium diphtheriae	Contact with infected person or carrier; contaminated raw milk
	Rocky Mountain spotted fever	Rickettsia rickettsii	Bite of infected tick
	Lyme disease	Borrelia burgdorferi	Bite of infected tick
	Cholera	Vibrio cholerae	Contaminated drinking water
	Tetanus	Clostridium tetani	Dirty wound; usually a puncture wound
Protozoans	African sleeping sickness	Trypanosoma	Spread by tsetse fly
	Malaria	Plasmodium	Spread by mosquitoes
Worms	Schistosomiasis	Schistosoma mansoni	Freshwater streams and rice paddies
	Beef tapeworm	Taenia saginata	Contaminated meat
Fungi	Athlete's foot	Imperfect fungi	Contact with infected person; shower stalls
	Ringworm	Imperfect fungi	Exchange of hats, combs, and athletic headgear with infected person

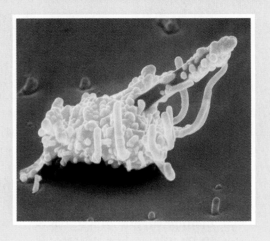

Figure 7–3
Although white blood cells normally trap and digest pathogens, this white blood cell is engulfing a cancer-causing asbestos fiber. Unfortunately, it cannot be digested.

INTEGRATING SOCIAL STUDIES

What effect did the bubonic plague have on the populations of Europe in the Middle Ages?

and are always present in uncooked meat. Many types of bacteria, especially the species known as *Salmonella*, can grow quickly enough to produce high levels of the toxins that produce food poisoning. The only way to make food completely safe is to cook it completely.

Although many pathogens are either viruses or bacteria, there are other pathogens as well. Fungi, protozoans, insects, and parasitic worms also cause disease.

Fighting Disease

Once a pathogen has been identified, biologists search for clues as to how it is passed from person to person. If a disease is thoroughly understood, preventing it usually becomes clear. Then, the best way to fight the disease is to avoid it.

Many diseases are spread by animals. The **vectors**—animals that carry disease-causing organisms from host to host—are the key to stopping such diseases. Malaria and yellow fever are fought by controlling the mosquito population.

Lyme disease can be prevented by avoiding deer ticks, which carry it. Bubonic plague, the "black death" that killed millions in Europe in the Middle Ages, is spread by fleas that live on rats and mice. ● Aggressive measures to control these rodents have made serious outbreaks of the plague rare.

Diseases that are spread from one person to another can be controlled by simple habits of personal hygiene. Washing one's hands thoroughly helps to prevent the spread of many pathogens. The common cold is spread by coughing, sneezing, and hand-to-hand contact. Such measures as covering your mouth with a tissue can limit infection.

If prevention fails, drugs have been developed for use against all sorts of pathogens. Perhaps the most useful single class of infection-fighting drugs are **antibiotics**—compounds that kill bacteria without harming cells of humans or animals. Many of these compounds are produced naturally. Antibiotics work by interfering with the cellular processes of microorganisms. For example, penicillin, the first antibiotic to be discovered, interferes with cell wall synthesis, disabling and killing bacteria. Streptomycin and tetracycline interfere with protein synthesis on bacterial ribosomes. Because viruses use the ribosomes of the infected cell to make their proteins, antibiotics are not effective against viruses.

Section Review 7–1

1. **Define** disease.
2. **State** the germ theory of disease.
3. **List** Koch's postulates.
4. **Critical Thinking—Drawing Conclusions**   Why might Koch's postulates be difficult to apply to a viral infection?
5. **MINI LAB**   How can you **predict** the growth of bacteria by using a model?

The Body's Defense System

SOMETIMES IT MAY SEEM THAT *we are surrounded by a world of pathogens that threaten our existence every moment of the day. In such a hostile environment, how does the body cope with the threat of infection? The answer is that the body has a protective system, a series of defenses that guard against disease.*

The body's defense against infection is provided by the immune system. Unlike many of the body's other systems, the work of the immune system goes on behind the scenes. In fact, if it is working properly, you may never notice it. But when something does go wrong with the immune system, life itself is threatened by the pathogens it normally holds at bay.

Nonspecific Defenses

The immune system is the body's primary defense against pathogens. It consists of nonspecific and specific defenses against infection. The skin is the body's most important nonspecific defense. Few pathogens can penetrate the tough layers of keratin protein at the skin's outer surface. The importance of these layers becomes obvious as soon as the skin is broken. As you know, even a small cut or scrape quickly becomes infected if it is not taken care of. Why does this happen? Because even the smallest cut breaks the protective barrier, giving microorganisms

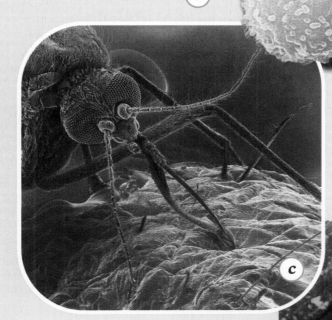

Figure 7–4

The body responds to infection with specific defenses and nonspecific defenses. (a) *Specialized white blood cells such as lymphocytes are the body's main specific defense (magnification: 1500X).* (b) *The skin provides the body with its most important nonspecific defense. It keeps bacteria, seen as green rods in this electron micrograph, from breaking through (magnification: 8000X).* (c) *When there is a break in the skin, such as from the bite of a mosquito, pathogens may enter the body (magnification: 50X).*

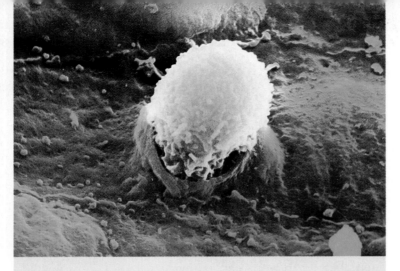

Figure 7–5
During the inflammatory response, white blood cells leak out of the blood vessels to attack a pathogen. In this scanning electron micrograph, a white blood cell is squeezing through the endothelium of a vein to join the attack (magnification: 3450X).

on the skin's surface a chance to enter the body.

The skin is considered a nonspecific defense because it is not directed against any one pathogen. Instead, a nonspecific defense guards against all infections, regardless of their cause. Other nonspecific defenses are found in the mouth and respiratory passages, where millions of microorganisms enter every day. Passages leading to the lungs are coated with mucus that traps airborne pathogens. Cells lining these passages sweep these trapped cells into the digestive system, where they are destroyed by digestive enzymes. Other pathogens that enter the mouth, eyes, and excretory system may be destroyed by lysozyme, an enzyme that breaks down cell walls of some bacteria.

☑ **Checkpoint** What is a nonspecific defense?

Inflammation

If pathogens do enter the body through a cut, they grow quickly, spreading and releasing toxins into the tissues. When this happens, a second nonspecific defense is activated. This is called the **inflammatory response** because it can cause the skin to turn a "flaming" red color. Blood vessels near the wound expand, and white blood cells leak from the vessels to invade the infected tissues. Many of these white cells, which are called **phagocytes,** engulf and destroy bacteria. The infected tissue may become swollen and painful as the battle between the pathogens and white blood cells rages.

☑ **Checkpoint** What is the inflammatory response?

Fever

When a serious infection causes pathogens to spread, the body responds in two ways. First, the immune system releases chemicals that increase the body's temperature. You have probably experienced this elevated body temperature, called a fever. Second, the immune system produces millions of white blood cells to fight the infection. An increased number of white cells in the blood is a sign that the body is dealing with a serious infection.

Specific Defenses

The immune system is also capable of powerful specific defenses that produce **immunity** against particular diseases. **Immunity is the ability of the body to resist a specific pathogen.** There are two kinds of immunity—antibody immunity and cell-mediated immunity.

Ever since ancient times, people have observed that individuals who recover from certain diseases, such as mumps and measles, never again become sick with the same disease. In other words, most people who recover from the mumps or measles are permanently immune—they will never get the mumps or measles again.

Antibody Immunity

Exposure to certain diseases produces permanent immunity because it stimulates cells in the immune system to make proteins called **antibodies.** The molecules that stimulate the production of antibodies are known as **antigens.** An antigen is any substance that triggers the specific defense of the immune system. The antibody is the basic functional unit of the specific immune response.

As *Figure 7–6* shows, an antibody is shaped like the letter Y and has two identical antigen-binding sites. This means that an antibody can attach to two antigens. Why is this good? If the antigen is on the surface of a virus particle, it means that antibodies can link the virus particles into a clump, preventing them from entering a cell. The clump of viruses and antibodies attract phagocytes, which engulf and destroy the whole mass. If the immune system produces enough antibodies to a particular virus, it can prevent that virus from causing disease.

Antibodies can prevent bacterial infections, too. When antibodies bind to the surfaces of bacteria, they mark the cells for destruction by phagocytes and other white blood cells.

Lymphocytes

The immune system also includes a special class of white blood cells called **lymphocytes.** One group of lymphocytes, the B lymphocytes, or **B cells,** matures in bone marrow. These cells produce antibodies.

How do B cells produce antibody proteins that fit their antigens so precisely? In a sense, they are custom-made. As B cells develop, the antibody genes within each of them rearrange themselves in a slightly different way. When their development is complete, the immune system

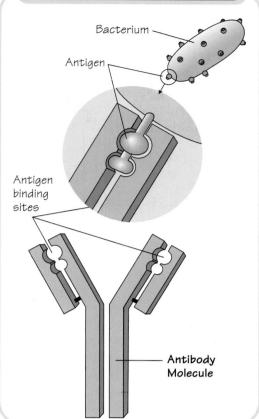

ANTIBODY STRUCTURE

Bacterium

Antigen

Antigen binding sites

Antibody Molecule

Figure 7–6
The antibody molecule is the basic functional unit of an immune response. Each antibody molecule has two antigen-binding sites, which are specific for a particular antigen.

contains literally millions of B cells—each capable of producing a slightly different antibody.

When a pathogen enters the body, molecules on its surface act as antigens to stimulate the immune system. This is helped along by **T cells,** lymphocytes that have matured in the thymus gland. In a few days, B cells whose antibodies closely match the shape of the antigen have started to grow and divide rapidly. This produces a large number of specialized B cells called **plasma cells,** which release antibodies into the bloodstream to fight the infection. Millions of plasma cells may be produced from a handful of B cells stimulated by antigen.

Although it may take many days for enough plasma cells to form and help to overcome an infection, these cells have another important function—they produce permanent immunity. When a person contracts measles, for example, antigens on the surface of the virus stimulate the production of millions of plasma cells to fight the infection. As a result, if the person survives the infection, his or her immune system retains those cells and is always ready to respond with a massive supply of the measles antibody.

Vaccines

Vaccines take advantage of this fact. A **vaccine** is a weakened or mild form of a pathogen that causes permanent immunity when injected into the body. For example, when you were vaccinated against polio, weakened polio viruses were used to stimulate the B cells in your body that are capable of making anti-polio antibodies. As a result, if you are ever exposed to the polio virus, your body is prepared to fight this virus with millions of plasma cells ready to make polio antibodies.

☑ *Checkpoint*   What is a vaccine?

Figure 7–7

If an infection occurs, the body responds by either of two immune responses—the production of antibodies or the production of killer T cells. In antibody immunity, antigens cause B cells to multiply. Some B cells develop into plasma cells that secrete antibodies. Other B cells develop into memory B cells, which store information about the pathogen in order to provide future immunity. In cell-mediated immunity, T cells multiply, producing three types of T cells—killer T cells, helper T cells, and suppressor T cells.

THE IMMUNE RESPONSE

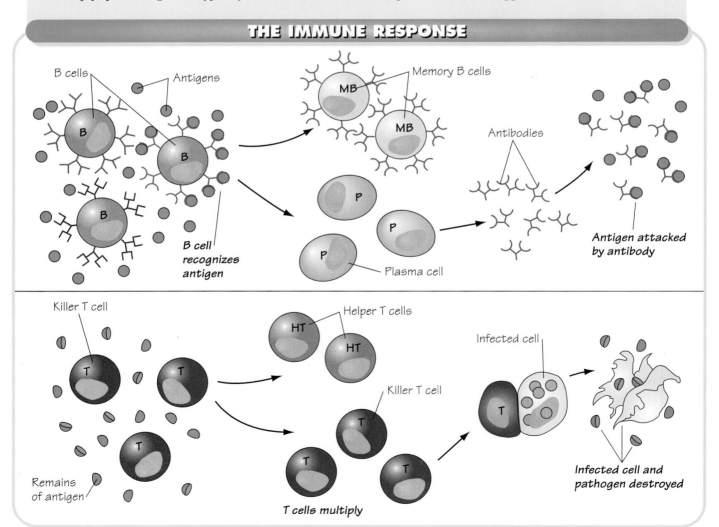

Cell-Mediated Immunity

Antibodies alone are not enough to protect the body against some pathogens. In these cases, the immune system has a powerful weapon—the **killer T cell.** Killer T cells make direct contact with antigen-bearing cells, disrupting their cell membranes and destroying them. This process is known as **cell-mediated immunity.** The actions of killer T cells are extremely important in fighting certain types of infections. Killer T cells attack and destroy virus-infected cells, and they are also important in fighting protozoans and multicellular parasites.

Unfortunately, killer T cells are also responsible for the rejection of tissue transplants. The cells of your body have a special set of protein markers on their surfaces that enable the immune system to recognize them as your own. If tissues from another person are transplanted into the body, the immune system checks these markers, recognizes them as foreign, and attacks them. To prevent tissue rejection, physicians search for an organ donor whose cell markers are nearly identical to those of the recipient. They may also use drugs, such as cyclosporine, that suppress the cell-mediated immune response.

In addition to killer T cells, there are other types of T cells that are involved in the immune response. **Helper T cells** are the first cells to identify the specific pathogen in the body. The helper T cells then send a message to the B cells "telling" them to produce antibodies for that particular pathogen.

A third kind of T cell is a **suppressor T cell.** After an infection has been fought off successfully, suppressor T cells shut off the immune response in both B cells and killer T cells.

☑ *Checkpoint* What is the function of helper T cells?

Figure 7–8
In this photograph, the killer T cells, which become elongated when active, are attacking a cancer cell's membrane (magnification: 6000X).

Immune Disorders

Although the immune system protects the body against many pathogens, sometimes disorders occur. There are two main types of disorders. In the first type, the body overreacts to harmless substances. Allergies and autoimmune diseases are examples of this type of disorder. In the second type, the immune system becomes too weak to fight infection. AIDS is an example of this type of disorder.

Allergies

When the immune system overreacts to an antigen in the environment, an **allergy** results. An allergic reaction occurs when antigens trigger a type of immune cell, called a mast cell, to release chemicals called **histamines.** Histamines produce an inflammatory response that includes sneezing, runny nose, and itchy eyes, which allergy sufferers know all too well. ● The offending antigens may be part of a pollen grain, a mold spore, the toxin from a bee sting, or even household dust.

INTEGRATING HEALTH

What are antihistamines? How do they help allergy sufferers?

AIDS

Although scientists do not have enough information to cure AIDS, they do know more than enough to prevent it. HIV, the virus that causes AIDS, is not easily spread. People who live with, care for, work with, or go to school with people with HIV are not at risk of contracting the virus by casual contact. The virus that causes AIDS can be spread only by coming into direct contact with an infected person's body fluids, such as blood, semen, and vaginal secretions.

Each square of this quilt is dedicated to a person who has died of AIDS.

Blood Transfusions

Prior to 1985, donated blood used for transfusions and other medical procedures, such as treatments for hemophilia, was not tested for the presence of HIV. As a result, several thousand people became infected with HIV and eventually died of AIDS. Today, blood supplies are carefully screened for HIV and other viruses.

Injected Drug Use

HIV infection among users of illegal drugs, on the other hand, has skyrocketed. Sharing needles to inject drugs may pass on HIV-laden blood directly from one person's bloodstream into the bloodstream of another. This action is one of the most dangerous and irresponsible things a person can do. Not only are drugs such as heroin and cocaine dangerous in their own right, but the injection of these drugs also carries with them the added risk of contracting AIDS.

A Sexually Transmitted Disease

AIDS can also be spread by sexual contact. The presence of the virus in the semen and vaginal fluids of an infected person means that every sexual contact that person has carries with it the risk of passing on AIDS. The most effective way to protect yourself from HIV infection is to abstain from sexual intercourse. By doing so, you help to prevent the spread of this deadly disease.

Making the Connection

How does information about AIDS transmission help you to make decisions about your behavior? How does it help you when you encounter someone who has HIV? Do you think employers should have the right to require all their employees to be tested for HIV? Why or why not?

Allergic reactions can create a dangerous condition called **asthma,** in which smooth muscle contractions reduce the size of air passageways in the lungs, making breathing difficult. Asthma attacks are usually triggered by a particular antigen, and so the best response to the condition is to avoid that antigen. New drugs make it possible to provide immediate relief from asthma attacks, relaxing the smooth muscles to make breathing easier.

Autoimmune Diseases

Sometimes the immune system makes mistakes and attacks its own cells, producing what is called an **autoimmune disease.** Myasthenia gravis and multiple sclerosis are two autoimmune diseases. In myasthenia gravis, antibodies attack the nerve receptors of the muscles. In multiple sclerosis, the immune system attacks the myelin sheath that surrounds nerve fibers. Multiple sclerosis, which may be triggered by a viral infection, usually strikes people between the ages of 20 and 40.

AIDS

The importance of a healthy, functioning immune system has been underscored by a disease that was first recognized in the early 1980s. At that time, physicians began to see an increase in the number of unusual infections. Some of these infections included protozoans in the lungs, severe fungal infections in the mouth and throat, and a rare

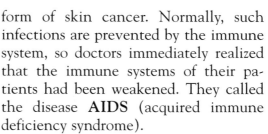

Figure 7–9
The helper T cell, colored green in this scanning electron micrograph, has been infected with HIV. The red objects are HIV, the virus responsible for causing AIDS (magnification: 6000X).

form of skin cancer. Normally, such infections are prevented by the immune system, so doctors immediately realized that the immune systems of their patients had been weakened. They called the disease **AIDS** (acquired immune deficiency syndrome).

The spread of the disease made scientists suspect that it was caused by a virus. In 1984, that virus—now known as **HIV** (human immunodeficiency virus)—was discovered. HIV infects, weakens, and gradually destroys the helper T cells. As the disease progresses, which may take many years, HIV-infected individuals suffer one infection after another from organisms that the immune system normally controls with ease.

To date, there is no cure for AIDS, although some progress has been made in developing drugs that make it difficult for HIV to infect cells and to reproduce. Fortunately, HIV does not spread easily from person to person, and the way in which the virus is transmitted—in blood and other body fluids—is now well understood. The best way to stop this dangerous disease is to avoid contact with the virus.

Section Review 7-2

1. **Describe** the function of the immune system.
2. **Define** immunity.
3. **Critical Thinking—Comparing** Compare the role of B cells and T cells in the immune response.

GUIDE FOR READING

- **Define** cancer.
- **Describe** some of the causes of cancer.

  MINI LAB
- **Interpret** data regarding cancer.

CANCER! FEW WORDS IN THE *English language conjure up the dread and fear that this word does. Cancers are the second leading cause of death in the United States, claiming more than half a million lives each year. And cancers are a worldwide threat, affecting people of every nationality and culture.*

What is this disease that takes such a toll on human life? Where does it come from, and why is it so difficult to treat? As you will see, one of the things that makes cancer so different from other diseases is that the cells that cause it are not invading pathogens— they are the body's own cells, which have, in a sense, turned against it.

A Cellular Disease

The growth of the many trillions of cells throughout the body is closely regulated. Controls on cell growth are necessary in a complex organism to keep tissues and organs together. **Cancer begins when a cell or a group of cells escapes the body's normal growth controls.** When this happens, the cells grow into a **tumor,** a mass of growing, unregulated cells.

If a tumor forms in a sensitive area of the body, such as the brain or spinal cord, its very presence can be dangerous.

Figure 7–10

Cancer occurs when cells multiply uncontrollably and destroy healthy tissue. (a) *In a healthy lung, the walls of the bronchi are covered with countless cilia (magnification: 4000X).* (b) *When cancer cells, the gray objects, invade the bronchi, they crowd out and destroy the healthy tissue (magnification: 3000X).* (c) *The invasion of cancer cells stimulates the production of T cells. In this electron micrograph, the smaller beige objects are T cells, which are trying to destroy a much larger cancer cell (magnification: 10,000X).*

However, the most dangerous tumors are those that are capable of spreading from their places of origin to invade other parts of the body.

Physicians classify tumors according to their ability to spread. A tumor that does not spread to surrounding tissue is called a benign tumor. A tumor that spreads and destroys healthy tissue is called a malignant tumor.

It is often said that cancer is not one disease but many. Cancers differ from each other according to the tissues in which they originate. Lung cancers originate in the tissues of the lung, skin cancers are produced when cells in the skin begin to grow out of control, and breast cancers begin in the tissues of the breast. Each type of cancer has its own pattern of growth and invasion, and each presents unique problems.

☑ *Checkpoint*   What is a tumor?

Causes of Cancer

One of the most baffling elements of the cancer puzzle has been the many different causes of cancer. **Some cancers are caused by biological agents, such as viruses. Others are caused by chemicals in the environment or in the foods we eat. And others have a physical cause—radiation.**

Viruses

Cancer-causing viruses were first discovered in animals. In the early 1900s, Peyton Rous discovered that a type of cancer in chickens could be caused by viruses passed from one animal to the next. Although many similar viruses have been discovered in animals, only a few human cancers seem to be caused by viruses. One of these is the human papilloma virus (HPV), which is sexually transmitted. Chronic HPV infections can lead to cancer of the reproductive

Figure 7–11
Immunofluorescence is a technique that uses antibodies to attach fluorescent dyes to specific structures within the cell. This immunofluorescent light micrograph shows a malignant form of skin cancer (magnification: 320X).

organs. Hepatitis, which infects the liver, may lead to liver cancer. And the Epstein-Barr virus, in very rare instances, can produce a cancer known as Burkitt's lymphoma.

Radiation

Radiation has been recognized as a cause of cancer ever since the first experiments with radioactive substances. Exposures to high levels of radioactivity can cause leukemia, a cancer of the blood, and several other cancers. However, the most common and most dangerous form of cancer-causing radiation is all around us—sunlight. Exposure to the ultraviolet radiation in sunlight brings with it a risk of skin cancer. Although most forms of skin cancer can be successfully treated with surgery, one often fatal form of skin cancer—malignant melanoma—is increasing in frequency at an alarming rate.

Chemicals

Chemicals can also cause cancer. A cancer-causing chemical is known as a **carcinogen,** and scientists have identified hundreds of them. Carcinogens

MINI LAB ·········· *Interpreting* ····

Going by the Numbers

PROBLEM *How can you **interpret** data regarding cancer?*

PROCEDURE

LUNG CANCER DEATH RATES *		
Gender	1960–1962	1990–1992
Male	40.2	74.4
Female	6.0	32.2

* per 100,000 U.S. population

1. Based on the data table, construct a bar graph.

2. After examining the data table and bar graph with your partner, discuss some reasons to explain the changes that occurred in lung cancer death rates over the 30-year span.

3. Discuss some reasons to explain why there are differences in lung cancer death rates between males and females.

ANALYZE AND CONCLUDE

1. Determine the percentage change in lung cancer death rates in males and females during the 30-year period.

2. Because 80 percent of lung cancers are caused by smoking tobacco, what can you infer about the use of tobacco in men over the past 30 years? In women?

cause cells to lose control of their normal functions, thus causing cancer. Some carcinogens are naturally occurring compounds, such as aflatoxin, a compound produced by fungi. Others, such as benzene, are synthetic compounds. Health researchers have worked hard to identify the most dangerous carcinogens so they can be removed from the workplace and the food supply.

Ironically, the single most damaging source of carcinogens in most countries is not a contaminant of food, water, or air. Some of the most powerful carcinogens are found in tobacco smoke. Smoking tobacco or inhaling tobacco smoke causes lung cancer, which is responsible for more than 30 percent of all cancer deaths in the United States.

Cancer Genes

For many years, researchers were puzzled as to how causes as different as sunlight, chemicals, and viruses could produce cancer. However, all the causes of cancer have one thing in common—they all produce mutations, or changes in DNA. Carcinogenic chemicals cause errors in DNA replication; sunlight and other forms of radiation damage nucleic acids directly; and cancer-causing viruses introduce new genes into the cells they infect.

Why should mutations be so important? In recent years, biologists have discovered that a series of important proteins regulate the rate at which cells pass through the phases of the cell cycle. These proteins, and the genes that encode them, are responsible for the controlled cell growth that occurs normally in the body. If one of these key genes is damaged or mutated, controls over cell growth would be lost. And a group of cells would begin to grow out of control, just like a tumor.

One of these key genes is a protein called p53. Although p53 has many functions, its most important function is to check the condition of a cell's genetic information before it is allowed to divide. If damage to DNA is detected, p53 prevents the cell from entering mitosis. In that way, it ensures that DNA damage is repaired before the cell is allowed to divide. How important is p53 in avoiding cancer? More than half of all human

Figure 7–12
CAREER TRACK
An immunologist studies how organisms defend themselves against infection by pathogens. Here, an immunologist is using a technique that analyzes and measures the concentration of antibodies in order to test for a parasitic disease.

tumors have a damaged or inactive p53 gene! Damage to p53 or the many other genes that help to regulate cell growth seems to be the source of nearly all human cancers.

Treating Cancer

In their early stages, most cancers produce few symptoms. This is unfortunate, because cancers are easier to treat if they are found early. Once a tumor is discovered, it should receive immediate medical attention. In some cases, surgery is the best treatment. In their early stages, all the skin cancers, as well as cancers of the breast, the intestine, and the bladder, can be completely removed by surgery. This often results in a complete cure.

If the cancer has spread or if the tumor cannot be completely removed, a different approach is needed. Some cancers can be treated with radiation, to which fast-growing cells are especially sensitive. Radiation is used for localized tumors. Other types of cancers are treated with **chemotherapy**—mixtures of drugs that interfere with important processes such as DNA replication and cell division.

Chemotherapy has proven especially useful against certain forms of childhood leukemia, a cancer of the white blood cells. However, the powerful drugs used in chemotherapy to kill cancer cells have serious side effects—they kill many normal cells as well, causing nausea, headaches, and sometimes a temporary loss of hair.

Because no drug has proven completely effective against all cancers, the search goes on for compounds that will do a better job of killing tumor cells with fewer side effects. Medical science is closer than ever before in pinpointing the exact genetic causes of cancer, and there is good reason to hope that new technologies may conquer this disease. ●

INTEGRATING
BIOLOGY
AND SOCIETY

Find out from the American Cancer Society the seven warning signs of cancer.

Section Review 7-3

1. **Define** cancer.
2. **Describe** some of the causes of cancer.
3. **MINI LAB** How can you **interpret** data regarding cancer?
4. **BRANCHING OUT ACTIVITY** Using reference materials, find out the ten leading causes of death from cancer in 1960 to 1962 for both men and women. Then find out the ten leading causes of death from cancer in 1990 to 1992 for both men and women. **Compare** the lists and try to explain any differences you see.

Laboratory Investigation

DESIGNING AN EXPERIMENT

Inhibiting Bacterial Growth

Disinfectants are products used to destroy bacteria and viruses. How do you know which type of disinfectant is effective against which type of bacteria? In this investigation, you will compare the bacteria-inhibiting powers of several kinds of disinfectants.

Problem

Which household disinfectant is the most effective in preventing the growth of bacteria? **Design an experiment** to find the answer.

Suggested Materials

2 Petri dishes containing sterile nutrient agar

glass-marking pencil

sterile medicine dropper

transparent tape

hydrogen peroxide

metric ruler

2 other types of household disinfectants

Suggested Procedure

1. **Obtain 2 Petri dishes. Open each Petri dish and have your partner rub his or her fingers over the entire surface of the sterile agar. Replace the covers.**

2. **Open the cover of one Petri dish and, using the medicine dropper, place 2 drops of hydrogen peroxide in the middle of the dish.**

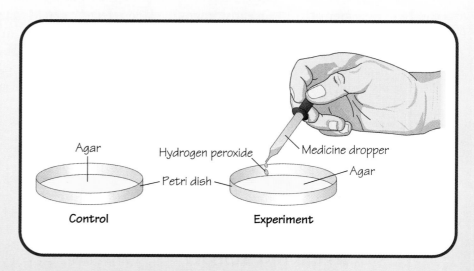

Agar · Hydrogen peroxide · Medicine dropper · Petri dish · Agar

Control · Experiment

3. Turn the dish over and, with the glass-marking pencil, label it Hydrogen Peroxide. Using transparent tape, tape the cover closed.

4. Turn over the other dish and label it Control.

5. Place the Petri dishes in an area where they will remain undisturbed and at room temperature for 24 hours. **CAUTION:** *Do not open the Petri dishes again.*

6. After 24 hours, without opening the Petri dishes, observe the surfaces of the nutrient agar in each dish. Record your observations in a data table similar to the one shown.

7. Return the Petri dishes to their storage place and observe them after 48 hours and after 72 hours. Record your observations.

8. Return the unopened Petri dishes to your teacher for sterilization and proper disposal. **CAUTION:** *Always wash your hands after handling a used Petri dish.*

9. Using a procedure similar to the one given in steps 1 to 8, design an experiment to determine the effectiveness of various disinfectants on the prevention of the growth of bacteria.

10. Be sure to include a control. Obtain the approval of your teacher before beginning your procedure.

Observations

1. What effect did hydrogen peroxide have on the growth of bacteria after 24, 48, and 72 hours?

2. What effect did each of the other disinfectants have on the growth of bacteria after 24, 48, and 72 hours?

DATA TABLE

Disinfectant	After 24 Hours	After 48 Hours	After 72 Hours
Hydrogen peroxide			

Analysis and Conclusions

1. Which disinfectant was the most effective against the growth of bacteria? Give evidence to support your answer.

2. Did every group in the class reach the same conclusion? How can you account for any differences?

3. What conclusion can you draw from your experiment about choosing disinfectants for your home?

More to Explore

Design an experiment to compare the effectiveness of disinfectants on bacteria samples from the soil.

$\mathcal{S}$tudy Guide

Summarizing Key Concepts

The key concepts in each section of this chapter are listed below to help you review the chapter content. Make sure you understand each concept and its relationship to other concepts and to the theme of this chapter.

7–1 Disease

- A disease is any change that disrupts the normal functions of the body.
- Pioneered by the French chemist Louis Pasteur and the German bacteriologist Robert Koch, the germ theory of disease suggested that infectious diseases were caused by microorganisms, which many people call germs.
- Koch's postulates include the following: The pathogen should always be found in the body of a sick organism and should not be found in a healthy organism. The pathogen must be isolated and grown in a pure culture. When purified pathogens are injected into a new host, they cause the disease. The same pathogen should be re-isolated from the second host and grown in a pure culture. The pathogen should still be the same as the original pathogen.

7–2 The Body's Defense System

- The immune system is the body's primary defense against pathogens. It consists of nonspecific and specific defenses against infection.
- Immunity is the ability of the body to resist a specific pathogen.

7–3 Cancer

- Cancer begins when a cell or a group of cells somehow escapes the body's normal growth controls.
- Some cancers are caused by biological agents such as viruses. Others are caused by chemicals in the environment or in the food we eat. And others have a physical cause—radiation.

Reviewing Key Terms

Review the following vocabulary terms and their meaning. Then use each term in a complete sentence.

7–1 Disease

pathogen	toxin
infectious disease	vector
Koch's postulates	antibiotic

7–2 The Body's Defense System

inflammatory response	lymphocyte
phagocyte	B cell
immunity	T cell
antibody	plasma cell
antigen	vaccine

killer T cell	histamine
cell-mediated immunity	asthma
helper T cell	autoimmune disease
suppressor T cell	AIDS
allergy	HIV

7–3 Cancer

tumor
carcinogen
chemotherapy

Recalling Main Ideas

Choose the letter of the answer that best completes the statement or answers the question.

1. Disease-causing organisms are called
   a. toxins.
   b. bacteria.
   c. pathogens.
   d. antigens.

2. Measles, smallpox, the common cold, and AIDS are caused by
   a. viruses.
   b. bacteria.
   c. fungi.
   d. parasitic worms.

3. Cholera, a disease caused by a bacterium, is spread by
   a. mosquitoes.
   b. contaminated water.
   c. fleas on rats and mice.
   d. hand-to-hand contact.

4. Antibiotics are drugs used against
   a. viruses.
   b. bacteria.
   c. fungi.
   d. AIDS.

5. Nonspecific defense mechanisms of the immune system include
   a. B lymphocytes.
   b. antibodies.
   c. vaccination.
   d. the skin and lysozymes.

6. Antibody production is stimulated by the presence of
   a. antigens.
   b. inflammation.
   c. killer T cells.
   d. phagocytes.

7. When antigens trigger mast cells,
   a. histamines are released.
   b. an allergic reaction occurs.
   c. the immune system overreacts.
   d. all of the above.

8. HIV weakens and gradually destroys
   a. mast cells.
   b. B cells.
   c. helper T cells.
   d. plasma cells.

9. Tumors capable of spreading from one part of the body to another are said to be
   a. malignant.
   b. cellular.
   c. benign.
   d. lung cancer.

10. All cancers seem to be caused by
    a. chemicals.
    b. mutations.
    c. radiation.
    d. viruses.

Putting It All Together

Using the information on pages xii to xiii, complete the following concept map.

DISEASE

caused by

1

including

2 — Worms — Fungi — Protozoans — 3

which are fought by the body's

4

Reviewing What You Learned

Answer each of the following in a complete sentence.

1. What is a pathogen?
2. Explain the germ theory of disease.
3. List two diseases caused by protozoans.
4. What kind of pathogen causes tuberculosis?
5. Give some examples of the body's nonspecific defense against pathogens.
6. How does the inflammatory response fight infection?
7. What is immunity?
8. What are B cells? T cells?
9. Name the two types of immunity.
10. Describe the function of killer T cells.
11. What are autoimmune diseases?
12. What is HIV?
13. What is a benign tumor? A malignant tumor?
14. Name three ways in which cancer can be treated.
15. What is a carcinogen?

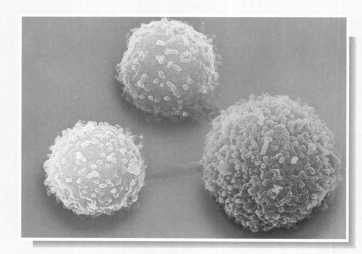

Expanding the Concepts

Discuss each of the following in a brief paragraph.

1. Explain some of the ways in which viruses differ from bacteria.
2. What are some ways in which humans encounter pathogens?
3. Explain the difference between nonspecific defenses and specific defenses.
4. How is inflammation of an injury part of the healing process?
5. How is cell-mediated immunity different from antibody immunity?
6. How does a vaccination protect you from a disease?
7. Explain why good personal hygiene is important to human health.
8. Explain the effect HIV has on the immune system.
9. Why is the cancer caused by smoking the most preventable type of cancer?
10. Why is cancer considered not one but many diseases?

Extending Your Thinking

Use the skills you have developed in this chapter to answer the following.

1. **Predicting** *E. coli* bacteria, which normally live in your large intestine, sometimes contaminate meat and cause food poisoning. Under ideal conditions, these bacteria can divide every 15 minutes. Starting with one bacterium, predict how many bacteria would be produced in 4 hours.

2. **Making judgments** The first vaccine was developed by Edward Jenner to fight smallpox. Jenner tested his theory of immunity on an eight-year-old boy. Do you think Jenner was right in doing so? Defend your answer.

3. **Applying concepts** Some scientists say that HIV has not been proven to cause AIDS. By referring to Koch's postulates, explain what they mean.

4. **Inferring** Because the immune system generally protects you with active immunity after an infection, why is it possible to get "the flu" year after year?

5. **Interpreting data** Examine the statistics for stomach cancer in the data table. How would you interpret the information found there?

STOMACH CANCER DEATH RATES*

Gender	1960–1962	1990–1992	Change
Male	16.2	6.7	− 59%
Female	8.2	3.0	− 63%

*per 100,000 U.S. population

Applying Your Skills

"This Will Only Hurt a Little"

When vaccinations are involved, a visit to the doctor's office is not always pleasant for a child. However, vaccinations are necessary in preventing many diseases.

1. Using library references, find out what vaccinations for children are recommended by the American Academy of Pediatrics.

2. Describe the pathogen and symptoms that each vaccine prevents.

3. Describe how each vaccine is made.

4. List any side effects associated with the vaccine.

5. Organize your data into a table.

• GOING FURTHER •

6. In your journal, discuss whether parents should be required to have their children vaccinated and who should pay for the vaccinations if the parents are unable to pay.

Periodic Table of the Elements

	1 1A								
1	1 **H** Hydrogen 1.00794	2 2A							
2	3 **Li** Lithium 6.941	4 **Be** Beryllium 9.0122							
3	11 **Na** Sodium 22.990	12 **Mg** Magnesium 24.305	3 3B	4 4B	5 5B	6 6B	7 7B	8 8B	9 8B
4	19 **K** Potassium 39.098	20 **Ca** Calcium 40.08	21 **Sc** Scandium 44.956	22 **Ti** Titanium 47.88	23 **V** Vanadium 50.94	24 **Cr** Chromium 51.996	25 **Mn** Manganese 54.938	26 **Fe** Iron 55.847	27 **Co** Cobalt 58.9332
5	37 **Rb** Rubidium 85.468	38 **Sr** Strontium 87.62	39 **Y** Yttrium 88.9059	40 **Zr** Zirconium 91.224	41 **Nb** Niobium 92.91	42 **Mo** Molybdenum 95.94	43 **Tc** Technetium (98)	44 **Ru** Ruthenium 101.07	45 **Rh** Rhodium 102.906
6	55 **Cs** Cesium 132.91	56 **Ba** Barium 137.33	57 to 71	72 **Hf** Hafnium 178.49	73 **Ta** Tantalum 180.95	74 **W** Tungsten 183.85	75 **Re** Rhenium 186.207	76 **Os** Osmium 190.2	77 **Ir** Iridium 192.22
7	87 **Fr** Francium (223)	88 **Ra** Radium 226.025	89 to 103	104 **Rf** Rutherfordium (261)	105 **Db** Dubnium (262)	106 **Sg** Seaborgium (263)	107 **Bh** Bohrium (262)	108 **Hs** Hassium (265)	109 **Mt** Meitnerium (266)

Key

6	Atomic number
C	Element symbol
Carbon	Element name
12.011	Atomic mass

57 **La** Lanthanum 138.906	58 **Ce** Cerium 140.12	59 **Pr** Praseodymium 140.908	60 **Nd** Neodymium 144.24	61 **Pm** Promethium (145)	62 **Sm** Samarium 150.36
89 **Ac** Actinium 227.028	90 **Th** Thorium 232.038	91 **Pa** Protactinium 231.036	92 **U** Uranium 238.029	93 **Np** Neptunium 237.048	94 **Pu** Plutonium (244)

Phase at 20°C

C	Solid
Br	Liquid
H	Gas

Metallic Properties

Li	Metal
B	Semimetal
C	Nonmetal

			13 **3A**	**14** **4A**	**15** **5A**	**16** **6A**	**17** **7A**	2 He Helium 4.003
10	**11** **1B**	**12** **2B**	5 B Boron 10.81	6 C Carbon 12.011	7 N Nitrogen 14.007	8 O Oxygen 15.999	9 F Fluorine 18.998	10 Ne Neon 20.179
			13 Al Aluminum 26.98	14 Si Silicon 28.086	15 P Phosphorus 30.974	16 S Sulfur 32.06	17 Cl Chlorine 35.453	18 Ar Argon 39.948
28 Ni Nickel 58.69	29 Cu Copper 63.546	30 Zn Zinc 65.39	31 Ga Gallium 69.72	32 Ge Germanium 72.59	33 As Arsenic 74.922	34 Se Selenium 78.96	35 Br Bromine 79.904	36 Kr Krypton 83.80
46 Pd Palladium 106.42	47 Ag Silver 107.868	48 Cd Cadmium 112.41	49 In Indium 114.82	50 Sn Tin 118.71	51 Sb Antimony 121.75	52 Te Tellurium 127.60	53 I Iodine 126.905	54 Xe Xenon 131.29
78 Pt Platinum 195.08	79 Au Gold 196.967	80 Hg Mercury 200.59	81 Tl Thallium 204.383	82 Pb Lead 207.2	83 Bi Bismuth 208.98	84 Po Polonium (209)	85 At Astatine (210)	86 Rn Radon (222)
110 Uun Ununnilium (269)	111 Uuu Unununium (272)	112 Uub Ununbium (277)						

The names of elements 104-108 are under dispute. This table provides proposed names from the International Union of Pure and Applied Chemistry (IUPAC).

Mass numbers in parentheses are those of the most stable or common isotope.

63 Eu Europium 151.96	64 Gd Gadolinium 157.25	65 Tb Terbium 158.925	66 Dy Dysprosium 162.50	67 Ho Holmium 164.93	68 Er Erbium 167.26	69 Tm Thulium 168.934	70 Yb Ytterbium 173.04	71 Lu Lutetium 174.967
95 Am Americium (243)	96 Cm Curium (247)	97 Bk Berkelium (247)	98 Cf Californium (251)	99 Es Einsteinium (252)	100 Fm Fermium (257)	101 Md Mendelevium (258)	102 No Nobelium (259)	103 Lr Lawrencium (260)

Care and Use of the Microscope

THE COMPOUND MICROSCOPE

One of the most essential tools in the study of biology is the microscope. With the help of different types of microscopes, biologists have developed detailed concepts of cell structure and function. The type of microscope used in most biology classes is the compound microscope. It contains a combination of lenses and can magnify objects normally unseen with the unaided eye.

The eyepiece lens is located in the top portion of the microscope. This lens usually has a magnification of 10×. A compound microscope usually has two other interchangeable lenses. These lenses, called objective lenses, are at the bottom of the body tube on the revolving nosepiece. By revolving the nosepiece, either of the objectives can be brought into direct line with the body of the tube.

The shorter objective is of low power in its magnification, usually 10×. The longer one is of high power, usually 40× or 43×. The magnification is always marked on the objective. To determine the total magnification of a microscope, multiply the magnifying power of the eyepiece by the magnifying power of the objective being used. For example, the eyepiece magnifying power, 10×, multiplied by the low-power objective, 10×, equals 100×. The total magnification is 100×.

A microscope also produces clear contrasts to enable the viewer to distinguish between objects that lie very close together. Under a microscope the detail of objects is very sharp. The ability of a microscope to produce contrast and detail is called resolution, or resolving power. Although microscopes can have the same magnifying power, they can differ in resolving power.

Learning the name, function, and location of each of the microscope's parts is necessary for proper use. Use the following procedures when working the microscope:

1. Remove the microscope from its storage area by placing one hand beneath the base and grasping the arm of the microscope with the other hand.

2. Gently place the microscope on the lab table with the arm facing you. The microscope's base should be resting evenly on the table, approximately 10 centimeters from the table's edge.

3. Raise the body tube by turning the coarse adjustment knob until the objective lens is about 2 centimeters above the opening of the stage.

4. Revolve the nosepiece so that the low-power objective (10×) is directly in line with the body tube. A click indicates that the lens is in line with the opening of the stage.

5. Look through the eyepiece and switch on the lamp or adjust the mirror so that a circle of light can be seen. This is the field of view. Moving the lever of the diaphragm permits a greater or smaller amount of light to come through the opening of the stage.

6. Place a prepared slide on the stage. Place the specimen over the center of the opening of the stage. Fasten the stage clip to hold the slide in position.

7. Look at the microscope from the side. Carefully turn the coarse adjustment knob to lower the body tube until the low-power objective almost touches

MICROSCOPE PARTS AND THEIR FUNCTION

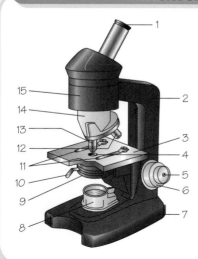

1. *Eyepiece*   Contains a magnifying lens
2. *Arm*   Supports the body tube
3. *Stage*   Supports the slide being observed
4. *Opening of the stage*   Permits light to travel up to the eyepiece
5. *Fine adjustment*   Moves the body tube slightly to sharpen the focus
6. *Coarse adjustment*   Moves the body tube up and down for focusing
7. *Base*   Supports the microscope
8. *Illuminator*   Produces light or reflects light up through the body tube
9. *Diaphragm*   Regulates the amount of light entering the body tube
10. *Diaphragm lever*   Opens and closes the diaphragm
11. *Stage clips*   Hold the slide in position
12. *Low-power objective*   Provides a magnification of 10× and is the shorter of the objectives
13. *High-power objective*   Provides a magnification of 43× and is the longer of the objectives
14. *Revolving nosepiece*   Contains the low- and high-power objectives and can be rotated to change magnification
15. *Body tube*   Maintains a proper distance between the eyepiece and the objective lenses

the slide or until the body tube can no longer be moved. Do not allow the objective to touch the slide.

8. Look through the eyepiece and observe the specimen. If the field of view is out of focus, use the coarse adjustment knob to raise the body tube while looking through the eyepiece. When the specimen comes into view, use the fine adjustment knob to focus the specimen. Be sure to keep both eyes open when viewing a specimen. This helps prevent eyestrain.

9. Adjust the lever of the diaphragm to allow the right amount of light to enter.

10. To view the specimen under high power (43×), revolve the nosepiece until the high-power objective is in line with the body tube and clicks into place.

11. Look through the eyepiece and use the fine adjustment knob to bring the specimen into focus.

12. After every use remove the slide. Clean the stage of the microscope and the lenses with lens paper. Do not use other types of paper to clean the lenses, as they may scratch the lenses.

PREPARING A WET-MOUNT SLIDE

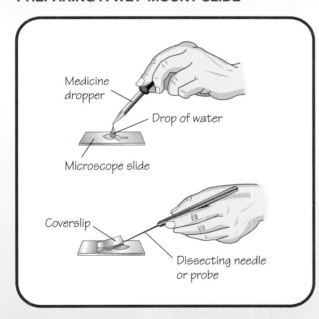

1. Obtain a clean microscope slide and a coverslip. A coverslip is very thin, permitting the objective lens to be lowered close to the specimen.

2. Place the specimen in the middle of the microscope slide. The specimen must be thin enough for light to pass through it.

3. Using a medicine dropper, place a drop of water on the specimen.

4. Lower one edge of the coverslip so that it touches the side of the drop of water at a 45-degree angle. The water will spread evenly along the edge of the coverslip. Using a dissecting needle or probe, slowly lower the coverslip over the specimen and water. Try not to trap any air bubbles under the coverslip because they will interfere with the view of the specimen. If air bubbles are present, gently tap the surface of the coverslip over the air bubble with a pencil eraser.

5. Remove any excess water at the edge of the coverslip with a paper towel. If the specimen begins to dry out, add a drop of water at the edge of the coverslip.

STAINING TECHNIQUES

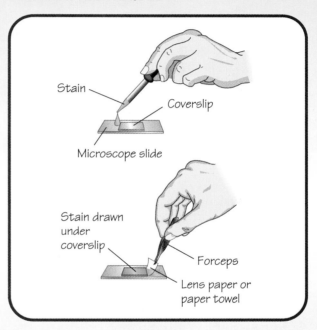

1. Obtain a clean microscope slide and coverslip.

2. Place the specimen in the middle of the microscope slide.

3. Using a medicine dropper, place a drop of water on the specimen.

4. Place one edge of the coverslip so that it touches the side of the drop of water at a 45-degree angle. After the water spreads along the edge of the coverslip, use a dissecting needle or probe to lower the coverslip over the specimen.

5. Add a drop of stain at the edge of the coverslip. Using forceps, touch a small piece of lens paper or paper towel to the opposite edge of the coverslip. The paper causes the stain to be drawn under the coverslip and stain the cells. Some common stains are methylene blue, iodine, fuchsin, and Wright's.

Science Safety Rules

ONE OF THE FIRST THINGS A SCIENTIST learns is that working in the laboratory can be an exciting experience. But the laboratory can also be quite dangerous if proper safety rules are not followed at all times. To prepare yourself for a safe year in the laboratory, read over the following safety rules. Then read them a second time. Make sure you understand each rule. Ask your teacher to explain any rules you don't understand.

DRESS CODE

1. Many materials in the laboratory can cause eye injury. To protect yourself from possible injury, wear safety goggles whenever you are working with chemicals, burners, or any substance that might get into your eyes. Never wear contact lenses in the laboratory.

2. Wear a laboratory apron or coat whenever you are working with any chemicals or heated substances.

3. Tie back long hair to keep it away from any chemicals, burners, candles, or any other laboratory equipment.

4. Before working in the laboratory, remove or tie back any article of clothing or jewelry that could hang down and touch chemicals and flames.

GENERAL SAFETY RULES

5. Read all directions for an experiment several times. Then follow the directions exactly as they are written. If you are in doubt about any part of the experiment, ask your teacher for assistance.

6. Never perform investigations that are not authorized by your teacher. Obtain permission before "experimenting" on your own.

7. Never handle any equipment unless you have specific permission.

8. Take extreme care not to spill any material in the laboratory. If spills occur, ask your teacher immediately about the proper cleanup procedure. Never simply pour chemicals or other substances into the sink or trash container.

9. Never eat in the laboratory.

FIRST AID

10. Report all accidents, no matter how minor, to your teacher immediately.

11. Learn what to do in case of specific accidents, such as getting acid in your eyes or on your skin. (Rinse any acids that may splash on your body with lots of water.)

12. Know the location of the first-aid kit. Your teacher should administer any required first aid due to injury. Or your teacher may send you to the school nurse or call a physician.

13. Know where and how to report an accident or fire. Find out the location of the fire extinguisher, phone, and fire alarm. Keep a list of important phone numbers, such as those for the fire department and school nurse, near the phone. Report any fires to your teacher at once.

HEATING AND FIRE SAFETY

14. Again, never use a heat source such as a candle or burner without wearing safety goggles.

15. Never heat a chemical you are not instructed to heat. A chemical that is harmless when cool can be dangerous when heated.

16. Maintain a clean work area and keep all materials away from flames.

17. Never reach across a flame.

18. Make sure you know how to light a Bunsen burner. (Your teacher will demonstrate the proper procedure for lighting a burner.) If the flame leaps out of a burner toward you, turn the gas off immediately. Do not touch the burner. It may be hot. And never leave a lighted burner unattended!

19. When you are heating a test tube or bottle, point it away from yourself and others. Chemicals can splash or boil out of a heated test tube.

20. Never heat a liquid in a closed container. The expanding gases produced may blow the container apart, causing injury to yourself or others.

21. Never pick up a container that has been heated without first holding the back of your hand near it. If you can feel the heat on the back of your hand, the container may be too hot to handle. Use a clamp or tongs when handling hot containers.

USING CHEMICALS SAFELY

22. Never mix chemicals "for the fun of it." You might produce a dangerous, possibly explosive substance.

23. Never touch, taste, or smell any chemicals in the laboratory. Many chemicals are poisonous. If you are instructed to note the fumes in an experiment, gently wave your hand over the opening of a container and direct the fumes toward your nose. Do not inhale the fumes directly from the container.

24. Use only those chemicals needed in the investigation. Keep all lids closed when a chemical is not being used. Notify your teacher whenever chemicals are spilled.

25. Dispose of all chemicals as instructed by your teacher. To avoid contamination, never return chemicals to their original containers.

26. Be extra careful when working with acids or bases. Pour such chemicals over the sink, not over your workbench.

27. When diluting an acid, pour the acid into water. Never pour water into the acid.

28. If any acids get on your skin or clothing, rinse them off with water. Immediately notify your teacher of any acid spill.

USING GLASSWARE SAFELY

29. Never force glass tubing into a rubber stopper. A turning motion and lubricant will be helpful when inserting glass tubing into rubber stoppers or rubber tubing. Your teacher will demonstrate the proper way to insert glass tubing.

30. Never heat glassware that is not thoroughly dry. Use a wire screen to protect glassware from any flame.

31. Keep in mind that hot glassware will not appear hot. Never pick up glassware that is not thoroughly dry.

32. If you are instructed to cut glass tubing, fire-polish the ends immediately to remove sharp edges.

33. Never use broken or chipped glassware. If any glassware breaks, notify your teacher and dispose of the glassware in the proper trash container.

34. Never eat or drink from laboratory glassware. Thoroughly clean glassware before putting it away.

USING SHARP INSTRUMENTS

35. Handle scalpels or razor blades with extreme care. Never cut material toward you; cut away from you.

36. Notify your teacher immediately if you cut yourself when in the laboratory.

ANIMAL SAFETY

37. No experiments that will cause pain, discomfort, or harm to mammals, birds, reptiles, fishes, and amphibians should be done in the classroom or at home.

38. Animals should be handled only if necessary. If an animal is excited or frightened, pregnant, feeding, or with its young, special handling is required.

39. Your teacher will instruct you as to how to handle each animal species that may be brought into the classroom.

40. Clean your hands thoroughly after handling animals or the cage containing animals.

END-OF-EXPERIMENT RULES

41. When an experiment is completed, clean up your work area and return all equipment to its proper place.

42. Wash your hands before and after you perform every experiment.

43. Turn off all burners before leaving the laboratory. Check that the gas line leading to the burner is off as well.

Metric System

THE METRIC SYSTEM OF MEASUREMENT *is used by scientists throughout the world. It is based on units of ten. Each unit is ten times larger or ten times smaller than the next unit. The most commonly used units of the metric system are given below. After you have finished reading about the metric system, try to put it to use. How tall are you in meters? What is your mass? What is your normal body temperature in degrees Celsius?*

COMMONLY USED METRIC UNITS

Length   The distance from one point to another

meter (m)	A meter is slightly longer than a yard.
	1 meter = 1000 millimeters (mm)
	1 meter = 100 centimeters (cm)
	1000 meters = 1 kilometer (km)

Volume   The amount of space an object takes up

liter (L)	A liter is slightly more than a quart.
	1 liter = 1000 milliliters (mL)

Mass   The amount of matter in an object

gram (g)	A gram has a mass equal to about one paper clip.
	1000 grams = 1 kilogram (kg)

Temperature   The measure of hotness or coldness

degrees	0°C = freezing point of water
Celsius (°C)	100°C = boiling point of water

METRIC—ENGLISH SYSTEM EQUIVALENTS

2.54 centimeters (cm) = 1 inch (in.)
1 meter (m) = 39.37 inches (in.)
1 kilometer (km) = 0.62 miles (mi)
1 liter (L) = 1.06 quarts (qt)
250 milliliters (mL) = 1 cup (c)
1 kilogram (kg) = 2.2 pounds (lb)
28.3 grams (g) = 1 ounce (oz)
$°C = 5/9 \times (°F - 32)$

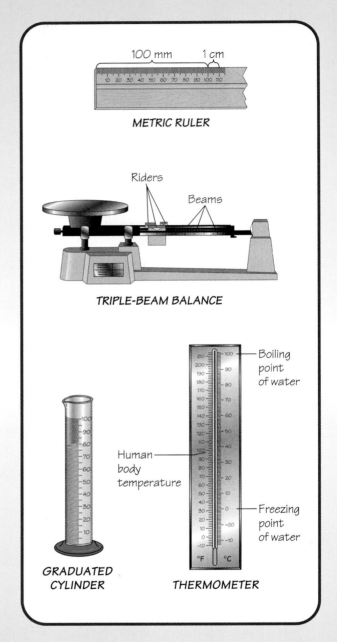

METRIC RULER

TRIPLE-BEAM BALANCE

GRADUATED CYLINDER

THERMOMETER

Six-Kingdom Classification System

Kingdom Eubacteria

Outer cell wall contains complex carbohydrates; all species have at least one inner cell membrane; live in diverse environments.

PHYLUM CYANOBACTERIA (blue-green bacteria)

Photosynthetic autotrophs, once called blue-green algae; contain pigments phycocyanin and chlorophyll *a*; some fix atmospheric nitrogen. Examples: *Anabaena, Nostoc.*

PHYLUM PROCHLOROBACTERIA

Photosynthetic autotrophs containing chlorophylls *a* and *b*; strikingly similar to chloroplasts; few species identified to date. Example: *Prochloron.*

Kingdom Archaebacteria

Single-celled prokaryotic organism; cell membrane contains lipids not found in any other organism; many survive in absence of oxygen; known as methanogens and produce methane gas; live in harsh environments. Examples: *Thermoplasma, Sulfolobus.*

Kingdom Protista

Eukaryotic; usually unicellular; some multicellular or colonial; heterotrophic or autotrophic organisms.

ANIMALLIKE PROTISTS Unicellular; heterotrophic; usually motile; also known as protozoa.

PHYLUM CILIOPHORA (ciliates)

All have cilia at some point in development; almost all use cilia to move; characterized by two types of nuclei: macronuclei and micronuclei; most have a sexual process known as conjugation. Examples: *Paramecium, Didinium, Stentor.*

PHYLUM ZOOMASTIGINA (animallike flagellates)

Possess one or more flagella (some have thousands); some are internal symbionts of wood-eating animals. Examples: *Trypanosoma, Trichonympha.*

PHYLUM SPOROZOA

Nonmotile parasites; produce small infective cells called spores; life cycles usually complex, involving more than one host species; cause a number of diseases, including malaria. Example: *Plasmodium.*

PHYLUM SARCODINA

Use pseudopods for feeding and movement; some produce elaborate shells that contain silica or calcium carbonate; most free-living; a few parasitic. Examples: *Ameba, foraminifers.*

PLANTLIKE PROTISTS Mostly unicellular photosynthetic autotrophs that have characteristics similar to green plants or fungi. A few species are multicellular or heterotrophic.

PHYLUM EUGLENOPHYTA (plantlike flagellates)

Primarily photosynthetic; most live in fresh water; possess two unequal flagella; lack a cell wall. Example: *Euglena.*

PHYLUM PYRROPHYTA (fire algae)

Two flagella; most live in salt water, are photosynthetic, and have a rigid cell wall that contains cellulose; some are luminescent; many are symbiotic. Examples: *Gonyaulax, Noctiluca.*

PHYLUM CHRYSOPHYTA (golden algae)

Photosynthetic; aquatic; mostly unicellular; contain yellow-brown pigments; most are diatoms, which build a two-part cell covering that contains silica. Examples: *Thallasiosira, Orchromonas, Navicula.*

PHYLUM CHLOROPHYTA (green algae)

Live in fresh and salt water; unicellular or multicellular; chlorophylls and accessory pigments similar to those in vascular plants; food stored as starch. Examples: *Ulva* (sea lettuce), *Chlamydomonas, Spirogyra, Acetabularia.*

PHYLUM PHAEOPHYTA (brown algae)

Live almost entirely in salt water; multicellular; contain brown pigment fucoxanthin; food stored as oils and carbohydrates. Examples: *Fucus* (rockweed), kelps, *Sargassum*.

PHYLUM RHODOPHYTA (red algae)

Live almost entirely in salt water; multicellular; contain red pigment phycoerythrin; food stored as carbohydrates. Examples: *Chondrus* (Irish moss), coralline algae.

FUNGUSLIKE PROTISTS

Lack chlorophyll and absorb food through cell walls. Unlike true fungi, the funguslike protists contain centrioles and lack chitin in their cell walls.

PHYLUM ACRASIOMYCOTA (cellular slime molds)

Spores develop into independent, free-living amebalike cells that may come together to form a multicellular structure; this structure, which behaves much like a single organism, forms a fruiting body that produces spores. Example: *Dictyostelium*.

PHYLUM MYXOMYCOTA (acellular slime molds)

Spores develop into haploid cells that can switch between flagellated and amebalike forms; these haploid cells fuse to form a zygote that grows into a plasmodium, which ultimately forms spore-producing fruiting bodies. Example: *Physarum*.

PHYLUM OOMYCOTA (water molds)

Unicellular or multicellular; mostly aquatic; cell walls contain cellulose or a polysaccharide similar to cellulose; form zoospores asexually and eggs and sperms sexually. Example: *Saprolegnia* (freshwater molds).

KINGDOM FUNGI

Eukaryotic; unicellular or multicellular; cell walls typically contain chitin; mostly decomposers; some parasites; some commensal or mutualistic symbionts; asexual reproduction by spore formation, budding, or fragmentation; sexual reproduction involving mating types; classified according to type of fruiting body and style of spore formation; heterotrophic.

PHYLUM ZYGOMYCOTA (conjugation fungi)

Cell walls of chitin; hyphae lack cross walls; sexual reproduction by conjugation produces diploid zygospores; asexual reproduction produces haploid spores; most parasites; some decomposers. Example: *Rhizopus stolonifer* (black bread mold).

PHYLUM ASCOMYCOTA (sac fungi)

Cell walls of chitin; hyphae have perforated cross walls; most multicellular; yeasts unicellular; sexual reproduction produces ascospores; asexual reproduction by spore formation or budding; some cause plant diseases such as chestnut blight and Dutch elm disease. Examples: *Neurospora* (red bread mold), baker's yeast, morels, truffles.

PHYLUM BASIDIOMYCOTA (club fungi)

Cell walls of chitin; hyphae have cross walls; sexual reproduction involves basidiospores, which are borne on club-shaped basidia; asexual reproduction by spore formation. Examples: most mushrooms, puffballs, shelf fungi, rusts.

PHYLUM DEUTEROMYCOTA (imperfect fungi)

Cell walls of chitin; sexual reproduction never observed; members resemble ascomycetes, basidiomycetes, or zygomycetes; most are thought to be ascomycetes that have lost the ability to form asci. Examples: *Penicillium*, athlete's foot fungus.

KINGDOM PLANTAE

Eukaryotic; overwhelmingly multicellular and nonmotile; photosynthetic autotrophs; possess chlorophylls *a* and *b* and other pigments in organelles called chloroplasts; cell walls contain cellulose; food stored as starch; reproduce sexually; alternate haploid (gametophyte) and diploid (sporophyte) generations; botanists typically use the term division rather than phylum.

DIVISION BRYOPHYTA (bryophytes)

Generally small, multicellular green plants; live on land in moist habitats; lack vascular tissue; lack true roots, leaves, and stems; gametophyte dominant; water required for reproduction. Examples: mosses, liverworts, hornworts.

DIVISION PSILOPHYTA (whisk ferns)

Primitive vascular plants; no differentiation between root and shoot; produce only one kind of spore; motile sperm must swim in water.

DIVISION LYCOPHYTA (lycopods)

Primitive vascular plants; usually small; sporophyte dominant; possess roots, stems, and leaves; water required for reproduction. Examples: club mosses, quillworts.

DIVISION SPHENOPHYTA (horsetails)

Primitive vascular plants; stem comprises most of mature plant and contains silica; produce only one kind of spore; motile sperm must swim in water. Only one living genus: *Equisetum*.

DIVISION PTEROPHYTA (ferns)

Vascular plants well-adapted to live in predominantly damp or seasonally wet environments; sporophyte dominant and well-adapted to terrestrial life; gametophyte inconspicuous; reproduction still dependent on water for free-swimming gametes. Examples: cinnamon ferns, Boston ferns, tree ferns, maidenhair ferns.

GYMNOSPERMS Four divisions of seed plants—Cycadophyta, Ginkgophyta, Coniferophyta, and Gnetophyta. Gymnosperms are characterized by seeds that develop exposed, or "naked," on fertile leaves—there is no ovary wall (fruit) surrounding the seeds. Gymnosperms lack flowers.

DIVISION CYCADOPHYTA (cycads)

Evergreen, slow-growing, tropical and subtropical shrubs; many resemble small palm trees; palmlike or fernlike compound leaves; possess symbiotic cyanobacteria in special roots; sexes are separate—individuals have either male pollen-producing cones or female seed-producing cones.

DIVISION GINKGOPHYTA

Deciduous trees with fan-shaped leaves; sexes separate; outer skin of ovule develops into a fleshy, fruitlike covering. Only one living species: *Ginkgo biloba* (ginkgo).

DIVISION GNETOPHYTA

Few species; live mostly in deserts; functional xylem cells are alive; sexes are separate. Examples: *Welwitschia, Ephedra* (joint fir).

DIVISION CONIFEROPHYTA (conifers)

Cones predominantly wind-pollinated; most are evergreen; most temperate and subarctic shrubs and trees; many have needlelike leaves; in most species, sexes are not separate. Examples: pines, spruces, cedars, firs.

DIVISION ANTHOPHYTA

Members of this division are commonly called angiosperms, or flowering plants. Nearly all familiar trees, shrubs, and garden plants are angiosperms. Seeds develop enclosed within ovaries; fertile leaves modified into flowers; flowers pollinated by wind or by animals, including insects, birds, and bats; occur in many different forms; found in most land and freshwater habitats; a few species found in shallow saltwater and estuarine areas.

Class Monocotyledonae (monocots) Embryo with a single cotyledon; leaves with predominantly parallel venation; flower parts in threes or multiples of three; vascular bundles scattered throughout stem. Examples: lilies, corns, grasses, irises, palms, tulips.

Class Dicotyledonae (dicots) Embryo with two cotyledons; leaves with variation in netlike patterns; flower parts in fours or fives (or multiples thereof); vascular bundles arranged in rings in stem. Examples: roses, maples, oaks, daisies, apples.

KINGDOM ANIMALIA

Multicellular; eukaryotic; typical heterotrophs that ingest their food; lack cell walls; approximately 35 phyla; in most phyla, cells are organized into tissues that make up organs; most reproduce sexually; motile sperm have flagella; nonmotile egg is much larger than sperm; development involves formation of a hollow ball of cells called a blastula.

SUBKINGDOM PARAZOA

Animals that possess neither tissues nor organs; most asymmetrical.

PHYLUM PORIFERA (sponges)

Aquatic; lack true tissues and organs; motile larvae and sessile adults; filter feeders; internal skeleton made up of spongin and/or spicules of calcium carbonate or silica. Examples: Venus' flower baskets, bath sponges, tube sponges.

SUBKINGDOM METAZOA

Animals with definite symmetry; definite tissues; most possess organs.

PHYLUM CNIDARIA

Previously known as coelenterates; aquatic; mostly carnivorous; two layers of true tissue; radial symmetry; tentacles bear stinging nematocysts; many alternate between polyp and medusa body forms; gastrovascular cavity.

Class Hydrozoa   Polyp form dominant; colonial or solitary; life cycle typically includes a medusa generation that reproduces sexually and a polyp generation that reproduces asexually. Examples: hydras, Portuguese man-of-wars.

Class Scyphozoa   Medusa form dominant; some species bypass polyp stage. Examples: lion's mane jellyfishes, moon jellies, sea wasps.

Class Anthozoa   Colonial or solitary polyps; no medusa stage. Examples: reef corals, sea anemones, sea pens, sea fans.

PHYLUM PLATYHELMINTHES (flatworms)

Three layers of tissue (endoderm, mesoderm, ectoderm); bilateral symmetry; some cephalization; acoelomate; free-living or parasitic.

Class Turbellaria   Free-living carnivores and scavengers, live in fresh water, in salt water, or on land; move with cilia. Example: planarians.

Class Trematoda (flukes)   Parasites; life cycle typically involves more than one host. Examples: *Schistosoma*, liver flukes.

Class Cestoda (tapeworms)   Internal parasites; lack digestive tract; body composed of many repeating sections (proglottids).

PHYLUM NEMATODA (roundworms)

Digestive system has two openings—a mouth and an anus; pseudocoelomates. Examples: *Ascaris lumbricoides* (human ascarid), hookworms, *Trichinella*.

PHYLUM MOLLUSCA (mollusks)

Soft-bodied; usually (but not always) possess a hard, calcified shell secreted by a mantle; most adults have bilateral symmetry; muscular foot; divided into seven classes; digestive system with two openings; coelomates.

Class Pelecypoda (bivalves)   Two-part hinged shell; wedge-shaped foot; typically sessile as adults; primarily aquatic; some burrow in mud or sand. Examples: clams, oysters, scallops, mussels.

Class Gastropoda (gastropods)   Use broad, muscular foot in movement; most have spiral, chambered shell; some lack shell; distinct head; some terrestrial, others aquatic; many are cross-fertilizing hermaphrodites. Examples: snails, slugs, nudibranchs, sea hares, sea butterflies.

Class Cephalopoda (cephalopods)   Foot divided into tentacles; live in salt water; closed circulatory system; sexes separate. Examples: octopuses, squids, nautiluses, cuttlefishes.

PHYLUM ANNELIDA (segmented worms)

Body composed of segments separated by internal partitions; digestive system has two openings; coelomate; closed circulatory system.

Class Polychaeta (polychaetes)   Live in salt water; pair of bristly, fleshy appendages on each segment; some live in tubes. Examples: sandworms, bloodworms, fanworms, feather-duster worms, plume worms.

Class Oligochaeta (oligochaetes)   Lack appendages; few bristles; terrestrial or aquatic. Examples: *Tubifex*, earthworms.

Class Hirudinea (leeches)   Lack appendages; carnivores or blood-sucking external parasites; most live in fresh water. Example: *Hirudo medicinalis* (medicinal leech).

PHYLUM ARTHROPODA (arthropods)

Exoskeleton of chitin; jointed appendages; segmented body; many undergo metamorphosis during development; open circulatory system; ventral nerve cord; largest animal phylum.

Subphylum Trilobita (trilobites)   Two furrows running from head to tail divide body into three lobes; one pair of unspecialized appendages on each body segment; each appendage divided into two branches—a gill and a walking leg; all extinct.

Subphylum Chelicerata (chelicerates)   First pair of appendages specialized as feeding structures called chelicerae; body composed of two parts—cephalothorax and abdomen; lack antennae; most terrestrial. Examples: horseshoe crabs, ticks, mites, spiders, scorpions.

Subphylum Crustacea (crustaceans)   Most aquatic; most live in salt water; two pairs of antennae; mouthparts called mandibles; appendages consist of two branches; many have a carapace that covers part or all of the body. Examples: crabs, crayfishes, pill bugs, water fleas, barnacles.

Subphylum Uniramia   Almost all terrestrial; one pair of antennae; mandibles; unbranched appendages; generally divided into five classes.

Class Chilopoda (centipedes)   Long body consisting of many segments; one pair of legs per segment; poison claws for feeding; carnivorous.

Class Diplopoda (millipedes)   Long body consisting of many segments; two pairs of legs per segment; mostly herbivorous.

Class Insecta (insects) Body divided into three parts—head, thorax, and abdomen; three pairs of legs and usually two pairs of wings attached to thorax; some undergo complete metamorphosis; approximately 25 orders. Examples: termites, ants, beetles, flies, moths, grasshoppers.

PHYLUM ECHINODERMATA (echinoderms)

Live in salt water; larvae have bilateral symmetry; adults typically have five-part radial symmetry; endoskeleton; tube feet; water vascular system used in respiration, excretion, feeding, and locomotion.

Class Crinoidea (crinoids) Filter feeders; feathery arms; mouth and anus on upper surface of body disk; some sessile. Examples: sea lilies, feather stars.

Class Asteroidea (starfishes) Star-shaped; carnivorous; bottom dwellers; mouth on lower surface. Examples: crown-of-thorns starfishes, sunstars.

Class Ophiuroidea Small body disk; long armored arms; most have only five arms; lack an anus; most are filter feeders or detritus feeders. Examples: brittle stars, basket stars.

Class Echinoidea Lack arms; body encased in rigid, boxlike covering; covered with spines; most grazing herbivores or detritus feeders. Examples: sea urchins, sand dollars.

Class Holothuroidea (sea cucumbers) Cylindrical body with feeding tentacles on one end; lie on their side; mostly detritus or filter feeders; endoskeleton greatly reduced.

PHYLUM CHORDATA (chordates)

Notochord and pharyngeal gill slits during at least part of development; hollow dorsal nerve cord.

Subphylum Urochordata (tunicates) Live in salt water; tough outer covering (tunic); display chordate features during larval stages; many adults sessile, some free-swimming. Examples: sea squirts, sea peaches.

Subphylum Cephalochordata (lancelets) Fishlike; live in salt water; filter feeders; no internal skeleton. Example: *Branchiostoma*.

Subphylum Vertebrata Most possess a vertebral column (backbone) that supports and protects dorsal nerve cord; endoskeleton; distinct head with a skull and brain.

Jawless Fishes Characterized by long eellike body and a circular mouth; two-chambered heart; lack scales, paired fins, jaws, and bones; ectothermic; possess a notochord as adults. Once considered a single class—Agnatha—jawless fishes are now divided into two classes: Myxini and Cephalaspidomorphi. Although the term agnatha no longer refers to a true taxonomic group, it is still used informally.

Class Myxini (hagfishes) Mostly scavengers; live in salt water; short tentacles around mouth; rasping tongue; extremely slimy; open circulatory system.

Class Cephalaspidomorphi (lampreys) Larvae filter feeders; adults are parasites whose circular mouth is lined with rasping, toothlike structures; many live in both salt water and fresh water during the course of their lives.

Class Chondrichthyes (cartilaginous fishes) Jaw; fins; endoskeleton of cartilage; most live in salt water; typically several gill slits; tough small scales with spines; ectothermic; two-chambered heart; males possess structures for internal fertilization. Examples: sharks, rays, skates, sawfishes.

Class Osteichthyes (bony fishes) Bony endoskeleton; aquatic; ectothermic; well-developed respiratory system, usually involving gills; possess swim bladder; paired fins; divided into two groups—ray-finned fishes (Actinopterygii), which include most living species, and fleshy-finned fishes (Sarcopterygii), which include lungfishes and the coelacanth. Examples: salmons, perches, sturgeons, tunas, goldfishes, eels.

Class Amphibia (amphibians) Adapted primarily to life in wet places; ectothermic; most carnivorous; smooth, moist skin; typically lay eggs that develop in water; usually have gilled larvae; most have three-chambered heart; adults either aquatic or terrestrial; terrestrial forms respire using lungs, skin, and/or lining of the mouth.

> *ORDER URODELA* (newts and salamanders) Possess tail as adults; carnivorous; usually have four legs; usually aquatic as larvae and terrestrial as adults.
>
> *ORDER ANURA* (frogs and toads) Adults in almost all species lack tail; aquatic larvae called tadpoles; well-developed hind legs adapted for jumping.
>
> *ORDER APODA* (legless amphibians) Wormlike; lack legs; carnivorous; terrestrial burrowers; some undergo direct development; some are viviparous.

Class Reptilia (reptiles) As a group, adapted to fully terrestrial life, although some live in water; dry, scale-covered skin; ectothermic; most have three-chambered heart; internal fertilization; amniotic eggs typically laid on land; extinct forms include dinosaurs and flying reptiles.

ORDER RHYNCHOCEPHALIA (tuatara) "Teeth" formed by serrations of jawbone; found only in New Zealand; carnivorous. One species: *Sphenodon punctatus*.

ORDER SQUAMATA (lizards and snakes) Most carnivorous; majority terrestrial; lizards typically have legs; snakes lack legs. Examples: iguanas, geckos, skinks, cobras, pythons, boas.

ORDER CROCODILIA (crocodilians) Carnivorous; aquatic or semiaquatic; four-chambered heart. Examples: alligators, crocodiles, caimans, gharials.

ORDER CHELONIA (turtles) Bony shell; ribs and vertebrae fused to upper part of shell; some terrestrial, others semiaquatic or aquatic; all lay eggs on land. Examples: snapping turtles, tortoises, hawksbill turtles, box turtles.

Class Aves (birds) Endothermic; feathered over much of body surface; scales on legs and feet; bones hollow and lightweight in flying species; four-chambered heart; well-developed lungs and air sacs for efficient air exchange; about 27 orders. Examples: owls, eagles, ducks, chickens, pigeons, penguins, sparrows, storks.

Class Mammalia (mammals) Endothermic; subcutaneous fat; hair; most viviparous; suckle young with milk produced in mammary glands; four-chambered heart; four legs; use lungs for respiration.

Monotremes (egg-laying mammals)

ORDER MONOTREMATA (monotremes) Exhibit features of both mammals and reptiles; possess a cloaca; lay eggs that hatch externally; produce milk from primitive nipplelike structures. Examples: duck-billed platypuses, spiny anteaters, short-beaked echidnas.

Marsupials (pouched mammals)

ORDER MARSUPIALIA (marsupials) Young develop in the female's uterus but emerge at very early stage of development; development completed in mother's pouch. Examples: opossums, kangaroos, koalas.

Placentals Young develop to term in uterus; nourished through placenta; some born helpless, others able to walk within hours of birth; about 16 orders.

ORDER INSECTIVORA (insectivores) Among the most primitive of living placental mammals; feed primarily on small arthropods. Examples: shrews, moles, hedgehogs.

ORDER CHIROPTERA (bats) Flying mammals, with forelimbs adapted for flight; most nocturnal; most navigate by echolocation; most species feed on insects, nectar, or fruits; some species feed on blood. Examples: fruit bats, flying foxes, vampire bats.

ORDER PRIMATES (primates) Highly developed brain and complex social behavior; excellent binocular vision; quadrupedal or bipedal locomotion; five digits on hands and feet. Examples: lemurs, monkeys, chimpanzees, humans.

ORDER EDENTATA (edentates) Teeth reduced or absent; feed primarily on social insects such as termites and ants. Examples: anteaters, armadillos.

ORDER LAGOMORPHA (lagomorphs) Small herbivores with chisel-shaped front teeth; generally adapted to running and jumping. Examples: rabbits, pikas, hares.

ORDER RODENTIA (rodents) Mammalian order with largest number of species; mostly herbivorous, but some omnivorous; sharp front teeth. Examples: rats, beavers, guinea pigs, hamsters, gerbils, squirrels.

ORDER CETACEA (cetaceans) Fully adapted to aquatic existence; feed, breed, and give birth in water; forelimbs specialized as flippers; external hindlimbs absent; many species capable of long, deep dives; some use echolocation to navigate; communicate using complex auditory signals. Examples: whales, porpoises, dolphins.

ORDER CARNIVORA (carnivores) Mostly carnivorous; live in salt water or on land; aquatic species must return to land to breed. Examples: dogs, seals, cats, bears, raccoons, weasels, skunks, pandas.

ORDER PROBOSCIDEA (elephants) Herbivorous; largest land animal; long, flexible trunk.

ORDER SIRENIA (sirenians) Aquatic herbivores; slow-moving; forelimbs modified as flippers; hindlimbs absent; little body hair. Examples: manatees, sea cows.

ORDER PERISSODACTYLA (odd-toed ungulates) Hooved herbivores; odd number of hooves; one hoof generally derived from middle digit on each foot; teeth, jaw, and digestive system adapted to plant material. Examples: horses, donkeys, rhinoceroses, tapirs.

ORDER ARTIODACTYLA (even-toed ungulates) Hooved herbivores; hooves derived from two digits on each foot; digestive system adapted to thoroughly process tough plant material. Examples: sheep, cows, hippopotamuses, antelopes, camels, giraffes, pigs.

Glossary

Pronunciation Key

When difficult names or terms first appear in the text, a pronunciation key follows in parentheses. A syllable in small capital letters receives the most stress. The key below lists the letters used in the pronunciations. It includes examples of words using each sound and shows how those words would be written.

Symbol	Example	Respelling
a	hat	(HAT)
ay	pay; late	(PAY); (LAYT)
ah	star; hot	(STAHR); (HAHT)
ai	air; dare	(AIR); (DAIR)
aw	law; all	(LAW); (AWL)
eh	met	(MEHT)
ee	bee; eat	(BEE); (EET)
er	learn; sir; fur	(LERN); (SER); (FER)
ih	fit	(FIHT)
igh	mile; sigh	(MIGHL); (SIGH)
oh	no	(NOH)
oi	soil; boy	(SOIL); (BOI)
oo	root; rule	(ROOT); (ROOL)
or	born; door	(BORN); (DOR)
ow	plow; out	(PLOW); (OWT)

Symbol	Example	Respelling
u	put; book	(PUT); (BUK)
uh	fun	(FUHN)
yoo	few; use	(FYOO); (YOOZ)
ch	chill; reach	(CHIHL); (REECH)
g	go; dig	(GOH); (DIHG)
j	jet; gently; bridge	(JEHT); (JEHNT-lee); (BRIHJ)
k	kite; cup	(KIGHT); (KUHP)
ks	mix	(MIHKS)
kw	quick	(KWIHK)
ng	bring	(BRIHNG)
s	say; cent	(SAY); (SEHNT)
sh	she; crash	(SHEE); (KRASH)
th	three	(THREE)
y	yet; onion	(YEHT); (UHN-yuhn)
z	zip; always	(ZIHP); (AWL-wayz)
zh	treasure	(TREH-zher)

A

abdomen: in arthropods, the body segment containing most of the internal organs, including the reproductive organs; in mammals, the cavity region between the diaphragm and the pelvis; in vertebrates, the part of the body cavity containing the digestive and reproductive organs

abiotic factor: physical environmental factor, such as climate, type of soil and its acidity, or availability of nutrients

acid: compound that donates H^+ ions

actin: protein found in the thin filaments of muscle fiber

action potential: rapid change in voltage on the inside of the axon from negative to positive and then back to negative

active site: region of an enzyme where a substrate binds

active transport: movement of a substance against a concentration difference; a process that requires energy

adaptation: evolution of physical and behavioral traits that make organisms better suited to survive in their environment

adaptive radiation: pattern of evolution in which selection and adaptation lead to the formation of a new species in a relatively short period of time

addiction: uncontrollable craving for a substance

age-structure diagram: diagram that illustrates the percentages of individuals within different age groups

AIDS (acquired immune deficiency syndrome): fatal disease of the immune system caused by HIV infection

air sac: in birds, an extension of the respiratory system where air collects

alcoholic fermentation: in yeasts, the process by which pyruvic acid is converted to alcohol and carbon dioxide

alga; pl. algae: single-celled photosynthetic organism classified as a protist

alimentary canal: one-way digestive track that begins at the mouth; includes the esophagus, stomach, small intestine, and large intestine; ends at the anus

allele (uh-LEEL): different form of a gene for a specific trait

allergy: overreaction of the immune system to an antigen in the environment

alternation of generations: variation in a life cycle that switches back and forth between the production of diploid (2n) and haploid (n) cells; in plants, pattern of reproduction in which the organism alternates between sporophyte and gametophyte phases

alveolus (al-VEE-uh-lus; pl. **alveoli**, al-VEE-uh-ligh): tiny air sac in the lungs appearing in a grapelike cluster surrounding a network of capillaries where gas exchange takes place

amebocyte (uh-MEE-boh-sight): wandering cell in sponges

amino acid: molecule of which proteins are made, containing a central carbon bonded to an amino group, a carboxyl group, a hydrogen atom, and another group called R group

amniocentesis (am-nee-oh-sehn-TEE-sihs): prenatal technique that involves withdrawing a small amount of fluid from the sac surrounding the fetus

amnion: membrane of the sac that envelops the embryo

amniotic (am-nee-AHT-ik) **egg:** self-sufficient developing egg encased in a shell that allows for gas exchange but keeps liquid inside

amylase: enzyme in saliva that breaks down the chemical bonds in starches, releasing sugars

anal pore: waste-discharging region on a paramecium

analogous structure: similar in appearance and function but dissimilar in anatomical development and origin

anaphase: third phase of mitosis during which duplicated chromosomes separate from each other

angiosperm: flowering plant whose seeds develop within a matured ovary (fruit)

animal society: any group of animals living together

annual: plant that completes its life cycle (from seed to maturity, flower, and seed production) within a single growing season

annual tree ring: layer of xylem cells produced in a tree stem in one year, with growth affected by seasonal variation; in cross section, seen as a concentric circle

anther: sac at the tip of a filament where pollen is produced and released

anthropoid (AN-thruh-poid): any of a higher order of primates; includes humans, apes, and monkeys

antibiotic: drug or compound that can destroy bacteria

antibody: large protein that is the basic functional unit of a specific immune response

anticodon: three nucleotides in transfer RNA that bind to a codon in mRNA

antidiuretic hormone (ADH): hormone that helps to regulate the fluid balance of the body

antigen: molecule that stimulates the production of an antibody

aorta: largest artery in the human body

artery: blood vessel that carries blood from the heart to the body

artificial selection: method of selective breeding of organisms to produce offspring with desirable characteristics

ascus: tough sac of an ascomycete that contains the spores produced by sexual reproduction

asthma: condition in which smooth muscle contractions reduce the size of air passageways in the lungs, making breathing difficult

atherosclerosis (ath-er-oh-skluh-ROH-sihs): condition in which fatty deposits build up on the inner surfaces of arteries, obstructing the flow of blood

atom: smallest unit of a chemical element

ATP (adenosine triphosphate): energy-storage compound in cells

atrium (AY-tree-uhm; pl. **atria**, AY-tree-ah): upper chamber of the heart that receives the blood

auditory canal: region where vibrations enter the ear

autoimmune disease: condition that results when the immune system attacks its own cells

autonomic nervous system: part of the motor division of the peripheral nervous system that regulates activities not under conscious control

autosome: any chromosome other than a sex chromosome

autotroph: organism that uses energy from the sun to change simple nonliving chemical nutrients in its environment into living tissue

auxin: plant hormone that produces phototropism, stimulating cell growth near the tip of a root or stem

axon: single long, branched extension of the cell body of a neuron that carries impulses away from the cell body

B

B cell: lymphocyte that matures in bone marrow and produces antibodies

bacillus (buh-SIHL-uhs; pl. **bacilli**, buh-SIHL-igh): rod-shaped bacteria

bacteriophage: any virus that infects bacteria

bacterium; pl. **bacteria**: prokaryote with a cell membrane and genetic material not surrounded by a nuclear envelope

base: compound that donates OH^- ions or accepts H^+ ions

behavior: animal's response to its environment

berry: soft ovary wall that encloses many seeds

biennial: plant that flowers and produces seeds in the second year of its life cycle

bilateral symmetry: body form of an organism that has identical left and right sides, specialized front and back ends, and upper and lower sides

bile: lipid and salt fluid produced by the liver to aid digestion

binary fission: asexual form of reproduction in which a cell divides in half to produce two identical daughter cells

binocular vision: ability to perceive depth using both eyes at the same time

biodegradable: capable of being broken down into unharmful products by the life processes of living things

biodiversity: variety of organisms, their genetic information, and biological communities in which they live

biological magnification: process whereby substances such as toxic metals and chemicals are passed up the trophic levels of the food web at increasing concentrations

biology: science of life

biome: ecosystem identified by its climax community

biotic factor: biological environmental factor, such as the living things with which an organism might interact

blood: fluid medium of transport of the circulatory system in vertebrates

blood pressure: measure of the force exerted by blood against the walls of arteries

bone marrow: blood-forming tissue that produces white and red blood cells

book gill: respiratory organ of some marine arthropods

book lung: respiratory organ of most spiders made of numerous layers of tissue that resemble the pages of a book

brain: bundle of nerves and neural connections that controls the nervous system

brainstem: structure that connects the brain to the spinal cord; includes the medulla oblongata and the pons

bronchitis: respiratory disease caused by the bronchi becoming swollen and clogged with mucus

bronchus (BRAHN-kus; pl. **bronchi**, BRAHN-kigh): one of many air tubes that enter the lungs and branch off, for gas exchange

budding: type of asexual reproduction in which an outgrowth of an organism breaks away and develops into a new organism

C

calorie: amount of heat energy needed to raise the temperature of 1 gram of water by 1°C

Calvin cycle: chemical pathway used to convert energy from ATP and $NADP^+$ into sugars; also called the light-independent reactions

capillary: small blood vessel in which the exchange of nutrients and wastes takes place

carbohydrate: class of macromolecules that includes sugars and starches; source of chemical energy

carcinogen: cancer-causing chemical

cardiac muscle tissue: muscle tissue found in the heart; not under direct control of the central nervous system

carpel: female leaf of a flower

carrying capacity: largest number of individuals of a particular species that can survive over long periods of time in a given environment

cartilage: strong, resilient connective tissue

catalyst: substance that speeds up a chemical reaction without itself being used up in the reaction

cell: smallest working unit of living things

cell body: largest part of the neuron in which metabolic activity takes place

cell cycle: period of time from the beginning of one cell division to the beginning of the next

cell division: process in which a cell divides into two independent daughter cells

cell-mediated immunity: immune response in which foreign cells are destroyed by contact with T cells

cell membrane: part of the cell's outer boundary; contains a lipid bilayer

cell theory: principle stating that all living things are composed of cells, cells are the smallest working units of living things, and all cells come from preexisting cells by cell division

cell transformation: the changing of a cell's genetic makeup by the insertion of DNA

cell wall: tough, porous boundary that lies outside the cell membrane; found in plant cells and in some bacteria but not in animal cells

centralization: concentration of nerve cells that form nerve cords or nerve rings around the mouth of most primitive invertebrates

centriole: small structure in animal cells that helps to organize microtubules

centromere: the part of a chromosome in which the chromatids are attached

cephalization (sehf-uh-lih-ZAY-shun): concentration of nerve cells and sensory cells in the head of an organism

cephalothorax: in chelicerates, body segment formed from fused head and thorax; carries the legs

cerebellum (ser-uh-BEHL-uhm): second-largest part of the brain; coordinates movement

cerebral cortex: deeply creased surface of the cerebrum

cerebrospinal (ser-uh-broh-SPIGH-nuhl) **fluid:** fluid that fills the space between the meninges to cushion the brain and spinal cord

cerebrum (SER-uh-bruhm): largest and most complex structure of the nervous system; consists of two lobes or hemispheres; controls voluntary activities

chelicera (kuh-LIHS-er-uh; pl. **chelicerae,** kuh-LIHS-er-ee): unique, specialized mouthpart of chelicerates used for grasping and crushing

chemical compound: substance formed by the bonding of atoms of different elements in definite proportions

chemical reaction: process that changes one set of substances into a new set of substances

chemiosmosis: process of ATP formation in chloroplasts and mitochondria

chemotherapy: mixture of drugs that interfere with important cell processes; used for treating cancer

chitin (KIGH-tihn): structural carbohydrate that is the main component of arthropod exoskeletons; reinforces the cell walls of fungi; also found in insect skeletons

chlamydia: sexually transmitted disease caused by a bacterium that can bring about infertility in females

chlorophyll: principal pigment of green plants

chloroplast: organelle found in plants and certain types of algae; harvests the energy of sunlight

chorionic villus (kor-ee-AHN-ihk VIHL-uhs) **sampling:** technique that involves the removal and examination of tissue surrounding the fetus

chromatid: strand of a chromosome that occurs in identical pairs; combined with its sister chromatid, constitutes a chromosome

chromatin: material of chromosomes that consists of DNA and proteins

chromatophore: specialized cell capable of changing color

chromosomal mutation: change in the number or structure of a cell's chromosomes; a mutation that affects the entire chromosome

chromosome: structure in the nucleus of a cell that contains DNA bound to proteins

chromosome deletion: phenomenon in which a broken-off piece of chromosome is left out during meiosis, which usually results in a genetic disorder

chromosome translocation: phenomenon in which a broken-off piece of chromosome becomes reattached to another chromosome

cilium; pl. cilia: short, hairlike projection of some cells; in ciliates, used to pull the organism through water with a coordinated rowing movement

circular muscle: in annelids, a muscle that surrounds the longitudinal muscle, lengthening the segment as it contracts

class: classification category of related orders

classical conditioning: associative learning; learning to associate a stimulus with either a reward or a punishment

climate: temperature range, average annual precipitation, humidity, and amount of sunshine that a region typically experiences

climax community: collection of plants and animals that results when an ecosystem reaches a relatively stable state in the interaction between organisms and their environment

clitellum: in an annelid, the structure that secretes a ring of mucus into which eggs and sperm are released

cloaca: body cavity into which the intestinal and genitourinary tracts empty

clone: group of genetically identical organisms produced by the division of a single cell

closed circulatory system: system in which blood moves only through blood vessels

cocaine: addictive stimulant drug that causes the brain to release dopamine and acts on the neurons of the brain

coccus (KAHK-uhs; pl. **cocci**, KAHK-sigh): spherical bacterium

cochlea (KAHK-lee-uh): fluid-filled portion of the inner ear that creates pressure waves

codominance: genetic condition in which both dominant and recessive alleles are expressed

codon: group of three nucleotides in mRNA that specifies an amino acid

coelom (SEE-lohm): mesoderm-lined cavity that provides an open space inside the body within which organs can grow and function

coevolution: simultaneous, progressive change of structures and behaviors in two different organisms in response to changes in each organism over time

collar cell: sponge cell made of fused cilia surrounding a whiplike flagella; used for beating water and filtering food

common descent: principle that species have descended from common ancestors

communication: passing information from one organism to another

compact bone: dense layer of hard bone with minuscule spaces for Haversian canals

compound light microscope: microscope that uses lenses and light to magnify an image

cone: reproductive structure of a conifer; male cone produces pollen and female cone produces ovules

conjugation: form of sexual reproduction that results in new combinations of genes

conservation: managing of natural resources in a way that maintains biodiversity

consumer: organism that eats other organisms to obtain energy and nutrients

continental drift: geological theory suggesting that continents move slowly over hundreds of millions of years

contour feather: strong, lightweight feather that provides a large surface area for a bird's flight

contractile vacuole: specialized structure in some protists; used to collect and expel water

control: in an experiment, the test group in which the variable is not altered; used as a benchmark to measure the variable's effect

convergent evolution: process by which unrelated species independently evolve superficial similarities when adapting to similar environments

cornea: tough transparent layer at the surface of the eye through which light enters

corpus luteum (KOR-puhs LOOT-ee-uhm): name given to the follicle after ovulation because of its yellow color

cortex: layer of spongy cells beneath the epidermis of a plant

cotyledon (kaht-uh-LEED-uhn): tiny seed leaf found in a plant embryo inside a seed

covalent bond: attraction between two atoms in which electrons are shared between two atoms

crop: widening in the digestive tract for the temporary storage of food

crossing-over: exchange between homologous chromosomes

cyclin: protein that regulates the timing of the cell cycle

cytokinesis: division of the cytoplasm that takes place during the anaphase and telophase phases of mitosis in most cells

cytoplasm: portion of the cell outside the nucleus

cytoskeleton: supporting framework of a eukaryotic cell

D

decomposer: organism that feeds on the dead bodies of animals and plants or on their waste products

demographic transition: change in growth rate resulting from changes in birth rate

dendrite: any of many small branched extensions of the cell body of a neuron that carry impulses toward the cell body

density-dependent limiting factor: population-limiting factor that operates more strongly on large, dense populations than on small, less crowded ones

density-independent limiting factor: population-limiting factor that acts on organisms regardless of the size of the population

depressant: one of a group of drugs that decreases the rate of brain activity and slows down the actions of the nervous system

dermis: inner layer of skin; supports the epidermis and contains nerve endings, blood vessels, smooth muscle, and glands

diaphragm: dome-shaped muscle that pulls the bottom of the chest cavity downward, increasing its volume; separates the chest cavity from the abdominal cavity

dicot: angiosperm that produces seeds with two cotyledons

diffusion: process by which substances spread through a liquid or gas from regions of high concentration to regions of low concentration

diploid: description of a cell that contains a double set of chromosomes; represented by the term 2n

DNA (deoxyribonucleic acid): nucleic acid that transmits genetic information from one generation to the next and codes for the production of proteins

DNA fingerprinting: technique used to identify an individual from the unique pattern of DNA

DNA replication: process in which DNA is copied

domesticate: to tame, raise, and breed animals for human purposes

dominant: form of gene that is expressed when present and excludes the recessive form; represented with a capital letter

dorsal hollow nerve cord: develops into the main nerve pathway from the body to the brain; characteristic of chordates

double fertilization: process of two fertilization events taking place inside an embryo sac

down feather: soft, fluffy feather that insulates the skin of a bird

drug: substance that causes a change in the body

drug-resistant bacteria: bacteria not susceptible to one or more antibodies

drupe: soft, fleshy ovary wall that encloses a single tough, stony seed of a fruit

E

ecological pyramid: diagram showing the decreasing amounts of energy, living tissue, or number of organisms at successive trophic levels

ecological succession: process by which an existing ecosystem is gradually and progressively replaced by another ecosystem

ecology: scientific study of interactions between different kinds of living things and the environments in which they live

ecosystem: collection of organisms—producers, consumers, and decomposers—interacting with each other and with their physical environment

ecosystem diversity: variety of habitats, living communities, and ecological processes in the living world

ectoderm: outer embryonic cell layer from which the nervous system, the skin, and other associated body coverings are derived in animal development

ectotherm: organism—such as a fish, amphibian, or reptile—that relies on interactions with the environment to control body temperature; cold-blooded organism

egg: female reproductive cell

electron: subatomic particle that carries a negative charge

electron microscope: microscope that uses a beam of electrons to examine a sample

electron transport chain: series of molecules located in the inner membrane of the mitochondrion that receive high-energy electrons from electron carriers

embryo: early stage of development of an organism resulting from fertilization

emphysema: respiratory disease in which the alveoli lose their elasticity and breathing becomes difficult

endocrine system: body system made up of a series of glands that produce and release chemicals into the bloodstream

endoderm: inner embryonic cell layer from which the tissues and organs of the digestive tract and other internal organs are developed

endodermis: layer of cells forming the inner boundary of the cortex of most roots and controlling entry into the vascular cylinder

endoplasmic reticulum: network of membranes within a cell that process and transport proteins and other macromolecules

endoskeleton: skeletal system located within the body

endosperm: food-rich tissue that surrounds the embryo of a plant

endospore: type of asexual spore formed inside a bacterial cell that develops a thick wall enclosing part of the cytoplasm and DNA, enabling the bacteria to survive for years

endosymbiont hypothesis: hypothesis that billions of years ago, eukaryotic cells arose as a combination of different prokaryotic cells

endotherm: organism, such as a mammal or a bird, that generates and maintains body heat through chemical reactions in the body; warmblooded organism

enhanced greenhouse effect: increased retention of heat in the Earth's atmosphere as a result of increased levels of carbon dioxide and other greenhouse gases to the atmosphere

environment: combination of physical and biological factors that influence life

enzyme: molecule that serves as a catalyst in organic reactions

epidemic: uncontrolled spread of disease

epidermis: outer layer of skin made up of layers of epithelial cells

epididymis (ehp-uh-DIHD-ih-mihs): tube in males that stores sperm

epiglottis: flap of tissue that prevents food from entering the trachea

esophagus: tube through which food passes from the pharynx to the stomach

estrogen: hormone in females involved in the development of the reproductive organs

eukaryote: organism made of cells that contain nuclei

evolution: process of change over a period of time

exon: expressed sequence of mRNA; a region that remains in mRNA after the introns are removed

exoskeleton: external skeletal system

experiment: controlled test to determine the validity of a hypothesis

exponential growth: rapid growth of a population whose living conditions are ideal

external fertilization: method of fertilization in which eggs and sperm meet outside the organism's body

extracellular digestion: process in which food is digested outside the cells

F

Fallopian tube: one of the two tubes in a female's reproductive system that receives the ovum from the ovary and passes it to the uterus

family: classification of a group of closely related genera

family group: group of related animals living together

feather: lightweight covering of a bird's body

fermentation: regeneration of NAD^+ to keep glycolysis running in the absence of oxygen

fertilization: fusion of egg and sperm to form a zygote

fetus: name given to an embryo after eight weeks of development

fibrin: netlike trap of plasma protein that forms a blood clot

filament: stamen that emerges from a flower

filtration: transport process that removes urea, excess water, and other wastes from the blood

fin: winglike structure on a fish used in swimming

fitness: an organism's ability to successfully pass on its genes to its offspring

fixed joint: joining place of two bones where there is little or no movement, such as in the skull

flagellum; pl. flagella: whiplike projection found on some cells; typically used for movement

flame cell: specialized cell with a tuft of cilia that conducts water and wastes through the branching tubes that serve as an excretory system in flatworms

flower: reproductive structure of an angiosperm

follicle: cluster of cells that contains a developing egg

follicle-stimulating hormone (FSH): hormone secreted by the pituitary gland that stimulates the development of sperm in males and the follicle in females

food chain: sequence of organisms related to one another as food and consumer

food web: interconnecting food chains in an ecological community

foot: in a mollusk, the muscular structure that usually contains the mouth

fossil: preserved bone or other trace of an ancient organism

frameshift mutation: gene mutation that involves the insertion or deletion of a nucleotide, thus changing the grouping of codons

freely movable joint: joining place of two bones where there is a wide range of movements, such as in the shoulders, hips, elbows, and knees

frond: large leaf of a fern

fruit: ripened ovary that contains angiosperm seeds

fruiting body: reproductive structure that produces spores

G

gamete (GAM-eet): haploid reproductive cell that can unite with another haploid cell to form a new individual

gametophyte: in plants, the haploid gamete-bearing generation that reproduces by fertilization

gastric gland: microscopic gland that appears in great numbers in the lining of the stomach and produces mucus, acid, and pepsin to aid digestion

gastritis: inflammation of the stomach caused by stomach acids making direct contact with the cells of the stomach lining

gastrovascular cavity: digestive sac with a single opening to the outside from which food enters and wastes leave

gastrulation (gas-troo-LAY-shuhn): process of cell migration during which the primary germ layers of the embryo are formed

gemmule (JEHM-yool): in sponges, a cluster of ball-shaped amebocytes that can grow into a new individual

gene: segment of DNA that codes for a specific protein; the unit by which hereditary characteristics are transmitted

gene mutation: mutation that involves only a single gene

gene pool: all the alleles of all the genes of the members of a population that interbreed

genetic code: language of the instructions in DNA and RNA that code for the amino acid sequence of a polypeptide

genetic diversity: genetic material in the gene pool of a species; variety of different forms of genes present in a population

genetic drift: random change in allele frequency, often producing offspring that will be different from the original population by chance

genetic engineering: manipulation and insertion of genes and DNA from different sources into an organism

genetics: study of heredity

genital herpes: sexually transmitted disease caused by a virus that affects the genital areas of males and females

genotype: genetic composition of an organism

genus; pl. genera: classification of a major group of closely related organisms

geologic time scale: unit of time—such as eons, eras, periods, and epochs—based on information contained in rocks

geotropism: response of an organism to the force of gravity, usually by turning downward or upward

gill: featherlike respiratory organ of many aquatic species; used to obtain oxygen from the water

gizzard: portion of digestive tract where food is ground into small, absorbable particles

global warming: prediction that the enhanced greenhouse effect will cause a significant rise in Earth's average temperature

glomerulus: ball of capillaries in a nephron that filters blood

glucagon: hormone that breaks down glycogen and fats and releases sugars into the blood

glycogen: compound that stores excess glucose in the body

glycolysis: series of reactions in which a molecule of glucose is broken down

Golgi apparatus: network of membranes within a cell that, in conjunction with the endoplasmic reticulum, processes and transports proteins and other macromolecules; contains special enzymes that attach carbohydrates or lipids to a protein

gonorrhea: sexually transmitted disease caused by a bacterium that infects the urinary and reproductive tracts

gradualism: theory that evolutionary change occurs slowly and steadily over long periods of time

grafting: artificial method of propagation

greenhouse effect: retention of heat in the Earth's atmosphere due to the presence of greenhouse gases

green revolution: substantial increase in crop yields that resulted from the introduction of modern agricultural practices

growth rate: change in the size of a population

gullet: depression on a paramecium used for the intake of food particles

gut: digestive tract

gymnosperm: seed plant in which the seeds are exposed to the air, usually in a cone-shaped structure

H

habitat: surroundings in which a species lives and thrives; defined in terms of the plant community and the abiotic factors

habituation: decreased response to a repeated stimulus

hair follicle: clusters of columns of epidermal cells anchored in the dermis; produce hair

half-life: length of time required for half of a radioactive element to decay to its more stable form

haploid: description of a cell that contains a single set of chromosomes; often represented by the letter n

Haversian (huh-VER-zhuhn) **canal:** small channel in compact bone through which nerve and blood vessels run

helper T cell: type of lymphocyte in the immune system that identifies a specific pathogen in the body

hemoglobin: iron-containing protein found in red blood cells that helps to transport oxygen

hepatitis B: disease caused by a virus that can cause inflammation of the liver; can be transmitted sexually

heredity: biological inheritance of traits from parent to offspring

hermaphrodite (her-MAF-ruh-dight): organism that has both male and female reproductive organs and produces both sperm and eggs

heterotroph: organism that cannot manufacture its own food

heterozygous (heht-er-oh-ZIGH-guhs): description of an organism that has a mixed pair of alleles for a trait

histamine: chemical released by a mast cell to produce an inflammatory response to an allergy

HIV (human immunodeficiency virus): virus that infects cells in the immune system and destroys helper T cells

homeostasis: process by which organisms respond to stimuli to keep conditions in their bodies suitable for life

hominid: any of a family of two-legged primates; includes humans and closely related primates but not apes

hominoid: any of a superfamily of primates; includes humans and apes

homologous structures: structures that have a common origin but not necessarily a common function

homozygous (hoh-moh-ZIGH-guhs): description of an organism that has an identical pair of alleles for a trait

hormone: chemical that travels throughout the bloodstream and affects the behavior of other cells

human chorionic gonadotropin (HCG): hormone produced by the cells' zygote that keeps the corpus luteum alive and preserves the uterine lining

hybrid: offspring of parents with different characteristics

hybridization: mating of two organisms with dissimilar genetic characteristics

hydrostatic (high-droh-STAT-ihk) **skeleton:** skeletal system in which the muscles surround and are supported by a water-filled body cavity

hypha (HIGH-fuh; pl. **hyphae**, HIGH-fee): threadlike, branching filament that is the most basic structure in a fungus

hypothalamus (high-poh-THAL-uh-muhs): region of the brain that directly or indirectly controls the release of hormones from the pituitary gland

hypothesis; pl. **hypotheses:** possible explanation of, preliminary conclusion about, or guess at the solution to a problem

I

immunity: ability of the body to resist a specific pathogen

implantation: process during which the cells of a zygote grow into the uterine wall

imprinting: learning mechanism in the early life of an animal in which a stimulus establishes a characteristic behavior

impulse: electrical signal carried by neurons in the nervous system

inbreeding: mating of organisms with similar genetic characteristics

incomplete dominance: genetic condition in which neither allele is completely dominant or recessive

independent assortment: process by which different genes do not influence each other's segregation into gametes

infectious disease: disease caused by a pathogen

inflammatory response: activation of a nonspecific defense to a pathogen

inorganic compound: very generally, a compound that does not contain carbon chains

insight learning: application of past experience to a new situation

instinct: genetically programmed, innate behavior

insulin: polypeptide hormone that removes sugar from the bloodstream

internal fertilization: method of fertilization in which the eggs and sperm meet inside the body of the egg-producing individual

interneuron: neuron that connects the sensory and motor neurons and carries impulses between them

interphase: G_1, S, and G_2 phases; occurs between cell divisions

intracellular digestion: process by which food is digested inside the internal cells of a simple multicellular animal

intron: intervening sequence that is removed from mRNA and thus not expressed

ion: charged particle formed by an atom that has gained or lost one or more of its electrons

ionic bond: attraction between oppositely charged ions

iris: disk of tissue located at the back of the cornea

islets of Langerhans: clusters of endocrine cells in the pancreas

K

karyotype (KAR-ee-uh-tighp): diagrammatic representation of individual chromosomes cut out from a photograph and grouped together

keratin: tough, flexible structural protein found in hair, fingernails, and epidermis

kidney: one of a pair of specialized excretion organs that removes nitrogen and other nonsolid wastes from the body and regulates water in the bloodstream

killer T cell: type of lymphocyte in the immune system that attacks and destroys a virus-infected cell

kingdom: highest ranking classification of living organisms that falls into one of the six major groups

Koch's postulates: series of rules used to identify the microorganism that causes a specific disease

Krebs cycle: series of reactions in which the chemical bonds in pyruvic acid are broken apart; also called citric acid cycle

L

lactic acid fermentation: in animals, the conversion of pyruvic acid to lactic acid

large intestine: colon; part of the digestive system that produces a waste material known as feces

larynx: structure in which air enters the respiratory system and the vocal cords are located

lateral line: collection of skin pores that connect to a system of tubes that help a fish detect patterns of movement in the surrounding water

leaf: specific outgrowth of a vascular plant that captures sunlight for photosynthesis

learning: ability to change behavior as a result of experience; acquisition of knowledge or a skill

legume: fruit with a pod that splits open on two sides

lens: flexible structure behind the pupil filled with a transparent protein that helps adjust eyes to focus to see near or far objects

ligament: band of tissue that connects the bones of a joint

light-dependent reaction: response that requires the direct involvement of light; produces NADPH

light-independent reaction: response that does not directly involve light; *see also* Calvin cycle

lipid: waxy, fatty, or oily compound used to store and release energy; one of the classes of macromolecules

lipid bilayer: double-layered pattern formed by phospholipids in water; the principal component of cell membranes

liver: large gland situated above the stomach that produces bile to aid digestion

longitudinal muscle: in annelids, a muscle that runs along the length of the body, shortening the segments as it contracts

loop of Henle: region of the nephron of the kidney where concentrated urine is produced

lung: respiratory organ in which gas exchange takes place

lung cancer: disease caused by small groups of cancer in the lungs; usually the consequence of smoking

luteinizing hormone (LH): hormone secreted by the pituitary gland that stimulates testosterone production in males and the development of the follicle, ovulation, and production of the corpus luteum in females

lymph (LIHMF): fluid found in intracellular spaces and in the lymphatic vessels of vertebrates

lymphatic (lihm-FAT-ihk) **system:** network of vessels that collects fluid that leaks from the capillaries and returns it to the circulatory system

lymphocyte: white blood cell that produces antibodies to assist the immune system

lysogenic infection: process in which viral genes combine with the host cell's DNA, produce viral mRNA, and gradually make new viruses

lysosome: saclike membrane filled with chemicals and enzymes that can break down almost any substance within a cell

lysozyme: enzyme in saliva that fights infection by digesting the cell walls of bacteria

lytic infection: process in which viral enzymes destroy a host cell's DNA, ribosomes, and resources to reproduce

M

macromolecule: large organic polymer, such as a carbohydrate, lipid, protein, or nucleic acid

macronucleus: the larger of the two nuclei of a ciliate; stores multiple copies of commonly used genes

Malpighian (mal-PIHG-ee-uhn) **tubule:** structure that excretes nitrogenous wastes; found in many arthropods

mammary gland: gland that enables a female to nourish her young with milk

mandible: in arthropods, specialized mouthpart used for biting

mantle: thin, delicate layer of tissue that covers the internal organs of a mollusk

mated pair: male and female living together

medulla oblongata (mih-DUHL-uh ahb-lahn-GAHT-uh): part of the brainstem that regulates the flow of information between the brain and the rest of the body; controls involuntary functions

medusa: free-swimming stage in the life cycle of a cnidarian

meiosis (migh-OH-sihs): process of cell division that reduces the number of chromosomes in the cell by half, from diploid to haploid; creates gametes used for sexual reproduction

melanin: dark-brown pigment that gives skin its color

meninges (muh-NIHN-jeez): three layers of tough, elastic tissues that cushion the brain and spinal cord

menstrual cycle: pattern of events in females that involves the development and release of an egg for fertilization and the preparation of the uterus to receive a fertilized egg

mesoderm: middle embryonic cell layer from which the skeletal, muscular, and other tissues are developed

mesoglea (mehs-oh-GLEE-uh): in cnidarians, the jellylike layer between the endoderm and ectoderm

messenger RNA (mRNA): form of RNA that carries genetic information from the DNA in the nucleus to the ribosomes in the cytoplasm

metamorphosis: process of changing form and shape

metaphase: second phase of mitosis during which the chromosomes complete their attachment to the spindle and line up across the center of the cell

microclimate: climate conditions of a particular area that vary over small distances

micronucleus: the smaller of the two nuclei of a ciliate; stores copies of all the cell's genes

mitochondrion; pl. mitochondria: an organelle found in the cells of most plants and animals; produces energy from a chemical fuel and oxygen

mitosis: process of cell division in eukaryotic cells

molar: tooth in the rear of the mouth adapted for grinding

molecular clock: theory that mutations in DNA occur at a constant rate; used to estimate time frames of departure from common ancestry

molecule: group of atoms united by covalent bonds

molting: process of shedding an exterior layer or exoskeleton to allow for renewal or growth

monocot: angiosperm that produces seeds with one cotyledon

monoculture: farming strategy whereby a single highly productive crop is planted in a large field

monomer: small, individual molecule that forms a polymer

morula (MOR-yoo-luh): solid ball of cells produced by cell division of a zygote

motor neuron: specialized neuron that carries impulses from the brain or spinal cord to muscles or other organs

mouth: opening through which food is taken in for digestion

multiple allele: type of gene that is determined by more than two alleles for a single trait

mutation: abrupt alteration in the genetic information of a cell

mutualism: reciprocal relationship in which two organisms benefit each other

mycelium (migh-SEE-lee-uhm): mass of hyphae that grows into the food source and forms the body of the fungus

myelin (MIGH-uh-lihn): material that forms a protective sheath around an axon; white fatty substance that surrounds many vertebrate nerve cells

myoglobin: reddish oxygen-storing protein found in skeletal muscles

myosin: protein that makes up the thick filaments of muscle fiber

N

natural selection: process in nature that over time results in the survival of the fittest

negative feedback: regulatory system that enables conditions within the body to remain constant

nematocyst: poisonous stinger used in cnidarians for defense and catching prey

nephridium (nee-FRIHD-ee-uhm; pl. **nephridia**, nee-FRIHD-ee-uh): excretory organ that removes nitrogen-containing wastes from the blood; found in many invertebrates

nephron: any of the numerous blood-filtering units of a kidney

nerve: bundle of nerve fibers

nerve cord: group of nerve cells that extend along the length of the body

nervous system: network of nerve cells and nervous tissue that receives and relays information about activities within the body and monitors and responds to internal and external changes

neuron: cell that carries impulses throughout the nervous system; consists of a cell body, dendrites, and an axon

neurotransmitter (NOO-roh-trans-miht-er): a chemical used by one neuron to signal another cell

neutron: subatomic particle that carries no charge

niche: full range of physical and biological conditions in which the organisms in a species can live and the way in which the organisms use those conditions

nictitating membrane: transparent eyelid that protects the eye underwater and keeps it moist in air

nonbiodegradable: incapable of being broken down into unharmful products by the life processes of living things

nondisjunction: failure of chromosome pair to separate correctly during meiosis

notochord: flexible, rodlike structure that provides body support; unique to chordates

nucleic acid: DNA or RNA that consists of nucleotides and genetic information

nucleotide: compound made of a phosphate group, a nitrogenous base, and a 5-carbon sugar; forms the basic structural unit of DNA

nucleus; pl. nuclei: in an atom, the compact core that contains the neutron and protons; in a cell, the structure that contains nearly all of the cell's DNA

nut: fruit with a hard ovary wall forming a protective shell around the seed

nutrient cycle: path along which nutrients that are available in fixed quantities on Earth are passed from one organism to another and from one part of the biosphere to another

O

ocellus (oh-SEHL-uhs; pl. **ocelli,** oh-SEHL-igh): simple eyespot that detects the presence or absence of light

olfactory bulb: part of the brain specialized for the sense of smell

open circulatory system: system in which blood is pumped from the heart through vessels and open spaces

operant conditioning: trial-and-error learning

operator: special region of DNA to which the repressor binds

operculum: bony structure that protects the gills; found in bony fishes

opiate: one of a group of drugs derived from the opium poppy; plant that mimics endorphins in the brain; often used as a pain-killing drug

optic lobe: structure in the brain that processes visual information

order: classification of several families of similar organisms

organ: group of tissues that work together to perform a specific function

organelle: small structure that performs a specialized function within a cell

organic compound: very generally, a substance that contains a chain of a least two carbon atoms

organism: individual living thing

organ system: group of organs that perform several closely related functions

osmosis: diffusion of water through a selectively permeable membrane

osteocyte (AHS-tee-oh-sight): cell embedded in both compact and spongy bone that helps build and maintain bones

ovary: in animals, the female reproductive gland that produces eggs and female hormones; in flowering plants, the structure that contains the egg cells of a flower

oviparous (oh-VIHP-uh-ruhs): producing eggs that develop and hatch outside the female's body

ovoviviparous (oh-voh-vigh-VIHP-uh-ruhs): producing eggs that develop and hatch within the female's body and are born alive

ovulation: process in which an egg is released from the ovary

ovule: in a seed plant, the place where female gametophytes are produced

ovum; pl. ova: female gamete or egg

oxytocin: pituitary hormone that stimulates contractions of the smooth muscles surrounding the uterus

P

pacemaker: area of the heart that regulates the heartbeat; the sinoatrial node

pancreas: gland situated below the stomach that produces digestive enzymes and regulates blood sugar

parasite: organism that takes nourishment from and lives at the expense of its host

passive transport: movement of substances across the cell membrane from regions of high concentration to regions of low concentration; occurs without the cell expending energy

pathogen: disease-causing organism

pedigree: diagram that tracks the inheritance of a single gene through several generations of a family

pedipalp: specialized leglike appendage of chelicerates that are used for grasping, sensing, and fertilizing

pepsin: protein-digesting enzyme produced by gastric glands in the stomach

peptic ulcer: lesion in the stomach wall caused by stomach acid

perennial: plant that lives for more than two years

periosteum (per-ee-AHS-tee-uhm): tough membrane that covers the bones

peristalsis: muscular contractions that pass food through the alimentary canal or digestive tract

petal: one of the white or colorful leaflike parts of a flower

phagocyte: white blood cell that engulfs and destroys bacteria

pharyngeal (fuh-RIHN-jee-uhl) **slit:** a narrow opening in the throat region of chordates

pharynx: muscular structure in the back of the mouth; connects the mouth with the rest of the digestive tract

phenotype: form of a genetic trait displayed by an organism

pheromone (FAIR-uh-mohn): chemical signal produced by an organism to influence the behavior or development of another organism of the same species

phloem (FLOH-ehm): vascular tissue that transports products of photosynthesis and substances from one part of the plant to another

photosynthesis: process by which green plants use the energy of sunlight to produce carbohydrates

phototropism: growth response of a plant to light, usually by turning toward or away from light

pH scale: measurement system that indicates the acidity or basicity of a solution

phylum (FIGH-luhm; pl. **phyla,** FIGH-luh): category made up of several classes of different organisms that share important characteristics

phytochrome: red-light-sensitive pigment that enables plants to sense day and night, changing seasons, and developmental processes

pigment: colored substances that reflect or absorb light

pistil: female reproductive organ of a flowering plant, composed of ovary, style, and stigma

pith: in dicots, the ground tissue inside the ring of a vascular bundle

pituitary gland: tiny endocrine gland at the base of the brain that secretes hormones that regulate the activity of other endocrine glands

placenta: organ that connects a mother with her developing embryo and provides a place for the exchange of nutrients, oxygen, wastes, and carbon dioxide

plasma: fluid part of the blood; constitutes about 55 percent of the total volume of blood

plasma cell: specialized B cell that releases antibodies into the bloodstream to fight infection

plasmid: small, circular DNA molecule in some bacteria that can be used for cell transformation

platelet: cell fragments in the blood that aid in blood clotting

point mutation: gene mutation that involves a single nucleotide

pollen: tiny spore that contains the male reproductive cells of a plant

pollination: transfer of pollen that precedes fertilization

polygenic trait: inherited characteristic controlled by more than one gene

polymer: large molecule assembled from small, individual molecules

polyp: sessile stage in the life cycle of a cnidarian

pons: region of connecting tissue at the base of the brainstem

population: group of organisms of a single species that live in a given area

powder feather: feather in aquatic birds that releases a water-repelling powder

premolar: teeth directly in front of the molar teeth

primary producer: organism that uses energy from the sun to change simple nonliving chemical nutrients in its environment into living tissue

progesterone: female hormone that promotes development of the uterine wall

proglottid (proh-GLAHT-ihd): segment of a tapeworm's body that contains reproductive structures

prokaryote: organism that does not contain nuclei; typically is small and single celled

prolactin: pituitary hormone that stimulates the production of milk in the breast tissue of the mother

promoter: special region of DNA to which RNA polymerase binds at the beginning of the process of transcription

prophase: first phase of mitosis during which each chromosome consists of two chromatids

prosimian (proh-SIHM-ee-uhn): any of a suborder of primates

protein: polymer of amino acids used for building cells, catalyzing reactions, and other purposes

protist: eukaryotic organism that does not share a unique set of characteristics

proton: subatomic particle that carries a positive charge

protonema (proht-oh-NEE-muh): tangle of thin filaments germinating from a moss spore and developing into a leafy moss plant

provirus: viral DNA that has become part of the host cell's DNA

pseudopod (SOO-doh-pahd): temporary projection from an ameboid cell used for movement and feeding; cytoplasm streams into the pseudopod and the rest of the cell follows

pulmonary circulation: pathway of blood vessels on the right side of the heart that carries blood between the heart and lungs

punctuated equilibrium: pattern of long periods of stability that are interrupted by episodes of rapid change

pupil: opening in the iris that regulates the amount of light that enters the eye

R

radial symmetry: arrangement of body parts that repeat around an imaginary line drawn through the center of an organism; shown in cnidarians and some adult echinoderms

radula (RAJ-oo-luh): the feeding structure in the mouth of many mollusks

reabsorption: process by which the material that was removed from the blood is put back into the blood without the toxic compounds

receptor: specific chemical binding site for a particular hormone

recessive: form of gene that is not expressed in the presence of the dominant form; represented with a lowercase letter

recombinant DNA: pieces of DNA from two or more sources that are reassembled to act as a single DNA molecule

red blood cell: blood cell that contains hemoglobin and constitutes almost half the total volume of blood; also called an erythrocyte

reflex: quick, automatic response to a stimulus

renal artery: artery through which blood flows into the kidney

renal vein: vein through which blood leaves the kidney

repressor: protein that blocks a gene's transcription by binding to the operator

reproductive isolation: separation of different species that cannot interbreed

respiration: release of energy from the breakdown of food molecules in the presence of oxygen

resting potential: product of a net excess of negative charges on the inside of the membrane

restriction enzyme: protein that cuts DNA at a specific sequence of nucleotides

retina: layer of cells at the back of the eye

retrovirus: virus containing an enzyme that copies its genetic information from RNA to DNA

RFLP (RIHF-lihp) (**restriction fragment length polymorphism**): dark band revealed when pieces of DNA are probed; can be used to identify and classify an individual's unique DNA pattern

rhizoid (RIGH-zoid): rootlike anchoring structure of moss plants that absorbs water and nutrients from the soil

rhizome: underground stem of a vascular plant

ribosomal RNA (rRNA): form of RNA that is an important component of ribosomes

ribosome: small particles in a cell that are made of RNA and protein; sites of protein assembly

ring vessel: in an anneid, structure that pumps blood, thus functioning as a miniature heart

RNA (ribonucleic acid): principal molecule that carries out the instructions coded in DNA

root: descending structure of a plant that branches into the soil, anchors the plant, and absorbs water and nutrients

S

salivary gland: gland in the mouth that produces saliva, a fluid that moistens food and makes food easier to chew

scale: in fish, one of many overlapping rigid plates that form a protective covering; in seed-bearing plants, the surface of a reproductive structure on which the seeds are exposed

scanning probe microscope: microscope that traces the surface of a sample with a small tip called a probe

science: process of thinking and learning about the world

scientific method: system of asking questions, developing explanations, and testing those explanations against the reality of the natural world

scolex (SKOH-lehks): front end of a tapeworm; contains suckers and hooks

scrotum: sac located outside a male's body cavity that contains the testes

sedimentary rock: kind of rock formed when silt, sand, or clay builds up on the bottom of a river, lake, or ocean

seed: reproductive structure that includes a developing plant and a food reserve enclosed in a resistant outer covering

seed cone: female cone that contains mature seeds

segment: one of several body compartments that allows an animal to increase in body size with minimal new genetic material

segregation: process that separates the two alleles of a gene during gamete formation

selective breeding: producing a new generation by mating individuals with desired characteristics

semicircular canal: one of three fluid-filled organs that help sense position in space and maintain balance

seminiferous (sehm-uh-NIHF-er-uhs) **tubule:** tightly coiled tubules in males in which sperm cells are produced

sensory neuron: specialized neuron that carries impulses from the sense organs to the brain and the spinal cord

sepal: structure that encloses and protects the developing flower bud and opens as the flower blooms

septum; pl. **septa:** dividing wall or membrane

seta; pl. **setae:** external bristles

sex chromosome: X and Y chromosomes that determine the sex of an individual

sex-linked gene: gene located on the sex chromosome

sexually transmitted disease (STD): disease spread from one person to another by sexual contact

shell: in mollusks, protective structure formed by glands in the mantle

siphon: tube through which water is forced out

skeletal muscle tissue: muscle tissue generally attached to bones; can be contracted voluntarily

skin: outer protective covering of the body; largest organ of the body

sliding filament theory: concept that thick and thin filaments slide past each other and cause the muscle to contract

slightly movable joint: joining place of two bones where there is a small amount of movement and flexibility, such as in the spinal column or ribs

small intestine: portion of the digestive tract in which most of the chemical work of digestion takes place

smooth muscle tissue: spindle-shaped, unstriated muscle tissue found in internal organs and blood vessels; not under conscious control of the nervous system

social insect colony: highly structured living group performing tasks that no single insect could accomplish

sodium-potassium pump: protein in nerve cell that moves sodium ions out of the cell and potassium ions into the cell

solution: uniform mixture of substances

somatic nervous system: part of the motor division of the peripheral nervous system that controls voluntary movements

speciation: formation of a new species brought about by genetic changes that prevent breeding between the new, genetically different groups

species: smallest group in the classification system of organisms that share similar characteristics and interbreed in nature

species diversity: number and variety of different life forms

sperm: male gamete

spicule: one of many small, spikelike structures that form the skeleton of a sponge

spinal cord: collection of nerve fibers that extends from the brain; part of the central nervous system of a vertebrate

spindle: cluster of microtubules that span the cell nucleus

spirillum (spigh-RIHL-uhm; pl. **spirilla,** spigh-RIHL-uh): spiral-shaped bacteria

spongin: protein that makes up the tough but flexible skeleton of some sponges

spongy bone: region of resilient, supportive bone tissue within the compact bone with an interlaced pattern that withstands stress

spore: small, typically single-celled structure capable of producing a new individual, either immediately or after a period of dormancy

sporophyte: in plants, the diploid spore-bearing generation that reproduces by spores

stamen: male leaf that produces pollen

statocyst: organ of balance found in many invertebrates

stem: main, upward-growing part of a vascular plant that provides support and conducts water and nutrients

stereoisomer: molecule that has the same atoms and bonds of another molecule but has atoms oriented differently in space

stigma: sticky tip of the style of a plant

stimulant: any one of a group of drugs that increase the release of neurotransmitters at some synapses in the brain to speed up the nervous system

stoma (STOH-muh; pl. **stomata,** STOH-muh-tuh): in the epidermis of a plant, one of many small openings that can open and close to allow gas exchange and to prevent water loss

stomach: large muscular sac where contractions mix food and enzymes and acids digest food

style: in a flower plant, the stemlike narrow part of the carpel

substrate: in a chemical reaction, the component that binds to an enzyme

superorganism: colony of interdependent organisms that act as a unit, able to achieve far more than individuals acting separately

suppressor T cell: type of lymphocyte in the immune system that shuts off the immune response in killer T cells and in B cells

sustainability: degree to which a human activity is in harmony with the biosphere and does not deteriorate the biosphere's living and nonliving parts

swim bladder: expandable structure that holds gas to change a fish's internal density and depth in the water

symbiosis (sihm-bigh-OH-sihs): beneficial relationship between two organisms that live together

synapse (SIHN-aps): place where a neuron can transfer an impulse to another cell

synovial (sih-NOH-vee-uhl) **fluid:** lubricant found in a joint that reduces friction and allows bones to slip past each other easily

syphilis: sexually transmitted disease caused by a bacterium that can result in death

systemic circulation: pathway of blood vessels on the left side of the heart that supplies the body with oxygen-rich blood and returns oxygen-poor blood to the heart

T

target cell: cell that has a receptor for a particular hormone

taste bud: one of many chemical receptors located on the tongue

taxonomy: science of naming organisms and assigning them to groups

T cell: white blood cell that matures in the thymus gland and regulates other cells of the immune system

telophase: fourth and final phase of mitosis during which two distinct nuclei form within the cell

tendon: cord of tissue that connects muscles and bones

testis (TEHS-tihs; pl. **testes,** TEHS-teez): male reproductive gland that produces sperm and male hormones

testosterone (tehs-TAHS-ter-ohn): male hormone produced in the testes that stimulates sperm production and the development of male sex organs and secondary sex characteristics

tetrapod: body plan that includes four limbs or legs

theory: logical explanation for a broad range of observations

thigmotropism (thihg-MAH-truh-pihz-uhm): response to touch

thyroid gland: an endocrine gland that produces the hormone thyroxine

tissue: mass of similar cells that performs a specific function

toxin: poisonous substance

trachea: tube that carries air from the larynx to the lungs; also called the windpipe

tracheal (TRAY-kee-uhl) **tube**: air-conducting passage for the diffusion of oxygen

tracheid (TRAY-kee-ihd): specialized water-conducting thick-walled tubelike cell of a vascular plant

trait: inherited characteristic that distinguishes one organism from another

transcription: process in which the nucleotide sequence of a DNA molecule is copied into RNA

transfer RNA (tRNA): form of RNA that carries an amino acid to the ribosome during the assembly of a protein

transformation: process of reproduction in which genetic material is added to or replaces portions of a bacteria's DNA

transgenic: description of an organism that has been transformed or altered with genes from another organism

translation: process by which the nucleotides in mRNA are decoded into a sequence of amino acids in a polypeptide

transpiration: loss of water vapor though the stomata of a vascular plant

trichocyst: tiny bottle-shaped structure embedded in the pellicle of a paramecium and discharged for purposes of defense

trisomy: condition caused by cells that contain three copies of a chromosome rather than two

trochophore (TRAHK-oh-for): free-swimming larva stage of a mollusk

trophic level: feeding level in the flow of food energy and nutrients from primary producers to highest level consumers

tropism: response of an organism to an environmental stimulus

tube foot: suction-cuplike structure connected to the water vascular system of an echinoderm

tumor: mass of cells

tympanic membrane: portion of the ear that vibrates in response to sound; eardrum

tympanum: eardrum

U

umbilical cord: thin tube of embryonic tissue that connects the embryo to the uterus

ureter: vessel that carries urine from the kidney to the urinary bladder

urinary bladder: sac that stores urine before it is eliminated from the body

uterus: muscular chamber in a female's reproductive system in which a fertilized egg can develop

V

vaccine: weakened or mild form of a pathogen that causes permanent immunity when injected into the body

vacuole: saclike structure in a cell that stores materials—such as proteins, fats, and carbohydrates—in animal cells, and water and dissolved salts in plant cells

valve: specialized flap of tissue that prevents a backflow of blood

variable: factor that differs among test groups in an experiment and is measured against a control

vascular cylinder: central region of xylem and phloem cells carrying water and nutrients between the roots and the rest of the plant

vascular plant: plant with tracheids that draw water upward

vascular tissue: specialized tissue that transports water and nutrients throughout a land plant

vas deferens (VAS DEHF-uh-rehnz): duct that extends from the scrotum to the ejaculatory duct

vector: animal that carries a disease-causing organism from host to host

vector pollination: spread of pollen from one plant to another by an insect or animal

vegetative reproduction: process of asexual reproduction in which offspring are produced from the division of cells of the parent plant

vein: blood vessel that returns blood to the heart

ventricle: lower chamber of the heart that pumps the blood out of the heart

vertebra; pl. vertebrae: any of the individual segments of bone that make up the backbone, or vertebral column

vertebral column: backbone that encloses and protects the spinal cord

vestigial organ: structure in an organism that seems to have little or no obvious purpose

villus; pl., villi: any of the numerous projections on the folded surfaces of the small intestine that increase the surface area for the absorption of food molecules

virus: nonliving particle that contains DNA or RNA and that can infect a living cell

vitreous (VIH-tree-uhs) **humor:** transparent fluid that fills the large chamber behind the lens of the eye

viviparous (vigh-VIHP-er-uhs): retaining the developing embryo inside the female's body and bearing offspring alive

vocal cord: elastic fold of tissue that vibrates and produces sound when exhaled air is passed by it

voltage-sensitive gate: one of thousands of tiny protein channels in the cell membrane of a neuron through which sodium or potassium passes

W

water vascular system: in echinoderms, a network of fluid-filled tubes and appendages, used for many purposes

white blood cell: blood cell that fights infection, parasites, and bacterial disease; also called a leukocyte

X

xylem (ZIGH-luhm): vascular tissue that carries water and nutrients from the roots to the branches and leaves of a plant

Z

zero population growth: lack of population growth due to equality of a population's birth rate and death rate

zoospore (ZOH-oh-spor): reproductive cell that produces a new individual by cell division

zygote (ZIGH-goht): fertilized egg

Index

Oxygen-poor blood, 66, 67
Oxygen-rich blood, 66, 67
   in arteries, 69
Oxytocin, 8, 127

P

p53 protein, 152
Pacemaker, 68
Pain, sensing of, 33
Pancreas, 7, 97
   hormones of, 8
Parasympathetic nervous system, 29
Parathyroid gland, 7
Parathyroid hormone (PTH), 8
Parietal lobe of brain, 26
Pasteur, Louis, 140
Patella, 48
Pathogen, 139-142
   types of, 141
Pelvic inflammatory disease (PID), 129
Pelvis, 48
Penicillin, 142
Pepsin, 97
Peptic ulcer, 105-106
   causes of, 106-107
Pericardium, 67
Periosteum, 128-129
Peripheral nervous system, 25, 26, 29
   divisions in, 29
Peristalsis, 96
Personal hygiene, 142
Phagocyte, 144
Phalanges, 48
Pharynx, 74
Photoreceptor cell, 31
Physical endurance, 57
Physical therapist, 51
Physiology, 12-13
Pigment,
   in humans, 46
   in iris, 30
Pituitary gland, 7-8
   hormones of, 8
   hypothalamus and, 8
Pivot joint, 50
Placenta, 125
Plasma, 70
Plasma cell, 145
Platelet, 48, 70, 71,
Pleural membrane, 74
Polypeptide, 11
Pons, 26
Potassium gate, 35
Potassium ion (K⁺), 35
   nerve impulse and, 34
Progesterone, 8, 116

Prolactin, 8, 127
Protein(s), 93
   metabolism of, 101
   p53, 152
Protozoan(s),
   diseases caused by, 141
Proximal tubule, 103
Pulmonary artery, 66, 67
Pulmonary circulation, 66
Pulmonary valve, 67
Pulmonary vein, 66, 67
Pupil, of eye, 30, 31

R

Radiation, cancer and, 151
Radius, 48
Reabsorption, by kidney, 102
Receptor(s), 7, 9, 11
   at synapse, 24
   touch, 33
Red blood cell, 48, 70
Red marrow of bone, 49
Red muscle fiber, 56
Reflex, 27
Renal artery, 101, 103
Renal cortex, 103
Renal medulla, 103
Renal pelvis, 103
Renal vein, 101, 103
Reproductive system, 115
   embryo and, 123
   female, 117-118
   fertilization and development and,
     120-122
   fetal development and, 125-126
   of humans, 4
   human sexual development and,
     115-116
   labor and birth and, 127
   male, 117
   menstrual cycle and, 118-119
   placenta and, 125
   sexually transmitted diseases and,
     128-131
Resistance exercise, 57
Respiration, 73
   aerobic, 57
   anaerobic, 57
   of humans, 4, 73-75
   smoking and, 80-81
Respiratory disorder, 80-81
Resting potential, 22, 23, 34-35
Retina, 31
Rib cage, 48
Right atrium, 67
   contraction begins in, 68

Credits

Photo Research: Natalie Goldstein

Photo Credits

Cover Frans Lanting/Minden Pictures, Inc.; Borders Corel Professional Photos CD-ROM™; **iv** t; Patricia Agre/Photo Researchers, Inc.; **iv** c; David Scharf/Peter Arnold, Inc.; **iv** bl; ©Philippe Plailly/ Science Photo Library/Photo Researchers, Inc.; **iv** br; Leonard Lessin/Peter Arnold, Inc.; **v** t; Corel Professional Photos CD-ROM™; **v** bl; ©Alfred Pasieka/Scince Photo Library/Photo Researchers, Inc.; **v** br; Rich Cane/Sports Chrome East/West ; **vi** tl; Corel Professional Photos CD-ROM™; **vi** t;r; Corel Professional Photos CD-ROM™; **vi** bl; Corbis-Bettmann; **vi** br; Corel Professional Photos CD-ROM™; **vii** t; ©Biophoto Associates/Photo Researchers, Inc.; **vii** c; Dr. Dennis Kenkel/ Phototake; **vii** b; Gopal Morti/CNRI/ Phototake; **viii** tr; K. G. Murti/Visuals Unlimited; **viii** cl; ©Oliver Meckes/Photo Researchers, Inc.; **viii** cr; ©Michael Fairchild/Peter Arnold, Inc.; **viii** b; Corel Professional Photos CD-ROM™; **ix** tl; Tui De Roy/Bruce Coleman, Inc.; **ix** tr; Frans Lanting/Minden Pictures, Inc.; **ix** bl; Gerard Lacz/Peter Arnold, Inc.; **ix** br; Corel Professional Photos CD-ROM™; **x** t; Corel Professional Photos CD-ROM™; **x** bl; Dan Budnik/Woodfin Camp & Associates; **x** br; Michael Fogden/DRK Photo; **xi** tl; Art Wolfe Incorporated; **xi** tr; Lionel Isy Schwart/The Image Bank; **xi** c; D. Cavagnaro/DRK Photo; **xi** b; Bullaty/Lomeo/The Image Bank; **xii** tl; ©Holt Studios International (Miss P. Peackock)/Photo Researchers, Inc.; **xii** tr; T.E. Adams/Visuals Unlimited; **xii** bl; David M. Phillips/Visuals Unlimited; **xii** b; r; ©Phil A. Dotson/Photo Researchers, Inc.; **xiii** tl; Visuals Unlimited; **xiii** tr; Larry Lipsky/DRK Photo; **xiii** c; Corel Professional Photos CD-ROM™; **xiii** b; Frans Lanting/Minden Pictures, Inc.; **xiv** tl; ©David Scharf/Peter Arnold, Inc.; **xiv** tr; Arthur J. Olson, The Scripps Research Institute, La Jolla, California, Copyr; 1988; **xiv** c; David Phillips/Visuals Unlimited; **xiv** b; ©Roger HartRainbow; **xv** t; Jeff Foot/DRK Photo; **xv** c; Robert & Linda Mitchell Photography; **xv** b; D. Cavagnaro/DRK Photo; **xvi** tl; Jeffrey L. Rotman; **xvi** tr; ©Jackie Lewin, EM Unit Royal Free Hospital/Science Photo Library/Photo Researchers, Inc.; **xvi** bl; Larry Lipsky/DRK Photo; **xvi** br; ©Photo Researchers, Inc.; **xvii** tl; photographer/ DRK Photo; **xvii** tr; Art Wolfe Incorporated; **xvii** bl; ©Andrew Syred/ Science Photo Library/Photo Researchers, Inc.; **xvii** br; S. Nielsen/DRK Photo; **xviii** t; ©Sophie de Wilde Jacana/Jacana Scientific Control/Photo Researchers, Inc.; **xviii** c; Runk/Schoenberger/Grant Heilman Photography; **xviii** bl; Martim Harvey/The Wildlife Collection; **xix** t; John Callanan/The Image Bank; **xix** c; Johnny Johnson/DRK Photo; **xix** bl; Mark Moffett/Minden Pictures, Inc.; **xix** br; Art Wolfe Incorporated; **xx** tl; ©Professors P.M. Motta and S. Correr/Science Photo Library/Photo Researchers, Inc.; **xx** tr; Rob Tringali, Jr./Sports Chrome East/West ; **xx** c; GJLP/CNRI/Phototake; **xx** b; ©Dr. Morley Read/Science Photo Library/Photo Researchers, Inc.; **xxi** tl; Paul J. Sutton/ Duomo Photography, Inc.; **xxi** tr; ©Prof. P. Motta/Dept. of Anatomy/ University "La Sapienza", Rome/Science Photo Library/ Photo Researchers, Inc.; **xxi** c; ©Prof. Arnold Brody/Science Photo Library/Photo Researchers, Inc.; **xxi** b; David Phillips/ Visuals Unlimited; **xxii** tl; William Sallaz/ The Image Bank; **xxii** tr; Lennart Nilsson ©Boehringer Ingelheim International GmbH; **xxii** c; ©Professors P.M. Motta and J. Van Blerkom/Science Photo Library/ Photo Researchers, Inc.; **xxii** b; Electra/ Phototake; **xxiii** t; ©Don Fawcett/Photo Researchers, Inc.; **xxiii** cr; ©Lennart Nilsson, THE INCREDIBLE MACHINE; **xxiii** cl; ©Boehringer Ingelheim International GmbH, Photo by Lennart Nilsson, THE INCREDIBLE MACHINE; **xxiii** b; **2** Leo Mason/The Image Bank; **3** l; Mel Di Giacomo/The Image Bank; c; Rob Tringali, Jr./Sports Chrome East/West; r; Silver Burdett Ginn; **6** t; Kagen/ Monkmeyer; bl; Bill Truslow/Tony Stone Images; br; Kopstein/Monkmeyer; **7** ©Professors P.M. Motta and S. Correr/ Science Photo Library/Photo Researchers, Inc.; **9** ©Geoff Tompkinson/Science Photo Library/Photo Researchers, Inc.; **10** Ken Karp Photography; **12** t; David Wagner/ Phototake; bl; Mark C. Burnett/Stock, Boston/PNI; br; Stock, Boston/PNI; **16** David Wagner/Phototake; **17** Kagen/ Monkmeyer; **18** ©Professors P.M. Motta and S. Correr/Science Photo Library/Photo Researchers, Inc.; **20** Robert Tringali/ Sports Chrome East/West; **21** l; Ken Karp